Ubertrends

How Trends And Innovation Are Transforming Our Future

Michael Tchong

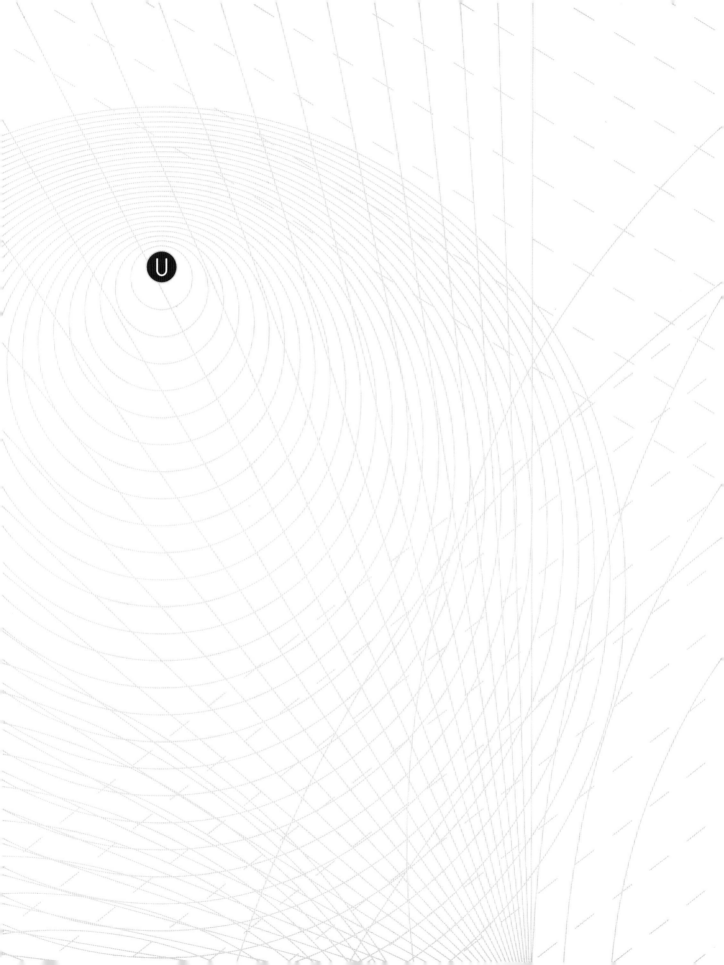

Ubertrends form in the eye of the storm. As these forces collide with the future they shapeshift society. When channeled with innovations, Ubertrends unleash a torrent of tsunamis.

First Edition

ISBN 978-0-9980898-0-5
1. Business — Strategy — Innovation. 2. Market Research — Consumer Insights.
Tchong, Michael. Ubertrends.

Library of Congress Control Number: 2018915202

Ordering Information

Quantity discounts are available for purchases by corporations, associations and others. For details, please contact the author at the address below. Orders by U.S. trade bookstores and wholesalers, please call (800) WAY-COOL or visit ubercool.com.

Printed in South Korea.

Ubercool Innovation LLC • 1925 Village Center Circle #150 • Las Vegas NV 89134 • 800-WAY-COOL • ubercool.com

Dedicated to my daughter Alexandra and her daughter Hailey.
May your future be inspired.

Table of Contents

The Digital Lifestyle is rewriting the rules of innovation. As technology becomes more tightly interwoven with the fabric of life, the dominant values that rule this technology-infused age are connectivity, convergence and convenience.

1

Digital Lifestyle
Marriage of Man and Machine

This massive wave has left a society so beholden to digital gadgetry that it's spending less on food, healthcare and travel to support its dependency. The marriage of man and machine has ushered in a whole new way of living, including innovative new ways of communicating, shopping and being infotained. A new social dialog has mainstreamed a Japanese expression, emoji, tiny pictograms that have become the new hieroglyphics. Yet disruptive Digital Lifestyle upheavals still loom on the horizon: artificial intelligence and robotics. Both will continue the convergence of computers with humankind leading to a profound societal revolution, one that will change the timbre of humanity forever.

More Important Than Life

Digital Lifestyle

> "[The iPod] didn't just change how we all listen to music, it changed the entire music industry."
>
> **Steven Jobs**
> Co-Founder, Apple Inc.

It was an astounding news story. A 16-year-old teen from Tampa, Fla. had dropped her iPod into the path of an oncoming truck. Thinking about it for a split second, she decided to save her iPod. Luckily, she only broke a leg. [1] It was a shocking example of how the Digital Lifestyle has affected human behavior. Imagine her thought stream: "My iPod or my life...iPod or life...iPod it is!"

It certainly wasn't the only strange behavior brought on by our love of technology. Three years earlier, the parents of 14-year-old Shannon Derrick sued her friend Stephanie Eick after she failed to return her new iPod nano. The families eventually settled but the Derrick's lawsuit and that teenage rescue dive demonstrate just how much value society now places on its digital gadgetry. [2]

1,000 Songs in Your Pocket

If ever there was a groundbreaking moment in the history of the Digital Lifestyle it was the 2001 introduction of Apple's legendary music player, the iPod. At the event, Apple CEO Steve Jobs waxed poetically, "music is a part of everyone's life." [3] Jobs had concluded earlier that after personal computing, music would be the next

---

1. Chris Matyszczyk, "Teen saves iPod, gets hit by truck," *CNET*, 29-May-09.
2. Jacqui Cheng, "Lost iPod nano lawsuit gets settled." *Ars Technica*, 13-Nov-06.
3. The Apple History Channel, "Apple Music Event 2001-The First Ever iPod Introduction," *YouTube*, 23-Oct-01.

iPod
1000 Songs in your pocket

Apple Ad for the Original iPod

Introduced in 2001, advertising for the Apple iPod music player stressed storage capacity and physical size with its "1,000 Songs in your pocket" pitch. Its white earphones became a globally recognized symbol of the Digital Lifestyle.

IMAGE COURTESY: APPLE INC.

frontier of the Digital Lifestyle.

His main selling point: "your entire music library fits in your pocket." It was a message that Apple would drive home with a global advertising campaign featuring this compelling headline, "1,000 Songs in your pocket." The message was not lost on music lovers. At the 2007 iPhone introduction, Jobs proudly announced that the "[iPod] didn't just change how we all listen to music, it changed the entire music industry." [4]

Little did Jobs realize that a scant eight years after the iPod's launch, a Tampa teenager would risk her life to save one.

Tech Addiction

Today, the Digital Lifestyle Ubertrend has taken an even more dramatic turn. In 2014, CNBC reported this startling finding: nearly half of Americans, 49%, had reduced spending on travel, food and healthcare in order to afford their technology. [5]

4. Jonathan Turetta, "Steve Jobs iPhone 2007 Presentation," *YouTube*, 09-Jan-07.
5. Steve Liesman, "A frugal trade? Americans spend less on food, more on technology," *CNBC*, 07-Oct-14.

So deeply rooted is the tech addiction that we're cutting back on vital spending categories, like food and healthcare, to buy more gadgets. That spending pattern resembles that of addicts who feed their insatiable appetite for drugs by cutting back on life's essentials.

Our technology obsession grew materially with the introduction of the smartphone, starting with the BlackBerry, also known as the "CrackBerry" for its addictive qualities.

One story that illustrates what a dominant force the BlackBerry became in life occurred during the October 2011 BlackBerry server outage in the Middle East. On any given day, a traffic accident occurs every three minutes in Dubai. [6] During the blackout, Dubai traffic accidents fell 20% compared to historical averages. In nearby Abu Dhabi accidents dropped a whopping 40%.

The addiction to the BlackBerry smartphone was even documented in a book, entitled, *CrackBerry: True Tales of BlackBerry Use and Abuse*. [7]

The importance of technology now exceeds that of money. Almost a third of U.K. smartphone users believe it would be worse to lose their phone than their wallet. [8]

Another study of students ages 17 to 23 in 10 countries, including the U.K., found that one in five participants reported feelings of withdrawal resembling addiction, after spending just 24 hours away from mobile phones, social media, the internet and TV. Worse, 11% said they were confused or felt like a failure. [9]

Researchers at the Stanford University School of Medicine conducted a phone survey in 2006 and found that 14% of Americans showed at least one possible sign of problematic internet use. [10]

While addiction measurements vary, other research studies in both the U.S. and Europe have found that between 1.5% and 8.2% of the population suffers from "Internet Addiction Disorder" or IAD. [11]

One organization, Redmond, Wash.-based reSTART Center for Technology Sustainability, offers treatments for IAD, by addressing "underlying mental health issues like depression, anxiety and ADD." [12]

My Lappy

It's a frequently repeated ritual. Trembling fingers eagerly peel away layer after layer. Anticipation builds as the object of lust is finally undressed: It's a beautiful, hot, sexy...new laptop. Welcome to the fascinating world of "unboxing" — a trend propelled by our pent-up desire for anything digital. [13]

At a MacRumors discussion forum, a topic speculating about "glass

The BlackBerry AKA "CrackBerry"

For many users, the omnipresent BlackBerry smartphone was as addictive as crack cocaine, cementing its popular reputation as the "CrackBerry."

6. Chris Shunk, "BlackBerry outage coincides with reduced number of traffic accidents," *Autoblog*, 18-Oct-11.
7. Al Sacco, "Official CrackBerry Addiction Guide on Sale Now," *CIO*, 03-Dec-08.
8. "Consumers would rather lose their wallets than their smartphones," *Mobile Today*, 17-Aug-11.
9. "Smartphone cold turkey: Scientists prove youngsters suffer gadget 'withdrawal,'" *Daily Mail*, 11-Apr-11.
10. "Internet addiction: Stanford study seeks to define whether it's a problem," *Stanford Medicine News Center*, 17-Oct-06.
11. "Technology Addiction," *Addiction.com*, ret. 02-Apr-16.
12. "reSTART," *netaddictionrecovery.com*, ret. 05-Jan-19.
13. "Unboxing," *Wikipedia*, ret. 05-Jan-19.

HP Spectre x360 Laptop

Users love their laptops so much that aficionados at NotebookReview have bestowed it with the oh-so-cute diminutive "lappy." The innovative new HP Spectre x360 folds into a tablet ($1,170) and qualifies as the latest seductress with its svelte lines and sexy copper accents.

> **66** As technology becomes more tightly interwoven with the fabric of life, the computer is becoming us and we're becoming the computer."
>
> **Michael Tchong**
> *Ubertrends*

trackpads" used in Apple's new MacBook began at 34 minutes past midnight on the day the company was set to launch its new laptops. Some 12 hours later, the thread had exploded to 60 pages, containing some 1,200 posts.

Such feverish anticipation is simply unheard of in any other consumer market. But then again, the birth of a new laptop is an extraordinary occasion. Over at NotebookReview, aficionados lovingly refer to their laptops as "my lappy." A computer is no longer merely a productivity tool. It has become an extension of our persona. Welcome to the Digital LIfestyle — the marriage of man and machine.

YouTube has become *the* voyeuristic showcase for digital disrobing. Melissa Lima, who is known to her 11.2 million YouTube subscribers as FunToys Collector, unboxes each toy slowly and deliberately, removing each element while describing and examining it from every angle. "It's incredibly seductive," writes Deb Amlen for Yahoo Tech.[14] Amlen can't decide whether she's more thrilled by the anticipation or whether it's the "ultimate satisfaction" of watching Lima do her thing.

As technology becomes more tightly interwoven with the fabric of life, humankind is evolving along with it. The computer is becoming us, and we're becoming the computer.

Not convinced? When we get tired, we "crash." We now love to multitask. And because we multitask so much, we tend to forget more, so we are in dire need of "memory protection." [15] Those also happen to be three core traits of CPUs — the central processing units or the brains of computers. [16]

Artful multitasking is steadily evolving into another computer trait,

14. Deb Amlen, "Why Unboxing Videos Are So Satisfying," *Yahoo Tech*, 10-Oct-14.
15. Dennis Fortier, "Multi-Tasking Linked to Forgetfulness," *Brain Today*, 13-Aug-10.
16. "Computer Multitasking," *Wikipedia*, ret. 05-Jan-19.

"multi-threading," multiple overlapping conversations that often manifest themselves in today's increasingly cacophonous and chaotic television debates. A cacophony that traces its history to the 1960s, when such conversation bazaars as the hit comedy show Laugh In and the game show Hollywood Squares introduced America to multi-threaded chatter.

The convergence of humankind and machine is particularly evident in the area of artificial intelligence, where mimicking how the human brain works is a major design challenge. The latest computer architectures increasingly spread computations across vast numbers of tiny, low-power specialty chips, which, much like the human brain, use energy more efficiently.

That decreased use of power has had a counter-intuitive impact on energy use. Despite an explosion in digital gadgetry, energy use is down 3%, as measured by residential electricity sales between 2010 to 2016, according to data from the U.S. Energy Information Administration. [17]

Convergence in the opposite direction, from computer to humans, is also taking shape. In April 2004, Barcelona's Baja Beach Club announced that it would offer VIP customers the option to embed an RFID microchip under their skin, which would not only guarantee them entry but also provide access to a debit account which they could use to pay for drinks. [18]

State-owned Swedish rail operator SJ boasted in October 2017 that it would become the first travel company to let passengers dispense with paper or e-tickets, by using a biometric chip implanted in their hand. [19]

A Wisconsin technology company, Three Square Market, lets employees embed a chip the size of a grain of rice (photo) between thumb and index finger. After being "chipped," the 50 out of 80 employees who participated in the program can swipe to gain entry to the office and pay for cafeteria food with a wave of the hand. [20]

Convergence is apparently already getting out of hand.

Digital *Enfant Terrible*

In August 2006, *The New York Times* noted that "as the number of home wireless networks grows, laptops — along with Treos, BlackBerries and other messaging devices — were migrating into the bedroom and onto the bed." [21] Technology had reached a tipping point, inserting itself into our lives, much like a digital *enfant terrible* who disrupts life's tender moments at the most inopportune times.

How far-reaching is this disruption? In January 2007, Kelton Research reported that "68% of Americans spend more time with their computer than with their spouse." [22]

To demonstrate just how pervasive the encroachment of the Digital Lifestyle is, Phrasee surveyed 940 U.S. people ages 18 and older in March

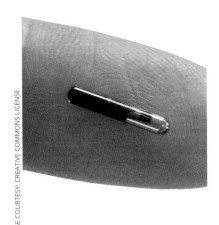

Biohacking: RFID Microchip

It's a trend that was sparked by Barcelona's Baja Beach Club, which was first to embed RFID chips under the skin of VIP customers in 2004. Today, members of the so-called bodyhacker movement are also implanting RFID chips and programming them to perform various tasks.

17. Rani Molla, "Even with all our gadgets, Americans are using less electricity than 10 years ago," *Recode*, 06-Aug-17.
18. Andrew Losowsky, "I've got you under my skin," *The Guardian*, 09-Jun-04.
19. "Swedish rail passengers use implanted microchip as ticket," *Springwise*, 17-Oct-17.
20. Maggie Astor, "Microchip Implants for Employees? One Company Says Yes," *The New York Times*, 25-Jul-17.
21. Katie Hafner, "Laptop Slides Into Bed in Love Triangle," *The New York Times*, 24-Aug-06.
22. "Cyber Stress," *Kelton Research*, 22-Jan-07.

2016 to find out about their, ahem, mobile multitasking and evacuation procedures. [23] The company found that 57% of men surveyed said they used their smartphones while in the restroom. By contrast, just 27% of women surveyed admitted to checking e-mail, social media, or the internet while in the bathroom.

What's most revealing is that 80% of 18-29-year-olds use their smartphone in the restroom, underscoring the acute digital dependency of millennials. Douglas Rushkoff, a professor of media studies at The New School University and producer of the PBS Frontline Digital Nation project, has a term for it — screenagers. [24]

But the Digital Lifestyle is also changing life in other subtle ways.

Of Cases and Wheelies

A little-noticed change was the disappearance of a status symbol of a bygone era, the slim, leather attaché case. Today, office workers are more apt to carry big, expandable bags, made from a flexible fabric, which are much better suited for lugging around smartphones, tablets, laptops, digital cameras, plus all necessary brick chargers.

Some have even opted for large cases with wheels, complete with retractable handles, capable of efficiently transporting those 10-plus extra pounds of digital gear people now routinely carry.

The trend has spread to women's handbags, which have grown markedly in size over the past decade. [25] Women lug so much gear now that feet sizes have increased to handle all that extra weight. [26] In three decades, the feet of the average U.K. woman has grown a full shoe size to an 8 or 9, up from a 7 or 8. The same goes for U.K. men.

Researchers blame the increase in foot size on diet and larger human bodies, but the fact remains that humans are now carrying extra body weight and a cadre of digital devices.

And still more devices are in the wings. The wearables trend (page 68) is ushering in a whole host of new tools, from smartwatches to fitness trackers to sleep trackers. Those devices may help fight the battle of the bulge, leading to a potential stabilization of foot sizes. According to Nielsen, fitness gadgets have surged in popularity, with 51 million American adults now using applications to track their health. [27]

The Digital Lifestyle is leading to yet another subtle change. As consumers pay more attention to how many calories they're consuming and burning, trailing 12-month revenue at Weight Watchers have fallen 16% in the past five years, as Fitbit, Garmin and other activity trackers have lured dieters away.

Of course, that's before those robot-assisted wheelie cases show up.

Kensington Contour Balance Laptop Roller "Wheelie"

This Kensington laptop bag with wheels is typical of a new generation of gear that has expanded along with our digital inventory. Long gone is that slim attaché case that was a status symbol among business people.

23. Ayaz Nanji, "Do Most Americans Check Their Smartphones in the Bathroom?," *MarketingProfs*, 01-Apr-16; *Phrasee*, Survey Monkey Audience Research, 14-Mar-16.
24. Douglas Rushkoff, "Playing the Future," *HarperCollins*, June 1996.
25. "Handbags grow larger with number of accessories," *Today's Zaman*, 08-Aug-08.
26. Sorcha Pollak, "Size 8 Is the New 7: Why Our Feet Are Getting Bigger," *Time*, 16-Oct-12.
27. "Fitness Trackers Eating Away At Weight Watchers," *AdAge*, 26-Feb-15.

FOMO: Fear Of Missing Out

Digital Lifestyle

Eyes are transfixed, gazing blankly at a stream of characters flowing by, like rivers of an obscure, cryptic language. A scene from the 1999 science-fiction hit movie, *The Matrix*? No, it's Twendz, a social media monitoring service that debuted a scant 10 years after the Wachowski sisters directed their futuristic movie scene. [28]

Launched on March 11, 2009 by PR agency Waggener Edstrom, Twendz was a realtime stream of trending topics from the Twitter social network. It provided a revealing snapshot of what was on the mind of about 5 million Twitter users at the time, which arguably represented the world's most forward-thinking community. [29]

The realtime nature of Twitter captured the imagination of computer users with live scoops of such major news events as the "Miracle on the Hudson" or a Turkish plane crash in the Netherlands. [30]

Mike Wilson, Twitter handle @2drinksbehind, made history on December 20, 2008, becoming the first person to tweet about Continental Airlines flight 737 after it slid off the runway during take-off. [31]

That was followed by another historic feat. The first eyewitness report of a US Airlines landing on the Hudson River in January 2009 from Jim Hanrahan, @Manolantern, who, four minutes after the crash, tweeted, "I just watched a plane crash into the hudson riv in manhattan." [32]

IMAGE COURTESY: JANIS KRUMS.

USAir Flight 1549 Tweet Photo

The 2009 landing of USAir flight 1549 on New York's Hudson River was captured by Janis Krums on an iPhone and uploaded to TwitPic. Realtime reporting like this sowed the seeds for FOMO — the Fear of Missing Out.

28. "The Wachowskis," *Wikipedia*, ret. 21-Dec-18.
29. Josh Lowensohn, "PR firm launches Twendz: A Twitter trend analyzer," *CNET*, 11-Mar-09.
30. Claudine Beaumont, "Amsterdam plane crash: Twitter, social media and the anatomy of a disaster," *The Telegraph*, 25-Feb-09.
31. Mike Wilson, "Tweet," *Twitter*, 20-Dec-08.
32. Jim Hanrahan, "Tweet," *Twitter*, 15-Jan-09.

Both of these breaking news reports scooped all mainstream media, demonstrating not only how much the world has changed due to the internet, but also the growing role social media played in the realtime dissemination of news.

It was Twitter's ability to break important news and provide other realtime insights that ushered in the trendy contraction, FOMO, the Fear Of Missing Out. Twitter put the spotlight on Janis Krums of Sarasota, Fla., who captured a newsworthy iPhone photo of ill-fated US Airlines flight 1549 after it crash-landed. [33]

Breaking news and celebrity tweets, such as the live birth of Erykah Badu's third child, amplified the feeling that if you were not on Twitter you were missing out. Badu, a singer from Texas, was so taken by Twitter that, as CNET put it, "she tweeted while she squeezed." [34]

Growing evidence suggests that social media use produces the same type of neurochemical stimulation as drugs and gambling. [35] Mobile Facebook users, for example, check Facebook 14 times a day. [36] That's just an average, of course. Some teens check their social media, such as their latest darlings Instagram and Snapchat, 100 times a day. [37] And it's not just Millennials or Digital Natives. Pew reports that social networking use among the 50-plus set has nearly doubled, from 22% to 42%. [38]

In May 2009, *The New York Times* reported that "time spent on social networks surpassed that for e-mail for the first time in February, signaling a paradigm shift in consumer engagement with the internet." [39] Social media had arrived, and it imbued the Digital Lifestyle with new social conventions, from poke to hashtag to unfriend.

Today, social media dominate the conversation, with Facebook boasting more than 2.2 billion and Twitter 336 million monthly active users, up considerably from the 5 million "tweeps" back in January 2009. [40][41]

> "Growing evidence suggests that social media use produces the same type of neuro-chemical stimulation as drugs and gambling."
>
> *The New Yorker*

Information as Entertainment

The rise of Twitter as the trend maven's favorite social network spurred yet another trend, the hashtag, a geeky form of communication that transformed Twitter users into database jockeys. Services like Twendz and others used a hashtag to track keywords trending on Twitter.

The ability to monitor hashtags lets social media users find news topics quickly or connect with others who share the same interest. Hashtags use the British word for the keyboard pound symbol, "hash," and add a keyword term, so for example #ubertrend.

33. Daniel Terdiman, "Photo of Hudson River plane crash downs TwitPic," *CNET*, 16-Jan-09.
34. Chris Matyszczyk, "Erykah Badu twitters while giving birth," *CNET*, 03-Feb-09.
35. Maria Konnikova, "Is Internet Addiction a Real Thing?," *The New Yorker*, 26-Nov-14.
36. Chris Taylor, "Smartphone Users Check Facebook 14 Times a Day," *Mashable*, 27-Mar-13.
37. Chuck Hadad, "Why some 13-year-olds check social media 100 times a day," *CNN*, 13-Oct-15.
38. Mary Madden, "Older Adults And Social Media," *Pew Internet*, 27-Aug-10.
39. Teddy Wayne, "Social Networks Eclipse E-Mail," *The New York Times*, 18-May-09.
40. Jason Abbruzzese, "Facebook hits 2.27 billion monthly active users as earnings stabilize," NBC News, 30-Oct-18.
41. "Number of monthly active Twitter users in the United States," *Statista*, ret. 21-Dec-18.

The First Hashtag

Hashtags were popularized during the 2007 San Diego forest fires when Nate Ritter used the hashtag "#sandiegofire" to identify his Twitter updates related to the California firestorm disaster.

NATE RITTER
@nateritter

Follow

#sandiegofire 300,000 people evacuated in San Diego county now.

10:30 PM - 22 Oct 2007

Former Google developer and UX designer Chris Messina is credited with inventing the hashtag, which he saw as a "better eavesdropping experience on Twitter." [42] The hash symbol convention, however, predates Twitter showing up earlier in internet chat, including IRC and Jaiku channels. [43]

While hashtags make it easier to find and group related tweets, it mainstreams an esoteric database technique, the database pointer, among the unwashed masses. [44]

Many observers believe Twitter represents the pulse of the internet. The theory is that if you track trends on Twitter, you're in tune with what's happening right now, and which was proven so true in the 2016 U.S. presidential election. The first person to reportedly use hashtags was Nate Ritter who identified updates relating to the 2007 San Diego forest fires with "#sandiegofire." [45]

A lot has changed since 2007. The hashtag has achieved pop culture status. It's used by advertisers and the media to drive traffic to their social media posts. It has become so overused by some Twitter users that Jimmy Fallon and Justin Timberlake created a hilarious spoof that made fun of the excessive use of hashtags. The YouTube video has been viewed nearly 33 million times. [46]

The hashtag lets Twitter act as a barometer of market opinion, an analytics facility made possible by Twitter's open data architecture, which is based on an open Application Programming Interface, or "API." This feature lets outside applications harvest user engagement data and analyze and dissect it in a myriad of ways. Social media marketers use this "engagement" data to optimize their social outreach.

How was your vacation?

I'm analyzing it now. The photo only got eight 'likes' but one of them was from someone really influential.

Blazek
© Dave Blazek

IMAGE COURTESY: DAVID BLAZEK.

Social Media Hashtag Mania

Society's latest fascination with social media influencers and its attendant tracking of "social engagement" metrics gets a humorous take in this David Blazek cartoon.

Many organizations have discovered to their chagrin that Twitter hashtags harbor a lot of power, notably BP. After its Gulf of Mexico oil spill, a spoof account calling itself @BPGlobalPR launched on Twitter. In just eight days, the account attracted 60,000 followers compared to BP's profile, @BP_America, which had only 7,200. The spoof account used disaster hashtags and humor to put BP's official account to shame, making its public relations effort all the more difficult.

Once Twitter gave rise to the discipline of social media marketing, a host of startups began offering "listening" solutions that track social user

42. Elana Zak, "How Twitter's Hashtag Came to Be," *The Wall Street Journal*, 03-Oct-13.
43. Martha Sperry, "What's A #Hashtag?," *Advocate's Studio*, 23-Oct-08.
44. Aleksandra Tesanovic, "Database Pointers," *COMET Publications*, 01-Jun-05.
45. Elana Zak, "How Twitter's Hashtag Came to Be," *The Wall Street Journal*, 03-Oct-13.
46. "#Hashtag with Jimmy Fallon & Justin Timberlake (Late Night with Jimmy Fallon)," *YouTube*, 24-Sep-13.

A Trendy Social Media-Fueled Term: Oversharing

The public's fascination with sharing too much information on social media has become the subject of much ridicule, as this meme so humorously illustrates.

conversations, such as Social Mention and BuzzSumo. Others offered simple metrics usually related to one's followers. One useful tool, Crowdfire, tracks follower growth metrics. Other services, such as Keyhole, let you dissect your Twitter followers.

These tools are part of a digital marketing sector that features more than 6,829 solutions able to output more digital data than anyone could productively analyze. [47]

A hot new social media trend is "influencer outreach." This marketing tactic connects marketers with social media influencers with large followings in the hope that they will help you spread the word virally. These esoteric social media marketing tactics are reaching a broader population, as the cartoon at left shows.

Influencer outreach services, such as Scrunch, let social media marketers discover influencers based on a keyword, for example, "innovation," Once entered, Scrunch shows a list of key social media influencers. As more people use hashtags to find trending conversations, social media has become spellbinding. And the beguiling nature of tracking keywords has made information the new entertainment.

Digital Natives

Think Millennials are the only ones pushing the buttons? Think again. Today's children, appropriately dubbed "Digital Natives," will create an even bigger digital logjam. Their proficiency with technology is second to none, as a study by the U.K. communications authority Ofcom found.

In its 2014 Communications Market Report Ofcom reported that "six-year-

Thumb Generation

In Asia, Digital Natives are referred to as the "Thumb Generation" due to their precocious keypad skills.

47. Scott Brinker, "Marketing Technology Landscape Supergraphic (2018)," *chiefmartec.com*, 24-Apr-18.

olds claim to have the same understanding of communications technology as 45-year-olds." [48]

Another telling finding: 69% of children ages 2-5 can operate a computer mouse, yet only 11% can tie their own shoelaces. [49]

The study surveyed 2,200 mothers in the U.S., UK, and eight other countries. Sample self-selection undoubtedly introduced a survey bias, but the study clearly points to a digital native future.

Influence Central's report, *Kids & Tech: The Evolution of Today's Digital Natives*, found that the average age at which children get their first smartphone is now 10.3 years. [50] Furthermore, 39% of children had a social media account at age 11, while 11% had one when they were 10 or younger.

Now consider that there are 74 million Digital Natives (see table). They follow another big wave, the Millennials. That generation, 75 million strong, is now the U.S.' largest demographic segment. As of 2015, there are more Millennials in the U.S. workforce than Generation Xers or Baby Boomers, reports Pew Research Center. [51] The consulting firm Accenture estimates that Millennials will spend $1.4 trillion annually by 2020, and they are expected to inherit about $30 billion in the coming years. [52]

Are you ready for this massive wave of the digitally savvy?

IMAGE COURTESY: FISHER-PRICE INC.

Fisher-Price iPad Activity Seat

To keep the Digital Natives generation duly occupied, Fisher-Price launched the "Apptivity Seat for iPad" ($80), because baby needs to multitask.

U.S. Population Generation Demographics				
Generation	Millions	Born	Ages	% Population
Digital Natives (Generation Z)	73.6	1998-2015	0-17	22.9%
Millennials (Generation Y)	75.3	1981-1997	18-34	23.4%
Gen-X (Generation X)	65.8	1965-1976	35-50	20.5%
Late Baby Boomers	43.8	1955-1964	51-60	13.6%
Early Baby Boomers	31.0	1946-1954	61-69	9.6%
Silent Generation	27.9	1928-1945	70-87	8.7%
G.I. "Greatest" Generation	3.7	1901-1927	88-100+	1.2%
Total	321.4			100.0%

Source: 25-Apr-16 Pew Research Center; 04-May-17 The Generational Imperative; 23-Jun-16 U.S. Census Bureau total measured population estimate; Michael Tchong.

E-books

One activity that is reeling from the changing habits of Digital Natives is book reading. A third of U.S. teenagers haven't read a book for pleasure in at least a year. [53]

> **"70% of Americans have not visited a bookstore in the past five years."**
>
> Dan Poynter
> Book Industry Statistics

A survey of 2,558 U.S. parents and children, conducted by YouGov for Scholastic, found that 51% of children today say they love or like reading books for fun, compared to 58% in 2012, and 60% in 2010. According to the report, children cite the pressure of schoolwork and certain other

48. "Techie teens shaping communications," *Ofcom*, 06-Aug-14.
49. "AVG Study Shows Young Kids Learn Tech Skills before Life Skills," *AVG*, 19-Jan-11.
50. Jay Donovan, "The average age for a child getting their first smartphone is now 10.3 years," *TechCrunch*, 19-May-16.
51. Richard Fry, "Millennials surpass Gen Xers as the largest generation in U.S. labor force," *Pew Research Center*, 11-May-15.
52. Hilary Stout, "Oh, to Be Young, Millennial, and So Wanted by Marketers," *The New York Times*, 20-Jun-15.
53. Jamie Ducharme , "A Third of Teenagers Don't Read Books for Pleasure Anymore," *Time*, 20-Aug-18.

"distractions." Feel free to insert computer and smartphone here, LOL. [54]

The outlook for the book market is growing increasingly dim with reading as a distraction falling across all age groups, replaced by digital diversions.

Consider these sobering statistics. In 2002, U.S. book market sales totaled a healthy $29.4 billion. [55] By 2014 that figure had declined 5% to $28 billion, despite a U.S. population increase of some 31 million people, or 11%, in the intervening years. [56]

More shocking still is a report suggesting that 70% of Americans have not visited a bookstore in the past five years. Yet one-third of all books sold around the globe, 1.6 billion in 2001 alone, are bought by U.S. consumers. [57]

The Digital Lifestyle Ubertrend, and as you will read later on, the Time Compression Ubertrend, are creating turbulence that makes finding quiet time to read a book challenging at best. That explains why most consumers will not get past page 18 in a typical book purchased. Our intentions are good but digital distractions and time limitations not so.

There is still hope that future e-books, perhaps best described as "immersive reading experiences," might help stem the tide. Or maybe someone will come up with a technological advance that lets digital readers absorb material faster, while also making them retain more information.

One such approach is offered by Spritz that with a little training promises to raise your reading speed to 350 words per minutes or 40% faster than average, while also improving your comprehension. [58]

I would raise my electronic comic book to toast such a device.

The Big Bang Theory

If the computer is beginning to mirror humankind, it's highly logical that entertainment should start reflecting all things digital. For the past 12 years, CBS' *The Big Bang Theory* has been making the world laugh, climbing from 68th place to the number two rated show on U.S. television by 2013. [59]

The Big Bang Theory is a story about four nerds, whose Digital Lifestyle adventures prove that geekdom is not only catching on but transforming the media landscape in the process. While the popularity of *The Big Bang Theory* is mainly due to exceptional writing and character development, the TV show's razor-sharp digital humor is catching on among the masses as their fluency with technology increases. Dialog from *The Big Bang Theory* reveals just how nuanced its tech humor is.

In one episode, Sheldon Cooper, the lead character played by actor Jim Parsons, asks, "What computer do you have? And please don't say a white one."

54. "Kids & Family Reading Report," *Scholastic*, 09-Jan-15.
55. Dan Poynter, "Book Industry Statistics," *ParaPublishing.com*, 01-Mar-08.
56. "U.S. Publishing Industry's Annual Survey Reveals $28 Billion in Revenue in 2014," *The Association of American Publishers*, 10-Jun-15.
57. Dan Poynter, "Book Industry Statistics," *ParaPublishing.com*, 01-Mar-08.
58. Spritz, ret. 21-Dec-18.
59. "The Big Bang Theory," *Wikipedia*, ret. 21-Dec-18.

Who Let the Dorks Out?

One of the most popular comedy shows on television, CBS' *The Big Bang Theory* — a story about four geeks and their Digital Lifestyle interactions, proves that geeks are not only winning but are transforming our media landscape.

In 2010, CBS scored another first: a TV show based on a Twitter feed, *$#*! My Dad Says*. While CBS canceled the show after just 18 episodes, it underscored the tremendous influence social media is having on pop culture. [60]

Another Digital Lifestyle concept that ended up inspiring a TV show was ABC's short-lived *Selfie*. However, as Quartz concludes, the show's racial diversity represents the future of television. [61]

Compatible Cars

> " The iPhone is the Ford Mustang of today."
>
> **Thilo Koslowski**
> Lead Automotive Analyst, Gartner

Fasten your seatbelts. North America's torrid love affair with the automobile is under attack from the Digital Lifestyle. In 2005, Mercedes became the first automaker to offer iPod integration in its 2006 Mercedes-Benz M-Class. [62] Today, cars are chosen as much based on their compatibility with Apple's iPhone or Google's Android as any other feature.

A Super Bowl ad campaign for GM's Chevrolet Malibu played up its Siri integration. [63] Another ad campaign from Kia boasted about its Apple CarPlay functionality. [64] New cars are so laden with technology that *Autoweek* titled its review of the 2017 Audi 4, "Nerd is the new black." [65]

Changes sweeping over the automotive market, however, extend beyond

60. "$#*! My Dad Says," *Wikipedia*, ret. 04-May-17.
61. Jeff Yang, "The TV show "Selfie" is now history—but it's also the future," *Quartz*, 08-Jan-15.
62. "Apple & Mercedes-Benz Unveil iPod Integration Kit," *Apple Press Info*, 11-Jan-05.
63. "2016 Chevrolet Malibu Shows Up In "Real People, Not Actors" Campaign," *GMAuthority.com*, 08-Jan-16.
64. "Kia Touts Ease of Apple Car Play System in Optima Spot," *Ad Age*, 03-Mar-16.
65. Jake Lingeman, "2017 Audi A4 review: Nerd is the new black," *Autoweek*, 15-Mar-16.

Volvo S90 Sedan Integrates Skype

No need to fumble for your phone or deal with forgettable PIN codes. With Skype for Business Conferencing built into your Volvo S90 dashboard, you can easily participate in conference calls while on the go. A partnership with Microsoft also adds support for voice commands via Cortana.

IMAGE COURTESY: VOLVO CAR CORPORATION

U.S. Population Ages 20-24 With a Driver's License

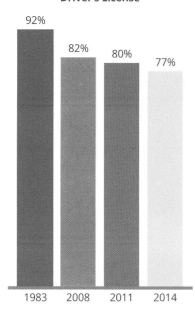

20-Jan-16 University of Michigan Transportation Research Institute

choices in connected technologies. Young adults are ditching driver's licenses at a quickening pace, raising a red flag for automakers as they grapple with the emergence of ride-sharing services and a growing indifference towards cars (sidebar).

Three in four people ages 20 to 24 possessed a driver's license in 2014, according to the University of Michigan's Transportation Research Institute. The exact figure, 77%, represents a sharp decline from 92% in 1983, or even 82% in 2008. [66]

The Digital Lifestyle is partly to blame for cars becoming less relevant to Millennials. Internet use is leading to a lower propensity to obtain a driver's license. Access to virtual connections via social media and video messaging is reducing the need for real-life contact among younger generations.

Gartner reports that 46% of people 18 to 24 would choose internet access over access to a car. By comparison, only 15% of Baby Boomers would ever admit that. This discovery made Gartner Lead Automotive Analyst Thilo Koslowski declare that "The iPhone is the Ford Mustang of today." [67] One factor that may be helping millennials give up cars is the popularity of ride-sharing, introduced by companies such as Lyft and Uber, and car-sharing ("A Changing Car Landscape," page 24).

The trend is not limited to North America. Young people worldwide are losing interest in cars. Toyota Head of Worldwide Marketing Masanao Tomozoe notes that it's an industry-wide phenomenon. [68]

To increase its appeal among Millennials, GM announced in 2010 that it would integrate Facebook into its OnStar system. Text messages and Facebook updates could be read to OnStar subscribers while they were driving. And users would also be able to text or update Facebook using

66. Nathan Bomey, "Millennials spurn driver's licenses, study finds," *USA Today*, 19-Jan-16.
67. Nick Bilton, "Disruptions: For Teenagers, a Car or a Smartphone?" *New York Times*, 20-Nov-11.
68. Chris Woodyard, "Toyota sales CEO says fewer teens globally want cars," *USA Today*, 16-Jun-14.

voice commands. [69] GM is not alone pushing connected cars. Thanks to a Microsoft alliance, Volvo now offers Skype for Business in its S90 vehicles. [70] The best part? No need to enter long participant PIN codes, one button does the job.

But carmakers may be facing a more significant challenge than mere Millennial boredom. Americans are driving less. The population-adjusted miles traveled peaked in June 2005 and has since declined 5%. [71]

While recessions typically affect driving behavior, and dips have been recorded during the Great Depression (1932), the Arab Oil Embargo (1975), 1979's "Stagflation" and, of course, the Great Recession of 2007, marketwatchers now believe that we are witnessing a long-term shift toward less driving, not just a cyclical variation.

The adjusted miles traveled by the 16-and-older age set is about where the U.S. was in October 1997, a period during which the internet and Amazon.com began to crest.

Could anyone have envisioned this mind-boggling scenario in historically car-crazy America?

Not without the Digital Lifestyle in the driver's seat.

69. Sharon Silke Carty, "Facebook updates can now be posted via GM's OnStar system," *USA Today*, 15-Sep-10.
70. "Volvo Cars adds Microsoft's Skype for Business to its 90 Series cars, heralding a new era for in-car productivity," *Volvo Car Group*, 29-Dec-16.
71. Doug Short, "Vehicle Miles Traveled: Another Look at Our Evolving Behavior," *Advisor Perspectives*, 24-Jun-16.

A Changing Car Landscape

The growing popularity of ride-hailing and car-sharing services, like Uber and Zipcar, are altering the automotive landscape.

Now add two more disruptions, Tesla's runaway success, and self-driving cars, and you know why automobile makers have pumped nearly $5 billion into car-related startups.

In January 2016, General Motors said it would invest $500 million in Lyft. [1] Shortly after that it bought the remains of ride-sharing upstart Sidecar. [2] In May 2016, Volkswagen announced a $300 million investment in Gett. [3]

That investment came weeks after Apple invested $1 billion into Chinese startup Didi Chuxing. [4] The action in car sharing is equally hot. It all began with the $500 million acquisition of Zipcar by Avis in January 2013. [5]

Daimler's car2go is now available in 25 global markets and boasts 3 million members. [6] BMW jumped in with DriveNow, while GM set up its Maven car-sharing service in 17 U.S. cities. [7]

Car sharing is forecast to grow globally from 5.8 million users in 2015 to 35 million by 2021. [8]

Toyota has launched Hui, pronounced "hooey," which means "group" in Hawaiian, in Honolulu, in addition to investing $1 billion in Southeast Asia's top ride-sharing company, Grab Holdings. [9]

Carmakers are so taken by these disruptions that they're bending over backward to accommodate emerging opportunities.

Maven's Gig service rents cars to Uber and Lyft drivers. BMW's latest auto lease lets you drive for ride-hailing services.

Next up are bike sharing services, like Maven Verity, and car subscription services, such as Fair, Flexdrive and Porsche's Passport program, which lets you swap out different Porsches for $2,000 a month.

A car and bike pile-up appear to be right around the corner.

1. Steve Trousdale, "GM invests $500 million in Lyft, sets out self-driving car partnership, *Reuters*, 05-Jan-16.
2. Ben Popper, "After investing in Lyft, General Motors buys up failed ride-sharing service Sidecar," *The Verge*, 19-Jan-16.
3. Brian Solomon, "Volkswagen Joins GM, Apple: Invests $300 Million In An Uber Rival," *Forbes*, 24-May-16.
4. Brian Solomon, "Apple Just Invested $1 Billion In Uber's Chinese Rival," *Forbes*, 12-May-16.
5. "Avis Budget Group to acquire Zipcar for $12.25 per share in cash," *Zipcar*, 02-Jan-13.
6. Kirsten Korosec, "Daimler's car2go car-sharing service adds its first US city in four years," *TechCrunch*, 26-Jul-18.
7. "Maven Debuts Elevated Car-Sharing Service in Baltimore, *GM Newsroom*, 05-Apr-17.
8. Caitlin Harrington, "Automakers Are Making Car Ownership Optional," *Wired*, 27-May-18.
9. "Toyota Launching App-Controlled Car-Sharing in Hawaii," *Bloomberg News*, 16-Jul-18.

A New Social Dialog

In her article, "Death to smiley," Salon writer Mary Williams describes the emoticon as "the rimshot of online communication." Her not-so-subtle feelings were best summed up by: "What is it about the emoticon that fills me with such loathing? Maybe it's the wastefulness of the enterprise, the redundancy of it, the implied lack of confidence in the writer's ability to communicate, or mine to comprehend." [72]

While Williams is not alone in her dislike of the emoticon, the "smiley" has become a significant form of mass expression. So much so that the vocabulary of the emoticon is now in the hands of the Unicode Consortium, a digital standards committee. [73]

The 2017 iteration of the Unicode standard assigned "rolling on the floor laughing," best known by its text *nom de plume* ROTFL, its own distinct round, yellow character.

A January 2010 Ubercool Innovation blog post advocated the creation of a service-independent emoticon standard, EmotiScript, a smiley *lingua franca* that would display the correct translation of the most popular emoticons then in use. [74]

That article preceded the arrival of Apple's iOS 4 mobile operating system in 2010, which added picture characters to the iPhone, although they

IMAGE COURTESY: APPLE INC.

Word of the Year: Face With Tears of Joy Emoji

In a remarkable twist of wordplay brought about by the Digital Lifestyle Ubertrend, an "emoji" was named "Word of the Year" by Oxford Dictionaries in 2015. Formerly known as "emoticons" or "smileys" they now go by the Japanese term emoji.

---

72. Mary Williams, "Death to smiley," *Salon*, 30-Nov-09.
73. "Emoji Charts," *Unicode Consortium*, ret. 05-Jan-19.
74. Michael Tchong, "Smiley Talk," *Ubercool Innovation*, 03-Jan-10.

The New Hieroglyphics

Purists believe emoji are interfering with text. The truth is that text has interfered with visual communications since the early cave drawings. Some messages now contain only emojis, turning these pictograms into the new hieroglyphics.

IMAGE COURTESY: APPLE INC.

> **"** Sony is developing a new movie about emojis. At this point we're just five years away from kids asking, 'Mom, what were words?'"
>
> **Jimmy Fallon**
> *The Tonight Show*

could only be enabled via an optional third-party app. [75] In 2011, Apple introduced iOS 5, which made the iPhone's emoticons more accessible via the Emoji keyboard. [76]

In the past five years, the popularity of emoticons has soared. Even its Japanese name, "emoji," has become part of pop culture's lexicon, all due to the iPhone. The word "emoji" (絵文字) is a contraction of the Japanese words for "picture character." These ideograms were initially used in electronic messages and social media and were added to Japanese mobile phones in the late 1990s. [77]

Apple initially limited its picture character set to the Japan market, but due to the runaway popularity of emoji among Japanese iPhone users, it made its stealth debut in North America through a kludgey third-party app.

The emoji's ascent reached a peak in late 2015 when the Oxford University Press, which publishes both the prestigious Oxford English Dictionary and Oxford Dictionaries Online, partnered with keyboard app company SwiftKey to determine which emoji was getting the most play that year and chose "Face with Tears of Joy" emoji, as its 2015 Word of the Year. [78]

That was a very appropriate choice. A study released earlier that year reported that "Face with Tears of Joy" was the most popular emoji on Instagram while revealing how widespread the use of emoji had become. Shortly after the introduction of the iOS emoji keyboard, 10% of the text on Instagram contained emoji. [79] By March 2015, nearly half of all Instagram text messages included emoji.

Concludes the study's author, Instagram Software Engineer Thomas Dimson, "if the overall trend continues, we might be looking at a future where the majority of text on Instagram contains emoji."

What attracts users to emoji are two centrifugal forces, the Digital Lifestyle and Time Compression. The Digital Lifestyle is changing the social dialog and making emoji an integral part of our communication toolbox.

The Time Compression Ubertrend, or "The Acceleration of Life," is responsible for the growing tendency of communicators to use shorthand to convey a feeling quickly.

Besides, it's easy to see why emoji are so popular. Emojis add a dash of

75. "Emoji," *Wikipedia*, ret. 05-Jan-19.
76. "Standard Emoji keyboard arrives to iOS 5, here's how to enable it," *9to5Mac*, 08-Jun-11.
77. "Emoji," *Wikipedia*, ret. 05-Jan-19.
78. Lizzie Plaugic, "The Oxford Dictionaries' word of the year is an emoji," *The Verge*, 16-Nov-15.
79. Thomas Dimson, "Emojineering Part 1: Machine Learning for Emoji Trends," *Instagram Engineering*, 06-Jul-15.

humor, sadness, or *divertissement* to trillions of black-and-white words each day. They are three-dimensional conversation aids in a two-dimensional text world. Think of emoji as the Hamburger Helper of conversation.

The quick rise of the pictogram is all the more remarkable given that our current form of communicating took tens of thousands of years to develop. The emoticon was first used by Carnegie Mellon University Professor Scott Fahlman in 1982. [80] Fahlman's version required turning your head sideways to grasp the meaning of his proposed smiley symbol, :).

That was before the fax, before the internet and more than 20 years before Facebook. Today, Facebook and WhatsApp users alone post a staggering 60 billion messages *each day*, providing ample opportunity for the emoji to spread widely. [81]

If the evolution of the spoken dialog is any indication, thou hast no reason to resist this pestilence, lest thy wasteth away.

Speak No More

In 2009, for the first time in the U.S., mobile data, i.e., text, e-mail messages and other services on devices surpassed voice data. [82] Fully 71% of millennials prefer receiving texts text messages to voice mail. [83] The evolution of text messaging replays that of answering machines. Early on, some callers would hang up on a call because they had an "I refuse to talk to a machine" attitude. Then came a period when people, particularly those in eastern time zones would leave a message for people in the west, knowing fully well that they were still sleeping when called. The ability to store messages for later retrieval is a feature called "store and forward." It's also why some prefer texting over talking. You can retrieve a message at your convenience. A call has to be answered in realtime and is far more intrusive.

Today, caller impatience and the ability to send e-mail or text messages are conspiring to make voicemail a thing of the past. [84] JPMorgan Chase has eliminated voicemail for its 136,000 employees, joining Coca-Cola in a trend that's bound to gather steam. [85]

Office Sign: 40 Days Without an On-the-job Conversation

Matthew Diffee brilliantly captures the impact digital technology has had on inter-office communication or lack thereof.

"We realized that hardly anyone uses voicemail anymore," Gordon Smith, head of the company's consumer bank told Bloomberg.

According to Pew, 53% of texters still prefer receiving a phone call over getting a text. [86] But that study dates back to 2011, which were pre-historic times. As the cartoon shows, we much prefer sending an e-mail to co-workers sitting at a desk right next to us than actually talk to them.

80. "Scott Fahlman," *Wikipedia*, ret. 21-Dec-18.
81. Lauren Goode, "Messenger and WhatsApp process 60 billion messages a day, three times more than SMS," *The Verge*, 12-Apr-16.
82. "Tellwut Online Survey Finds 71% of Millennials Prefer Text Messages To Voice Mail," *Tellwut/PRWeb*, 25-Jan-17.
83. Aaron Smith, "Americans and Text Messaging," *Pew Research*, 19-Sep-11.
84. Roger Yu, "Voice mail in decline with rise of text, loss of patience," *USA Today*, 03-Sep-12.
85. Robert Hackett, "This Massive Bank Just Killed Voicemail," *Fortune*, 02-Jun-15.
86. Aaron Smith, "Americans and Text Messaging," *Pew Research*, 19-Sep-11.

Photoshopping

In 1987, an engineering student at the University of Michigan, Thomas Knoll, wrote a software program that converted monochrome images on his computer monitor to grayscale. After demoing his creation to his younger brother, John Knoll, who worked at George Lucas' Industrial Light and Magic, the Knoll brothers joined forces and shipped their first finished product, Image Pro, in 1988. [87]

The following year, the Knolls sold their software program to Adobe Systems, which renamed and shipped it as Photoshop 1.0 in 1990. And so began a journey that would one day lead to "photoshopping" becoming part of the popular vernacular. [88]

The editing of real-life details has made photoshopping today's equivalent of xeroxing. Reactions to its use range from blushing avoidance to angry social media users upset by its overuse by the media to make celebrities and models look better, like when Modeliste photoshopped Zendaya for its cover. [89] And the use of Photoshop is not limited to professional retouching artists. Celebrities, such as Beyoncé and Lady Gaga have been called out for photoshopping their own Instagram images. [90]

IMAGE COURTESY: MIRROR.CO.UK.

Unlike any other software program, Photoshop has achieved near omnipresent ubiquity due to one particular Photoshop filter called Pixelate.

You may not know what the Pixelate Photoshop filter does, but you see its results almost daily in the media, where it's used to blur out sensitive details, a credit card number, e-mail address, license plate number or a person's name or face.

Technology terms are infusing the human dialog, ranging from app to cyberspace to GIF to googling, bandwidth, Bitcoin, hashtag, meme, pwn (sometimes rhyming with "own"), tweep and webinar.

"Pwn" — a term derived from the verb own — was coined by the videogame community and is used to taunt an opponent who has just been soundly defeated (e.g., "You just got pwned!"). [91]

Another saying, "epic fail," was also born in videogame circles. Perhaps the first internet videogame meme was an idiosyncrasy that reared its alien head during the 90s dotcom boom, "All your base are belong to us," which

Blurring an Image Using a "Pixelation" Technique

Photoshop, a digital imaging tool, has become such an integral part of the Digital Lifestyle that "photoshopping" is now a common verb. The blurring of potentially embarrassing parts of an image is a practice widely seen on the internet, television and in print media.

87. Angela West, "20 Years of Adobe Photoshop," *WebdesignerDepot*, 01-Dec-10.
88. Vangie Beal, "Photoshopping," *Webopedia*, ret. 21-Dec-18.
89. "Model-actress Zendaya 'shocked' to find herself Photoshopped," *CNN*, 22-Oct-15.
90. Katie Corvino, "8 Celebrities Who Have Been Called Out For Fake Social Media Photos," *Elite Daily*, 03-Nov-15.
91. "Pwn," *Wikipedia*, ret. 21-Dec-18.

was based on an opening scene of the 1989 arcade game Zero Wing. [92]

The internet history of "sockpuppet" is equally fascinating. The traditional definition, a simple hand puppet made from a sock, gained an entirely new meaning on the internet, where it refers to an online identity used for purposes of deception. [93]

Another term that gained an entirely new online meaning is "astroturfing," which also involves deception. As Wikipedia defines it, "Astroturfing is the practice of masking the sponsors of a message or organization (e.g., political, advertising, religious or public relations) to make it appear as though it originates from and is supported by a grassroots participant(s)." [94] Astroturfing apparently requires the use of sockpuppets.

Social media is fertile ground for new social conventions, starting with such terms as a Facebook poke and Twitter tweeps — a contraction of Twitter and "peeps." Another word that caught on due to social media is avatar — the image that appears beside messages identifying the poster — which is a Sanskrit word meaning incarnation or embodiment. [95]

But the most famous social media-specific word of all is "unfriend." The New Oxford American Dictionary chose unfriend as its 2009 word of the year. [96] In 2013, the Oxford Dictionaries followed by selecting "selfie" as its word of the year. [97] Although not a social media term per se, selfies were popularized by social media users, which allowed the word to achieve hall-of-fame status a scant eight years after it became the thing to do on social network MySpace. [98]

A myriad of abbreviations was initially propelled by texting and social media messaging, including BRB, OMG, WTF, LMAO (laughing my ass off) and LOL. An emoji that approximates the two last terms was named the Oxford Dictionaries' 2015 Word of the Year, continuing a long streak of Digital Lifestyle terms infiltrating the human vocabulary. [99] Doxxing" is another term that recently caught on. This slang verbiage, which is used by hackers to describe the process of obtaining and posting private information about an individual, usually a rival or enemy, gained widespread currency after the white supremacist march on Charlottesville, Va.

On the horizon lies even more esoteric terminology, ready to become part of your word stream. One such jargon is "virtual spelunking," which refers to the practice of using Google Earth to see the world. You might call it desktop travel.

The spectacular growth of both Instagram and Snapchat is a testament to our visually oriented future. The popularity of graphic memes and animated GIFs as a way of communicating key messages is a major anthropological turning point. You know you have adopted the Digital Lifestyle when you start referring to a new phase in your, or someone else's, life as 2.0.

Welcome to Human Lingo 2.0.

> 66 Perhaps the first internet videogame meme was an idiosyncrasy that reared its alien head during the 90s dotcom boom, 'All your base are belong to us.'"
>
> Michael Tchong
> *Ubertrends*

92. "All your base are belong to us," *Wikipedia*, ret. 21-Dec-18.
93. "Sockpuppet (Internet)," *Wikipedia*, ret. 21-Dec-18.
94. "Astroturfing," *Wikipedia*, ret. 21-Dec-18.
95. "FAQ for Avatar," *IMDB*, ret. 21-Dec-18.
96. Doug Gross, "Dictionary word of the year: 'Unfriend'," *Wikipedia*, ret. 21-Dec-18.
97. Trey Barrineau, "'Selfie' named word of the year for 2013," *USA Today*, 18-Nov-13.
98. "Selfie," *Wikipedia*, ret. 21-Dec-18.
99. Katy Steinmetz, "Oxford's 2015 Word of the Year Is This Emoji," *Time*, 16-Nov-15.

Electronic Dance Music

In March 2018, some 165,000 people descended on the city of Miami to attend Ultra, an electronic dance music (EDM) festival. [100] Ultra coincides with an EDM stalwart, the Winter Music Conference, a gathering of DJs, dance club owners, music producers and promoters, held every year since 1985. [101]

The Winter Music Conference, or "WMC" as devotees of electronic dance music like to call it, celebrates the dance culture and its music, *née* electronica, a derivative of the 1970s work of German band Kraftwerk and Giorgio Moroder.

The 1960s popularized a novel concept, "disco" — a club where the entertainment consisted of music played on a turntable, explaining today's trendy moniker for DJs, "turntablist." [102]

In 1970, Ralf Hütter and Florian Schneider formed Kraftwerk in Düsseldorf, Germany, which introduced a signature sound combining driving, repetitive rhythms with strictly electronic instruments. [103] Kraftwerk's distinctive sound was revolutionary for its time and had a lasting impact across many genres of modern popular music.

It was Kraftwerk's trademark "metallic sound" that gave rise to the new kind of "electronica" — music propelled by the electric guitar, which got a further boost in the 1960s with the introduction of the "wah-wah" pedal, the electronic organ and other electronic instruments. Frank Zappa was

IMAGE COURTESY: MYNT.

The City of Miami Beach's Booming Dance Club Scene

Miami New Times says it best, "The players change and institutions come and go. Velvet ropes line the street, then vanish, only to return under new blinking signs." Mynt, pictured above, was one of those cool clubs then vanished. Today's hottest one-name brands are LIV, Ora, WALL and Story.

100. Sara Vogelsanger, "Ultra Music Festival Floods Miami with Record-Breaking Attendance," *Relentless Beats*, 29-Mar-18.
101. "Winter Music Conference," *Wikipedia*, ret. 21-Dec-18.
102. "Turntablist," *The Urban Dictionary*, ret. 21-Dec-18.
103. "Kraftwerk," *Wikipedia*, ret. 21-Dec-18.

DJ Console for the Rest of Us

The Numark iDJ Live II controller is designed for those who already own an iPad, which is used as the controller's display. The iDJ's low price (under $100), combined with its portability factor makes it ideal for the budding DJ in all of us.

IMAGE COURTESY: NUMARK.

IMAGE COURTESY: D&M HOLDINGS INC.

Denon DJ SC5000 Controller

One glance at the Denon DJ SC5000, shown at the NAMM tradeshow, provides convincing evidence of the digital evolution of DJ gear: HD touchscreen, customizable RGB color jog wheel, plus USB and SD card inputs.

the first major artist to use the wah-wah pedal after it was introduced my manufacturer Thomas Organ in 1967. [104] But it was Jimi Hendrix who made the wah-wah pedal gain prominence, with his famous rendition of *The Star Spangled Banner* at Woodstock. Giorgio Moroder's groundbreaking synthesizer work in the 1970s and 1980s was also influential on electronic music. [105] Moroder gained fame by working with legendary disco queen Donna Summer on such songs as *I Feel Love*.

Kraftwerk and Moroder, in turn, put their imprint on music that began emanating from Detroit in 1979, called "techno," which was pioneered by such DJs as Juan Atkins, Derrick May and Kevin Saunderson. Techno featured "industrial" sounds that mirrored those produced by Detroit's automotive industry. A second electronica vein, house music, began pulsing in Chicago in 1983 and was based on the groundbreaking work of Frankie Knuckles and Kool Herc, nicknamed "the godfather of house." [106] House was a permutation of R&B music and often featured vocals, particularly female ones.

The dance culture built momentum fast and got its own festival in 1989, Berlin's Love Parade, which at its peak drew more than 1 million electronica fans, making it by far the world's largest music extravaganza. [107]

The EDM scene today is dominated by DJs who use iPads to spin their digital "discs," although many traditionalists remain beholden to old-school records. A new generation of "iDJs" have had such an impact on the DJ scene that many traditional and new suppliers to the industry have created new digital solutions, like the Numark iDJ Live II (photo).

That a digital culture would eventually reinvent its music scene was a long time in the making. In 1948, CBS Records introduced what was then considered a major music milestone, the long-playing record. The CD, launched in 1983, upped the ante with a continuous, 74-minute playback time, far exceeding the 23 minutes per side of the original LP. [108] In 1997, the MP3 compression standard made its appearance, which four years later would play an essential role in the launch of the iPod music platform. MP3 was a "codec" — a COmpression/DECompression algorithm that created digital music files that were one quarter to 1/20 the size of uncompressed versions. [109]

MP3 changed the industry in less than a decade. Thanks to this format, EDM fans can now listen to whatever type of music they like, from drum and bass to breakbeats. In 2014, the total number of electronic dance music tracks streamed in the U.S. skyrocketed 55% to 11.2 billion, year-over-year. [110]

Many Ubertrends are at play in electronic dance music. Both Time Compression and Generation X-tasy have joined forces with the Digital Lifestyle to create a powerful, turbulent effect that is reshaping many markets, including entertainment.

104. Zachary Crockett, "The Invention of the Wah-Wah Pedal," *Priceonomics*, 05-Nov-15.
105. "Giorgio Moroder," *Wikipedia*, ret. 21-Dec-18.
106. "Kool Herc," *Wikipedia*, ret. 21-Dec-18.
107. "Love Parade," *Wikipedia*, ret. 21-Dec-18.
108. "LP record," *Wikipedia*, ret. 21-Dec-18.
109. "MP3," *Wikipedia*, ret. 21-Dec-18.
110. Daniel Terdiman, "Electronic Dance Music Is Hot, And Here's the Data To Prove It," *Fast Company*, 17-Jun-15.

Robot Love

It may sound like a terrible joke but David Levy, an artificial intelligence researcher at the University of Maastricht in the Netherlands, is serious when he speculates that we will be marrying robots by 2050 and that Massachusetts will be the first state to allow it. [111] Think we'll find robot love, anybody?

> " Around 2050, the state of Massachusetts will be the first jurisdiction to legalize marriages with robots."
>
> **David Levy**
> A.I. Researcher,
> University of Maastricht

Adds Levy irreverently, "At first, sex with robots might be considered geeky, but once a story like 'I had sex with a robot and it was great!' appears someplace like Cosmo magazine, I'd expect many people to jump on the bandwagon."

A skeptical University of Edinburgh robot scientist provides a sober counterpoint, "who," he asks, "would want to marry a robot?" But why not? Those donning avatars and leading double lives in Second Life have already succumbed to the charms of virtual reality affairs. [112] Others have reportedly even married a video game character. [113]

The real question is how far will our robotic future take us? Society's infatuation with all things digital suggests that a man-machine relationship is not all that far-fetched.

The movie *Her* already shows just how involving a digital relationship could become. [114] In the film, actor Joaquin Phoenix falls in love with an intelligent computer operating system called Samantha, voiced by the actress Scarlett Johansson.

111. Charles Choi, "Forecast: Sex and Marriage with Robots by 2050," *Live Science*, 12-Oct-07.
112. Alexandra Alter, "Is This Man Cheating on His Wife?," *The Wall Street Journal*, 10-Aug-07.
113. Kyung Lah, "Tokyo man marries videogame character," *CNN*, 17-Dec-09.
114. Spike Jonze, "Her," *Warner Bros.*, 13-Oct-13.

U.S. Consumers' Autonomous Vehicles Purchase Intention

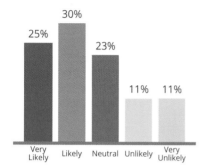

15-Oct-14 Boston Consulting Group
Revolution in the Driver's Seat: The Road to Autonomous Vehicles

Suffice it to say that many an entrepreneur is hard at work developing the ultimate love robot. One market watcher predicts that by 2050 "Amsterdam's red light district will all be about android prostitutes." [115]

Our love affair with robotics is already beginning to gather momentum. According to Boston Consulting Group, 55% of car buyers are very likely to buy a partially autonomous vehicle — an automobile that can almost drive itself. [116] However, had the study respondents been informed before filling out the questionnaire that they would be able to check e-mail or scroll through Facebook while the car was driving itself, that figure would likely have been much higher.

There are a host of videos on YouTube that show people driving their Tesla Model S or X automobiles in Autopilot mode, supported by such autonomous features as Autosteer and Auto Lane Change. [117] As with any new technology, there are bound to be accidents, either due to human error or some type of device failure.

The first accident involving a Tesla on autopilot drew worldwide attention because it involved an exotic new type of automotive technology. [118] The media blamed the crash mainly on a lack of regulation. [119] Tesla stresses that Autopilot "is an assist feature that requires you to keep your hands on the steering wheel at all times." [120] And there's growing evidence that the driver was not paying close attention. [121]

Another story that caught the fancy of the social media world was a February 2015 video and matching animated GIF that showed a man kicking a "robot dog" made by Boston Dynamics. [122] After CNN aired the story, a London-based reporter told me that the global news broadcaster had received "hundreds of complaints" about "animal cruelty."

Animal cruelty? It's a robot dog for heaven's sake! CNN clearly understood the broad implications, concluding that "As robots begin to act and look more and more like living things, it's increasingly hard not to see them in that way. And while in principle kicking a robot is not abusing a living being, after watching the video many felt uncomfortable." [123]

The Digital Lifestyle is blurring the boundaries between reality and the virtual world. Robot love, anyone?

Rise of the Machines

In 1987's *RoboCop*, Peter Weller plays a superhuman cyborg law enforcer in a distant dystopian future. That future has arrived. After reportedly spending hours negotiating the surrender of Micah Johnson, the sniper responsible for killing five police officers in July

115. Ian Yeoman, Michelle Mars, "Robots, Men and Sex Tourism," *Elsevier*, May-12.
116. Mark Phelan, "Buyers want self-driving cars," *USA Today*, 15-Oct-14.
117. "Model S Software Version 7.0," *Tesla Motors*, ret. 04-May-17.
118. Greg Gardner, "Tesla driver crashes, dies while car in Autopilot mode," *Detroit Free Press*, 01-Jul-16.
119. Jim Puzzanghera, "Fatal Tesla crash exposes lack of regulation over autopilot technology," *L.A. Times*, 01-Jul-16.
120. The Tesla Team, "A Tragic Loss," *Tesla Motors Blog*, 30-Jun-16.
121. Sam Levin, Nicky Woolf, "Tesla driver killed while using autopilot was watching Harry Potter, witness says," *The Guardian*, 01-Jul-16.
122. "Watch robot dog 'Spot' run, walk...and get kicked," *YouTube*, 15-Feb-15.
123. Phoebe Parke, "Is it cruel to kick a robot dog?," *CNN*, 13-Feb-15.

Tesla Autopilot Control Panel

Tesla Model S instrument cluster shows in realtime information the car uses to intelligently determine vehicle behavior relative to its surroundings. Tesla's self-driving technology paces the industry.

2016, Dallas police detonated a bomb near the suspect, using a bomb robot's extension arm. [124] It was the first, and certainly not last, manifestation of a real-life Robocop.

But our robot present is not all dystopia; a particular utopia is also being erected. For at the opposite end of the bomb robot spectrum lies, seductively, the sex bomb robot. At the January 2010 Adult Entertainment Expo in Las Vegas, a negligee-clad robot, dubbed Roxxxy, would mechanically intone "I love holding hands with you" each time it sensed its creator, Douglas Hines, touching its, um, her hand. [125]

Given the event's name, there's no real need to explain some of Roxxxy's other talents, suffice it to say that they also involve an extension. The company developing Roxxxy, True Companion, reports that despite its prohibitive $7,000 price, pre-orders for the sex robot are running "in the thousands." [126] But as *The Guardian*'s Jenny Kleeman notes, "[Roxxxy] was the talk of the show before her unveiling, and the laughing stock after." [127]

The prophecy of future robots to come was also foretold in the 2003 movie *Terminator 3: Rise of Machines*. A few years after that film's release, the London Aquarium featured an exhibit of three robot fish, developed by a University of Essex team. [128]

The "fish" resembled the real thing, undulating their bodies to propel themselves and equipped with sensors that enabled them to navigate autonomously while avoiding obstacles. Team Project Leader Professor

124. Patrick McGhee, Manny Fernandez, et al., "Dallas Shooting Suspect, Micah Johnson, 'Upset at White People'," *The New York Times*, 08-Jul-16.
125. Rosemary Brennan, "Meet Roxxxy, the Super Pricy Sex Robot Unveiled at the Adult Entertainment Expo," *Glamour*, 11-Jan-10.
126. Vittorio Hernandez, "Despite $7,000 Price, Pre-Orders For Roxxxy Sex Robot In Thousands," *Yibada*, 15-Sep-15.
127. Jenny Kleeman, "The race to build the world's first sex robot," *The Guardian*, 27-Apr-17.
128. "Robotic fish in action at London Aquarium," *Physics.org*, 06-Oct-05.

Huosheng Hu noted, "This work has many real-world applications including seabed exploration, detecting oil leaks in pipelines, mine countermeasures and improving the performance of underwater vehicles."

In 2006, Ryomei Engineering of Hiroshima, Japan, announced a "robot carp" that could monitor real-life koi by monitoring the level of oxygen in water, a key indicator of fish health. [129] The 32-inch-long (81 cm) robo-fish was equipped with a camera so it could survey bridges and oil platforms for underwater damage.

The early fruits of Japan's research and development efforts have been on prominent display. In 2004, Toyota introduced a trumpet-playing robot that played a rendition of the Stevie Wonder's *I Just Called To Say I Love You*. [130]

That was quite a feat, given that shaping one's lips correctly, dubbed *embouchure*, is one the of most challenging aspects of playing a woodwind instrument. Toyota accomplished the feat with a set of pneumatic bladders that continuously change pressure to play a variety of pitches. [131]

In a musical return volley, Honda's ASIMO robot conducted the Detroit Symphony Orchestra on May 13, 2008, performing *The Impossible Dream* from *Man of La Mancha* with cellist Yo-Yo Ma. [132]

No Chasing Windmills Here

On May 13, 2008, Honda's stair-stepping Asimo robot led the Detroit Symphony Orchestra in a performance of *The Impossible Dream* from *Man of La Mancha* with cellist Yo-Yo Ma.

Before long, the robot race between Honda and Toyota became a constant game of one-upmanship. In 2009, Toyota showed its robot running 7 kilometers per hour (4 mph), which was faster than the 6 km per hour ASIMO was capable of. [133]

ASIMO, which stands for Advanced Step in Innovative Mobility, has been in development since 1986 and like Toyota's robot is aimed at the non-industrial business market comprising of service robots. In June 2018,

129. Colin Joyce, "Robot koi carp designed to get up close and friendly with real fish," *The Telegraph*, 16-Mar-06.
130. "Toyota Robot," *YouTube* 18-Sep-07.
131. Astiles, "Robot Of The Week: Toyota's Trumpet Playing Robot," *Google Lunar XPRIZE*, 04-Mar-09.
132. Lawrence Van Gelder, "A Robot as Conductor," *The New York Times*, 25-Apr-08.
133. "Toyota Humanoid Robot Runs At 7 Km/hr," *SingularityHUB*, 29-Jul-09.

Honda announced that it would cease ASIMO production to focus on more practical uses in nursing and road transportation, or service robotics. [134] Could that be a repeat of the Sony Aibo decision and later about-face?

Service Robots

Japan is facing a ticking time bomb. The number of Japanese living in Japan is forecast to *decline* to fewer than 100 million by 2050, from 127 million today. [135] That year, about 40% of the population will be 65 or older. And because Japan only issues 50,000 work visas each year, elder care is set to become a significant challenge. [136]

An entirely different set of imperatives influences Japan's robot design principles. The government is focusing its robotic development efforts on helping an aging population, a smart goal indeed given that Japan and Italy share the distinction of having the world's oldest citizens.

The Japanese government's role in robot research has resulted in a quickened development pace. Robots of every possible function and size have been introduced, from Citizen's tiny Eco-Be, a miniature, 2.5-centimeter (1-inch), two-wheeled robot powered by a Citizen watch motor, to Japan's RI-MAN humanoid, being developed by RIKEN, a government-supported-supported research institute.

RIKEN's original goal was to design a service robot able to carry at least 70 kilograms (154 pounds), the average weight of a Japanese individual of advanced age. In 2015, RIKEN, demonstrated its latest iteration of RI-MAN, Robear, a robot able to carry as much as 80 kg (176 pounds).

Robear is the brainchild of Toshiharu Mukai, who has lead the Robot Sensor Systems Research Team since 2007 at the now-closed RIKEN-SRK Collaboration Center for Human-Interactive Robot Research. Robear is designed to perform strenuous tasks such as lifting elderly patients out of bed into a wheelchair, which is performed an average of 40 times a day by care workers, according to Mukai. [137]

Service robots will not be limited to nursing care. According to MarketsandMarkets, service robotics will top $24 billion by 2022. [138]

Say Hi to Robear, Your Care Robot

Optimized for human care, RIKEN-designed Robear features smart capacitive sensors, precise actuators and torque sensors that lends Robear a gentle touch and softer, more precise movement. Perfect for caring for individuals weighing up to 176 pounds (80 kg).

IMAGE COURTESY: RIKEN-SRK.

134. Dani Deahl, "Honda retires its famed Asimo robot," *The Verge*, 28-Jun-18.
135. Sam Byford, "This cuddly Japanese robot bear could be the future of elderly care," *The Verge*, 28-Apr-15.
136. Alec Ross, "Could our future nurses and caregivers be robots?," *LinkedIn*, 27-Feb-16.
137. Sam Byford, "This cuddly Japanese robot bear could be the future of elderly care," *The Verge*, 28-Apr-15.
138. "Service Robotics Market worth $24 Billion by 2022," *Markets and Markets*, Jan-17.

Service Robots Infiltrate the Hospitality Industry

At the Aloft hotel in Cupertino, Calif., guests are greeted by "Botlr," the robot bellhop, made by the start-up Savioke, which is used to make small deliveries to guest rooms. At the Hilton in McLean, Va., guests are met by "Connie" — a robot named after founder Conrad Hilton (middle). At Japan's Henn-na Hotel, which means "strange" in Japanese, a bevy of SoftBank robots do duty, like a desk clerk dressed as a velociraptor (right).

IMAGES COURTESY: SAVIOKE INC., HILTON WORLDWIDE INC., HENN-NA HOTEL.

> ❝ Welcome to the Henn-na Hotel. Please don't ask any difficult questions, because I'm a robot."

Robot Receptionist
Henn-na Hotel
Nagasaki, Japan

That growth will be driven by continuous technological advancements, including the development of autonomous robots; increased demand for domestic robots and home security and surveillance robots; child and elderly assistance, plus the growing use of service robots in defense, agricultural, medical, marine and aerial applications. [139]

Stay at the Aloft hotel in Cupertino, Calif. and meet Botlr, a Relay robot made by Savioke. The start-up claims that its team of robots has made more than 100,000 guest deliveries. [140] The Vdara in Las Vegas is the latest hotel to add Savioke robots to its staff, which deliver small items to guest rooms for a fee of $3 vs. $8 for regular room service. [141] Hilton Hotels announced that its McLean hotel in Virginia would feature a service robot called "Connie," named after company founder Conrad Hilton. [142]

Connie is based on the Nao platform, an $8,000 humanoid bot made by French robotics company Aldebaran. SoftBank took a majority stake in Aldebaran in 2012. SoftBank has announced that its Nao service robots, currently employed at stores in Japan and dubbed Pepper (see page 41), would eventually be sold at its Sprint company stores in the U.S. but it remains a no-show four years later. [143]

SoftBank robots are also used at the Henn-na Hotel In Japan, part of a Netherlands-themed "Huis Ten Bosch" amusement park, that is staffed by robots. Nao robots, skinned either as a life-sized velociraptor or a woman, check patrons into the Henn-na. Here's a sample of the velociraptor robot's dialog, "Welcome to the Henn-na Hotel. Please don't ask any difficult questions, because I'm a robot." [144] Robots are already starting to resemble their human counterparts. They're ready for customer service!

139. "Service Robotics Market Worth 18.02 Billion USD by 2020," *Markets and Markets*, 04-Dec-15.
140. "Savioke," ret. 04-May-17.
141. Terry Gardner, "At a Las Vegas hotel, this pair will bring snacks, drinks and more to your room," *L.A. Times*, 17-Jul-18.
142. Nick Statt, "Hilton and IBM built a Watson-powered concierge robot," *The Verge*, 09-Mar-16.
143. Cassandra Khaw, "Humanoid robots with a heart to be sold in the US next year," *The Verge*, 02-Sep-14.
144. Gideon Lewis-Kraus, "Check In With the Velociraptor at the World's First Robot Hotel," *Wired*, 02-Mar-16.

The Robot Invasion Has Begun

The LG HOM-BOT robot vacuum cleaner bears a striking resemblance to an amoeba (below) — a type of cell or organism that typically represents the first evolutionary steps of a new species.

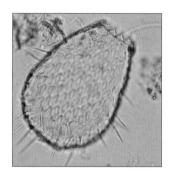

Rocco the Parrot Hijacks Alexa

Marion Wischnewski, from Great Shefford, U.K., took in a homeless African gray parrot that, besides liking to swear, also learned how to order strawberries, watermelons and ice-cream using Amazon's voice-activated assistant. Alexa, please tell me a clean bird joke.

Domestic Robots

In the 1973 movie *Sleeper*, Woody Allen plays a hapless robot impersonator in a futuristic society where domestic robot servants are *de rigueur*. [145] What could be dismissed as a 1970s comedic farce is well on its way to becoming a reality some 46 years later. But today's domestic robot is more like a rudimentary organism.

At the January 2013 Consumer Electronics Show (CES) in Las Vegas, LG introduced a new robot vacuum cleaner, the LG HOM-BOT, boasting "dual eye-mapping" — two cameras that take several images per second, scanning walls, ceilings and floors to better navigate its cleaning course. [146]

HOM-BOT avoids collisions using ultrasound and infrared sensors to detect obstacles, and its 1.5-centimeter (0.6-inches) long "brushes" provide improved location analysis. Not only does the LG HOM-BOT respond vocally, but once the machine has determined that it's finished, it automatically returns to its charging station and sings a little victory song. [147]

As the above images show, the LG HOM-BOT bears a striking resemblance to an amoeba — a unicellular organism thought to be one of the oldest forms of life on earth. [148]

Amoebae are predatory single-cell organisms that do not have a fixed shape, but project parts of their cell to create jellylike tentacles called pseudopods. It moves and feeds using these pseudopodia, which closely resemble the brushes of the Hom-Bot.

If single-cell organisms represent the first signs of new life, has the robot invasion already begun?

145. "Sleeper," *Wikipedia*, ret. 21-Dec-18.
146. Edwin Kee, "LG Hom-Bot Square Vacuums To Hit CES 2013 Showfloor," *Übergizmo*, 02-Jan-13.
147. Ry Crist, "LG Hom-Bot Square Review," *CNET*, 08-Sep-13.
148. "Unicellular organism," *Wikipedia*, ret. 21-Dec-18.

A Field Guide to the Robot Research and Development Industry

This directory of robot manufacturers sheds light on an industry of the future

IF ROBOTS ARE OUR FUTURE, THEN ROBOTIC MANUFACTURERS WILL FORM THE ELITE RANKS OF THE NEXT AGE. MANY ARE VIRTUALLY UNKNOWN, BUT DOMINANT PLAYERS WILL EMERGE IN THE NEXT DECADE.

This list is by no means all-inclusive. Also, there has been a noticeable trend of startups using industrial robot platforms, like Switzerland's ABB and Germany's KUKA, to create a host of robots, ranging from pizza-making bots to robot DJs.

AIST – Japanese industrial automation company AIST developed PARO, a robot baby harp seal covered in soft white fur. PARO behaves like a real pet: It enjoys being held, gets angry when slapped and likes to nap. PARO costs $6,000 but received a "Class II exempt pre-marketing notification" from the FDA in 2009. [1]

ASUS – In May 2016. ASUS has announced a domestic robot called Zenbo that looks like the mutant offspring of the desk-lamp iMac G4 and Wall-E. [2] Zenbo is equipped with facial recognition, can play music and includes a Siri-like voice interface. The ASUS bot also has a camera for sentry duty or taking photos. What's groundbreaking is that Zenbo will retail for $599.

Boston Dynamics – Acquired by Alphabet (aka Google) for $500 million in 2013, Boston Dynamics' "BigDog" robot is featured in numerous viral videos, including one where it's "kicked." Another YouTube video, featuring its Atlas next-generation robot, was shown on Jimmy Fallon's Tonight Show and has been viewed some 22 million times. [3] Alphabet has put Boston Dynamics up for sale. [4]

Honda – Introduced in 1996, Honda's childlike 1.3-meter (51-inch) tall ASIMO robot jogs at speeds of up to 7 km per hour (4 mph), serves tea, it's Japanese after all, and can carry on a simple conversation. ASIMO also walks up stairs, plays football (soccer), and is even able to pour you a drink or push a mail cart — giving it an early head start to climb from mailroom to CEO suite. [5]

iRobot – The iRobot Roomba, the first robot vacuum cleaner, was launched in 2002. Today, iRobot makes half a dozen robot vacuum cleaners. Given iRobot's track record it's not surprising that the Roomba is the most popular robot on the U.S. market today. Two models of the company's latest generations, the Roomba 960 ($449) and Roomba 690 ($279), are among the highest rated and best-selling iRobot vacuum cleaners on Amazon.com. In 2007, iRobot announced a 250-pound, weapons-firing, stair-climbing, ammo-carrying military bot, called Warrior X700, that would be able to carry a 500-pound payload, use its robotic arm to lift 150 pounds and run 16 kph (10 mph). [6] The latest bot is the iRobot Looj 330 Gutter Cleaning Robot, which blasts away leaves, dirt, clogs and sludge on its own. [7]

Kawada Industries – Kawada Industries' HRP-2 "Promet" is a 1.54-meter (five-foot) tall silver-and-blue robot, weighing 58 kilograms (128 pounds), that can walk, carry small objects, sit on the floor and pull itself up. Promet speaks a few words and can wave goodbye. [8]

LG – The LG HOM-BOT Square ($450), introduced in 2013, features seven Smart Clean modes and a Dual Eye 2.0 mapping system that learns your home's layout and automatically adjusts to various floor types. [9]

RIKEN – RIKEN, a government-supported research institute in Japan, initially developed a robot, called "RI-MAN," that could see, hear, smell and even carry a 12-kilogram weight (26 pounds). Its latest project, jointly created by the RIKEN-SRK Collaboration Center, is Robear, designed to carry at least 176 pounds (80 kg). [10]

1. Elena Ponte, "Recent FDA Medical Device Regulation And Its Relevance To Robotics," *Tech Policy Lab*, 27-Jan-14.
2. Brian Heater, "The $599 ASUS Zenbo robot is just trying to help out around the house," *TechCrunch*, 31-May-16.
3. "Atlas, The Next Generation," *YouTube*, 23-Feb-16.
4. Brad Stone and Jack Clark, "Google Puts Boston Dynamics Up for Sale in Robotics Retreat," *Bloomberg*, 17-Mar-16.
5. Mark Prigg, "Ascent of Asimo: From a clunky pair of legs to a football playing, disco dancing robot friend who can even pour you a drink," *Mail Online*, 17-Cot-14.
6. Noah Shachtman, "Roomba-Maker Unveils Kill-Bot," *Wired*, 17-Oct-07.
7. Len Calderone, "National Robotics Week Was A Hit!," *Robotics Tomorrow*, 02-Jun-14.
8. "Humanoid Robot HRP-2 'Promet'," *Kawada Industries*, ret. 04-May-17.
9. Jonathan Chan, "LG Hom-Bot Robot Vacuum Cleaner Review," *Reviewed.com*, 25-May-16.
10. Sam Byford, "This cuddly Japanese robot bear could be the future of elderly care," *The Verge*, 28-Apr-15.

Ryomei – Hiroshima-based Ryomei Engineering, a subsidiary of Mitsubishi Heavy Industries, developed a robot koi carp, at a cost of $300,000, which gathers information about the swimming koi surrounding it. The remote-controlled koi not only looks like a carp but also moves like one, maneuvering with a flick of its tail, while monitoring the water's oxygen level, a key indicator of fish health. In 2006, Ryomei said that it had no plans to market the robot fish and there has been no update since. [11]

Savioke – This startup's "Relay" robots are used in the hospitality business and have made more than 100,000 guest deliveries as of 2017. [12]

SoftBank Robotics – French robotics company Aldebaran, renamed SoftBank Robotics, is the developer of Pepper (formerly "Nao"), a bipedal robot that is currently on sale in Japan for about $1,800. At Google I/O in May 2016, the company announced that its platform is being opened more widely to Android developers. [13] Pepper is the platform chosen by Hilton, which partnered with IBM's Watson division to launch Hilton's "Connie" robot. [14] You can get a close-up look at our robotic future at Oakland airport, where Pepper is currently employed at the Pyramid Taproom restaurant. [15]

Sony – Sony makes the best-known consumer robot, Aibo, a robot dog that can act as a virtual pet. Since its May 11, 1999 launch, consumers purchased 150,000 of the toy-poodle-sized bot. [16] In 2006, Sony ceased production of Aibo, which, given the future potential of robotics, was a poor decision indeed. At the 2018 Consumer Electronics Show, Sony announced it was bringing Aibo back to the U.S., a move welcomed by those present, who were impressed by the new Aibo. [17] The resurrected robodog, boasting many new state-of-the-art features, will retail for $2,899. [18] The company also developed the bi-pedal Qrio robot but also abandoned that effort in 2006.

Tokai Rubber Industries – Working with Japanese research institute RIKEN, Tokai developed the Robot for Interactive Body Assistance (RIBA), which can lift humans weighing up to 80 kilograms (176 pounds). RIBA is the predecessor of Robear.

Toyota – In March 2004, Toyota unveiled its Partner robot that walked, waved its arms, bowed and was able to play the trumpet. At Toyota headquarters a robotic tour guide, Robina, greets visitors. Robina is part of Toyota's Partner Robot line, which also includes a bot called Humanoid. The 1.22-meter (4-foot) tall Humanoid is prototype for a series of "harmony with people" robots that Toyota hopes to build to serve as personal assistants, aides for the elderly and laborers.

ZMP – In April 2005, Tokyo-based ZMP, a robot research and rental firm, launched the $6,000 Nuvo, a 39-cm (15-inch) tall, two-legged robot that was able to pick itself up after falling and recognized voice commands such as "advance" and "stop." [19] ZMP has ceased development of Nuvo and is focusing on a home delivery robot called CarriRo. [20]

Zora Bots – This Belgium-based robot provider has sold more than 1,000 of its robots to healthcare facilities around the world. Zora robots, which can cost up to $18,000, can hold conversations, controlled by laptop, and are designed to offer elderly patients companionship.

There is a ready market for these types of robots as the number of people over 60 will more than double to 2.1 billion by 2050, according to the United Nations.

11. "Robocarp, the future of pond enforcement," *The Engineer*, 16-Mar-06.
12. "Savioke," ret. 05-Jan-19.
13. Brian Heater, "Pepper the Robot gets increased access for Android developers ahead of its US launch," *TechCrunch*, 19-May-16.
14. Nick Statt, "Hilton and IBM built a Watson-powered concierge robot," *The Verge*, 09-Mar-16.
15. Brian Heater, "Pepper the robot gets a gig at the Oakland airport," *TechCrunch*, 25-Jan-17.
16. The Associated Press, "Sony puts robot dog Aibo to sleep," *NBCNews.com*, 01-Feb-06.
17. Sam Byford, "I played with Sony's new Aibo robot dog, and I miss it already," *The Verge*, 11-Jan-18.
18. Brian Heater, "Sony's adorable new Aibo comes to the US in Sept," priced at $2,899," *TechCrunch*, 23-Aug-18.
19. Mark Allen, "I, Roommate: The Robot Housekeeper Arrives," *The New York Times*, 14-Jul-05.
20. "Delivery robot CarriRo Delivery," *ZMP Products*, ret. 04-Jan-19.

Moving Millions of Stock Units Without Nary a Collision

Kiva robots move inventory at an Amazon fulfillment center in Tracy, Calif. Amazon.com has about 100,000 of these robots buzzing about its warehouses around the globe.

IMAGE COURTESY: BLOOMBERG INC.

Will Robots Replace Work Done By Humans?

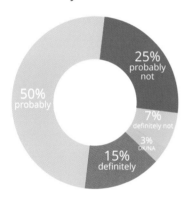

25% probably not

7% definitely not

3% DK/NA

15% definitely

50% probably

10-Mar-16 Pew Research Center

Industrial Robotics

One glance at a YouTube video of Amazon.com's "pick" but not yet "pack" robots will immediately convey the future potential of industrial robotics. In the video, Amazon bots whir through cavernous warehouses in a ballet of motorized movements, stopping just in time to avoid a collision. [149]

Statista estimates that worldwide shipments of industrial robots reached 371,400 units in 2018, up from around 249,000 in 2015. [150] Since the average industrial robot costs north of $100,000, this suggests a 2018 market of about $37 billion. [151] By 2023, the industrial robotics market will nearly double to $72 billion, according to MarketsandMarkets. [152]

The economics of employing industrial robots are very compelling. Amazon operates about 100,000 robots in its warehouses across the globe. Dave Clark, the retailer's senior vice president of worldwide operations and customer service, estimates that the robots reduce operating expenses by about 20%. [153]

That explains why Amazon paid $775 million in 2012 to buy Kiva Systems LLC, the developer of Amazon's industrial robots. The acquisition effectively put Amazon CEO Jeff Bezos in control of a critical industrial robotics market segment. Although Kiva initially promised to continue selling its technology to other retailers that pipe dream ended in April 2015 when Kiva was renamed Amazon Robotics and prospective buyers of Kiva robots were "encouraged" to let Amazon provide fulfillment services using Amazon warehouses and robots.

149. "Amazon warehouse robots," *YouTube*, 02-Dec-14.
150. "Estimated annual industrial robot shipments in selected regions worldwide," *Statista*, 2018.
151. "How Much Do New Robots Cost?," *RobotWorx*, ret. 04-May-17.
152. "Industrial Robotics Market worth US$72 Billion by 2023," *MarketsandMarkets*, Jul-17.
153. Kim Bhasin and Patrick Clark, "How Amazon Triggered a Robot Arms Race," *Bloomberg*, 29-Jun-16.

According to an analysis by Deutsche Bank, adding robots to one new warehouse saves Amazon $22 million in fulfillment expenses. Installing Kivas in the 100 or so distribution centers that still haven't implemented the technology would save Amazon an additional $2.5 billion.

The Future of Robotics

The big debate today is, how fast will robots start to replace workers? While 70% of Americans believe their job won't be automated, the Boston Consulting Group studied 21 industries in the world's 25 leading manufacturing export economies and concluded that the share of tasks performed by robots would rise from a global average of about 10% across all manufacturing industries today to around 25% by 2025. [154] [155]

That is a troubling prospect knowing that 5 million fewer manufacturing jobs exist today than in 2000. [156] Far more jobs have been lost to robots and automation than trade with China, Mexico or any other country.

The International Federation of Robotics puts the total number of industrial robots in operation currently at about 1.75 million, a number that will increase to between 4 and 6 million by 2025, according to BCG. [157] [158]

PricewaterhouseCoopers believes that by the early 2030s up to 38% of U.S. jobs could potentially be at high risk of automation. [159] Most Americans agree, with 65% thinking it's highly probable that robots will replace work done by humans, according to a Pew Research study.

And that convergence of humanity and machines discussed earlier is advancing rapidly. If you think robots will be limited to metal or plastic, perish the thought. In 2014, researchers at the University of Illinois developed a walking bio-bot powered by heart cells. [160]

At the École polytechnique fédérale de Lausanne, a team is developing soft, flexible and reconfigurable robots that resemble walking worms in action. Air-actuated, they behave much like human muscles and could be used in physical rehabilitation. The EPFL says the soft robots are made of low-cost materials and can easily be produced on a large scale. [161]

The 2017 debut of robot lawyers and surgeons suggests that professional jobs are also not immune from the trend of automation and AI.

But perhaps the biggest news comes from FANUC, a Japanese manufacturer of industrial robots, which says it's applying advanced video graphics and artificial intelligence technology to create robots that can learn from other bots. [162] That would be a significant leap forward for robotics.

Now you know why the BBC reported that robots could one day demand "legal rights." [163] The robot revolution is dawning, and it will be disruptive.

Robot Rage Ready to Roil

The news headline said it all: "Hotel Workers Fret Over a New Rival: Alexa at the Front Desk." The drumbeat that automation will replace jobs is growing louder. King's College London researchers Lukas Schlogl and Andy Sumner believe the effects of automation will not likely be mass unemployment, but wage stagnation and labor market polarization. [1] Research authored by economists Daron Acemoglu of MIT and Pascual Restrepo of Boston University supports that view. [2] When one or more industrial robots were introduced into the workforce between 1993 and 2007, it led to the elimination of 5.6 jobs within a local area where people commute for work. The report also found that wages declined, dropping 0.5% per 1,000 employees when one or more robots entered the picture. A McKinsey Global Institute report predicts that technology will drive a 30% decline in food service and lodging jobs between 2016 and 2030. That forecast resembles the 38% decline in manufacturing jobs from 1960 to 2012. [3] As Arnold Schwarzenegger said in the 1984 sci-fi thriller *The Terminator*, "I'll be back."

1. Lukas Schlogl and Andy Sumner, "The Rise of the Robot Reserve Army: Automation and the Future of Economic Development, Work, and Wages in Developing Countries," *Center for Global Development*, Jul-18.
2. Daron Acemoglu and Pascual Restrepo, "Robots and Jobs: Evidence from US Labor Markets," *National Bureau Of Economic Research*, Mar-17.
3. "Jobs Lost, Jobs Gained: Workforce Transitions in a Time of Automation," *McKinsey Global Institute*, Dec-17.

154. Christopher Rugaber, "Will your job be automated? 70% of Americans say no," *The Associated Press*, 04-Oct-17.
155. Hal Sirkin et al., "The Robotics Revolution: The Next Great Leap in Manufacturing," 23-Sep-15.
156. Patrick Gillespie, "Rise of the machines: Fear robots, not China or Mexico," *CNN Money*, 30-Jan-17.
157. "Robots and jobs: Evidence from the US," *America's Trade Policy*, 17-Apr-17.
158. Harold Sirkin et al.," The Robotics Revolution: The Next Great Leap in Manufacturing," *BCG*, 23-Sep-17.
159. Richard Berriman and John Hawksworth, ""Will robots steal our jobs?," *PwC*, 24-Mar-17.
160. Liz Ahlberg, "Muscle-powered bio-bots walk on command, *Illinois News Bureau*, 30-Jun-14.
161. EPFL, "Soft robots that mimic human muscles," *YouTube*, 11-Oct-16.
162. April Glaser, "These industrial robots teach each other new skills while we sleep," *Recode*, 14-Oct-16.
163. "Robots could demand legal rights," *BBC News*, 21-Dec-06.

Videogaming

It's a mild winter evening in San Francisco and art galleries, restaurants and clubs are overflowing with crowds buzzing about the latest and greatest in videogaming. It's another gathering of the Game Developers Conference, which attracts more than 28,000 industry insiders to the City.

Two thousand miles away in Columbus, Ohio, the buzz is much the same at the MLG.tv Columbus Arena — the nation's first eSports arena, a 14,000 square-foot facility that plays host to hundreds of spectators who come to watch America's newest pass-time, eSports. [164]

Attendees follow all the eSports action on huge video screens, which frequently feature organized, multiplayer video game competitions. Wait a minute! Are you telling me that people gather in large facilities to watch others play videogames? Yes, they do. eSports is expected to generate more than $1.6 billion in annual revenue by 2020, according to PwC. [165]

The 28,000 game developers gathered in San Francisco form the top of the pyramid that feeds the insatiable appetite of a market that generated $138 billion in revenues in 2018. [166] And 2018 was a cataclysmic year due to another big wave: It was the first year that the gaming industry garnered more than half of its revenues from mobile, with mobile gaming registering a scorching 26% growth rate in 2018 to top $70 billion.

More than 2.3 billion people worldwide play videogames, and despite a deeply held belief that videogaming is the territory of teens, the average age

Trendy Game: Fortnite

After launching in July 2017, Fortnite has attracted 125 million registered players in less than a year. About 40 million people play the game once a month. Fortnite's staggering growth is due to its availability on almost every major platform, including iOS devices and the Nintendo Switch, plus the fact that it's free. Publisher Epic Games offers character skins and other cosmetic add-ons for purchase.

IMAGE COURTESY: EPIC GAMES INC.

164. Kevin Parrish, "America's First eSports Arena Arrives In Columbus, Ohio," *Tom's Hardware*, 25-Sep-14.
165. Niraj Chokshi, "What You Might Not Know About E-sports, Soon to Be a $1 Billion Industry," *The New York Times*, 27-Aug-18.
166. Brendan Sinclair, "Global games market to hit $137.9 billion this year - Newzoo, *gamesindustry.biz*, 30-Apr-18.

of a gamer today is 37, according to Entertainment Software Association. [167]

In 2014, videogames outsold both music and video. And videogamer wanderlust has already propelled eSports to a $612 million global market with an audience of some 134 million people.

Grand Theft Auto V, released on September 17, 2013, for the PlayStation 3 and Xbox 360 consoles, sold 11.2 million units in its first 24 hours, generating $816 million in revenues, and went on to reach $1 billion in sales in just *three days*. Those figures smashed records previously held by the *Call of Duty* videogame and such blockbuster movies as *The Avengers* and *Avatar*. Yet it was still not enough to make the list of the 10 most popular videogame franchises of all-time that together have generated a staggering $82 billion in revenues (table):

Top Grossing Videogames of All-Time				
Rank	Title	Platform	Year	Billions
1.	Space Invaders	Arcade/Atari 2600	1978	$13.9
2.	Pac-Man	Arcade/Consoles/Mobile/PC	1980	$12.8
3.	Street Fighter II	Arcades, SNES, Genesis	1991	$10.6
4.	World of Warcraft	PC	2004	$8.5
5.	CrossFire	PC	2007	$6.8
6.	Wii Sports	Wii	2006	$6.0
7.	Lineage series	PC	1998	$5.7
8.	Wii Fit	Wii	2007	$5.0
9.	Donkey Kong	Arcade/NES/Coleco	1981	$4.4
10.	Dungeon Fighter Online	PC	2005	$4.0
Total				$81.6
Source: 15-Aug-15 Business Insider; Video Game Sales Wiki; Encylopedia Gamia				

And to demonstrate how much videogames have evolved *vis-à-vis* movies. Even the No. 10 videogame on the above list, *Dungeon Fighter Online*, has generated more money than the highest grossing film of all-time, *Avatar*, which at $2.8 billion trails the videogame's revenues of $4 billion. [168] Surprisingly, some Broadway musicals fare better. *The Lion King*, at $6.2 billion in worldwide revenues, would rank sixth in the above table, ahead of "Wii Sports." [169]

The consumer videogame market did not develop overnight. It took a long time to reach its exalted status. The Magnavox Odyssey videogame console and the Atari Pong arcade game both debuted in 1972. [170]

The Odyssey was a groundbreaking development. It was the first videogame device to use a television set and the first videogame to be advertised on TV. Odyssey retailed for $100 and shipped with several games, including Table Tennis. Magnavox sold more than 100,000 Odyssey units in 1972, and more than 350,000 by the end of 1975.

Now compare that 350,000 figure to the 500 million units Sony has sold during four generations of its PlayStation videogame console, and you get a sense for how far the videogame market has progressed over these past 47 years. [171]

Is it any surprise then that videogames have transformed our vocabulary? As seen earlier, such terms as "All your base are belong to us," and an

167. Tom Gibson, "Bigger Than Hollywood: The Numbers Behind Video Gaming," *Bloomberg*, 04-Aug-15.
168. "All Time Highest Grossing Movies Worldwide," *The Numbers*, ret. 04-May-17.
169. Marine Cole, "The 10 Top-Grossing Broadway Musicals," *The Fiscal Times*, 24-Sep-14.
170. "Early history of video games," *Wikipedia*, ret. 04-May-17.
171. Chaim Gartenberg, "Sony celebrates selling 500 million PlayStations with a limited edition 2TB PS4 Pro," *The Verge*, 09-Aug-18.

uncharacteristically harsh treatment readily doled out on social media these days, "FAIL," are two prime examples. And if FAIL is not forceful enough to describe a person's or business' failing, then "EPIC FAIL" is in order, in all caps of course. The word "epic" has a clear-cut connection to adventure gaming.

And who doesn't like a secret? An "easter egg" is a hidden feature buried deep in applications by software developers. An easter egg that created a sensation was the 2005 discovery that the videogame Grand Theft Auto: San Andreas contained a hidden graphic of two game characters having sex.

Another term born in gaming lingo is "nOOb," which wittily, and perversely, refers to a newbie. "FTW" — for the win — is now part of mainstream jargon and is quite often used in social media posts. "Pwn" — which rhymes with own — reportedly was the result of the accidental use of the "P" key on a keyboard instead of its close neighbor, the "O" key, when trying to type "Own." [172]

Deliberate mistyping produces the term "prOn," which disguises "porn," a word that's frequently filtered out of online forums.

MMORPG

In an alternate reality where a microsecond can make the difference between winning and losing, it's a given that time-saving abbreviations rule.

WOW stands for World of Warcraft, a massively multiplayer online role-playing game (MMORPG) released by Blizzard Entertainment in 2004. At its peak in October 2010, World of Warcraft boasted 12 million subscribers, making it the world's most-subscribed MMORPG and setting a Guinness record for paid, subscription-based games.

Another popular MMORPG, MapleStory, created by a South Korea game development studio Wizet and published by Nexon, attracted some 39 million user accounts globally by 2006. [173] MapleStory players assume identities of warriors, magicians and thieves and collectively fight monsters. MapleStory is free to play but Nexon's Cash Shop, a cyber bazaar of sorts, charges players anywhere from 30 cents to $25 for virtual accessories for their in-game characters, from souped-up vehicles to wacky hairstyles.

Closely held Wizet revealed in 2006 that it earned more than $300 million from MapleStory. [174] The studio eventually merged with parent company Nexon. [175] Zynga adopted Nexon's pioneering revenue model in its games, which helped the San Francisco-based company raise a $1 billion IPO in 2011. [176] [177] Nexon's success proves that even in the virtual world of videogaming, shopping can be therapeutic.

MapleStory's "Cash Shop" Sells In-Game Character Accessories

MapleStory, a massively multiplayer role-playing game (MMORPG) from South Korea, has reportedly earned as much as $300 million in one year selling virtual trinkets to its videogame players.

IMAGE COURTESY: WIZET.

172. Larry Hester, "12 Video Game Buzzwords to Make You Sound Smart," *Complex*, 04-Jun-13.
173. "MapleStory," *Wikipedia*, ret. 22-Dec-18.
174. "MapleStory," *Wikipedia*, ret. 22-Dec-18.
175. "Wizet," *Fandom by Wikia*, ret. 22-Dec-18.
176. Dean Takahashi, "Online gaming giant Nexon raises $1.2B in Toyko IPO," *VentureBeat*, 23-Dec-11.
177. JP Mangalindan, "Today in Tech: Zynga goes public," *Fortune*, 16-Dec-11.

Wii Haptic Interface Helps Patients Rehabilitate Faster

The Nintendo Wii features an innovative haptic, or gesture-based, interface that requires physical use, an activity that helps patients rehabilitate faster. The therapy is dubbed "Wiihab" and in this photo provided by Nintendo, Lillian Faybik, 87, of Manhattan, plays baseball on the Wii at The Carter Burden Center for the Aging in New York City.

IMAGE COURTESY: NINTENDO OF AMERICA INC.

> "The Wii takes the place of some physical therapy to get your strength back."
>
> **Roy Heathcoat**
> Veteran, VA Medical Center
> Milwaukee, Wisc

Videogame Therapy

You know things have changed when you tune into the evening news and see a senior citizen, ahem "active adult," playing a Nintendo Wii videogame. The trend is called "Wiihab," and it's casting a whole new light on an activity once reserved for trigger-happy teens.

Nintendo's Wii can play a significant role in rehabilitation therapy for patients recovering from strokes, broken bones, surgery and even combat injuries. In a Department of Veteran Affairs report, paraplegic Roy Heathcoat observes, "The Wii takes the place of some physical therapy to get your strength back." [178]

The Wii was the first console to feature a motion-sensitive controller that requires body movements similar to traditional therapy exercises. Patients become so engrossed they're almost oblivious to the workout. In Colorado Springs, Recreational Therapist Colleen Roy uses Wii basketball in her therapy sessions. [179] Wii games and activities remain an excellent tool for therapy because, as patient Andres Schmidt puts it, "The Wii does help you forget about all the problems that you have."

Another area where videogames are proving their mettle is brain fitness. Inspired by Tohoku University Professor Dr. Ryuta Kawashima's work in neurosciences, Nintendo developed the "Brain Age" videogame series for the DS. [180]

Designed to help fight memory loss, Brain Age and its successor, Brain Age 2, have been big hits for Nintendo, with nearly 34 million copies sold, according to the company. [181]

178. Megan Tyson, "Wii-hab: Veterans Get More Than Fun With Wii Rehab," *U.S. Dept. of Veteran Affairs*, 08-Mar-10.
179. "Your Healthy Family: Wii basketball therapy," *KOAA*, ret. 04-May-17.
180. "Brain Age: Train Your Brain in Minutes a Day!," *Wikipedia*, ret. 22-Dec-18.
181. "Top Selling Software Sales Units," *Nintendo*, ret. 04-May-17.

Videogame Violence

In 1982, when videogaming was a mere $10 billion market, U.S. Surgeon General C. Everett Koop shocked the audience at a University of Pittsburgh seminar on family violence when he warned, "There's nothing constructive in the [video] games. Everything is eliminate, kill, destroy." [182]

In 2011, Anders Breivik dismayed the world when he killed eight people in an Oslo, Norway bomb attack and 69 more in a youth camp rampage. Breivik was a fan of violent videogames, and news reports suggest that these games may have contributed to his violent behavior. Police found a manifesto that talked about two games, in particular, *World of Warcraft* and *Call of Duty: Modern Warfare 2*, which were two of the most popular video games at the time. [183]

So will the violence featured in videogames negatively influence future generations? One study, *Psychology, Crime & Law*, concludes that violent videogames affect juveniles in differing ways, based on the subject's natural personality. [184] The researchers discovered that in only two of the 125 cases studied did rising anger reach levels that might be considered cause for concern, suggesting that dangerous levels of anger were rarely triggered by gaming. Angry gamers will cool off, and calm players will get agitated, but then again it only takes two to create havoc.

IMAGE COURTESY: THRESHOLD GLOBAL STUDIOS.

Most Popular Video Game Tetris Set to Become a Movie

Chinese billionaire Bruno Wu is investing $80 million to produce a movie based on the classic videogame Tetris, titled *Tetris The Movie*. At 495 million units, Tetris is the best-selling videogame of all-time.

Videogame Movies

The trend of turning a videogame into a film began with *Super Mario Brothers* in 1993 and gained momentum with *Mortal Kombat* in 1995 and *Lara Croft: Tomb Raider* in 2001. It exploded with *Angry Birds* and *World of Warcraft* in 2016, which earned, respectively, $352 million and $434 million (table, right).

But the most significant impact of videogaming may well be the move to mobile. That was quite evident in July 2016 when the videogame Pokémon Go burst onto the scene, zooming from zero users to 45 million in the span of two weeks. [185] Videogames are still in their infancy. Up next is virtual reality, which may provide this form of entertainment with its biggest adrenaline shot yet.

182. Joseph Dominick, "Videogames, Television Violence and Agression in Teenagers," *Journal of Communication*, Jun-84.
183. Lucy Goodchild van Hilten, "Can video games cause violence?," *Elsevier*, 19-Aug-15.
184. John Timmer, "Study finds stable personalities unaffected by violent games," *Ars Technica*, 03-Apr-07.
185. Jacob Kastrenakes, "People are quickly losing interest in Pokémon Go," *Bloomberg*, 23-Aug-16.

Rnk	Title	Release Date	Box Office Revenue	Publisher
	Top 40 Films Based On Video Games Ranked By Revenues			
1.	Warcraft	June 10, 2016	$433,537,548	Blizzard Entertainm.
2.	Rampage	April 13, 2018	$423,900,102	Warner Bros. Inter.
3.	The Angry Birds Movie	May 20, 2016	$352,333,929	Rovio Entertainment
4.	Prince of Persia: The Sands of Time	May 28, 2010	$336,365,676	Ubisoft
5.	Resident Evil: The Final Chapter	January 27, 2017	$312,257,250	Capcom
6.	Resident Evil: Afterlife	September 10, 2010	$300,228,084	Capcom
7.	Lara Croft: Tomb Raider	June 15, 2001	$274,703,340	Eidos
8.	Tomb Raider	March 16, 2018	$273,521,715	Square Enix
9.	Assassin's Creed	December 21, 2016	$240,558,621	Ubisoft
10.	Resident Evil: Retribution	September 14, 2012	$240,004,424	Capcom
11.	Need for Speed	March 14, 2014	$203,277,636	Electronic Arts
12.	Pokémon	July 18, 1998	$163,644,662	Nintendo
13.	Lara Croft: Tomb Raider - Cradle of Life	July 25, 2003	$156,505,388	Eidos
14.	Resident Evil: Extinction	September 21, 2007	$148,412,065	Capcom
15.	Pokémon 2000	July 17, 1999	$133,949,270	Nintendo
16.	Resident Evil: Apocalypse	September 10, 2004	$129,394,835	Capcom
17.	Mortal Kombat	August 18, 1995	$122,195,920	Midway Games
18.	Resident Evil	March 15, 2002	$102,441,078	Capcom
19.	Hitman	November 21, 2007	$99,965,792	Eidos
20.	Street Fighter	December 23, 1994	$99,423,521	Capcom
21.	Silent Hill	April 21, 2006	$97,607,453	Konami
22.	Max Payne	October 17, 2008	$85,416,905	Rockstar Games
23.	Final Fantasy: The Spirits Within	July 11, 2001	$85,131,830	Square
24.	Hitman: Agent 47	August 21, 2015	$82,347,656	Square Enix
25.	Pokémon 3	July 8, 2000	$68,411,275	Nintendo
26.	Doom	October 21, 2005	$55,987,321	id Software
27.	Silent Hill: Revelation	October 26, 2012	$52,302,796	Konami
28.	Mortal Kombat: Annihilation	November 21, 1997	$51,376,861	Midway Games
29.	Super Mario Bros.	May 28, 1993	$20,915,465	Nintendo
30.	Pokémon Heroes	July 13, 2002	$20,867,919	Nintendo
31.	House of the Dead	October 10, 2003	$13,818,181	Sega
32.	In the Name of the King: A Dungeon Tale	January 11, 2008	$13,097,915	Microsoft Studios
33.	Street Fighter: The Legend of Chun-Li	February 27, 2009	$12,764,201	Capcom
34.	Ratchet & Clank	April 29, 2016	$11,821,329	Sony Interactive Ent.
35.	Wing Commander	March 12, 1999	$11,578,059	Origin Systems
36.	Alone in the Dark	January 28, 2005	$10,442,808	Infogrames
37.	DOA: Dead or Alive	September 7, 2006	$7,516,532	Tecmo
38.	Kingsglaive: Final Fantasy XV	July 9, 2016	$6,479,980	Square Enix
39.	BloodRayne	January 6, 2006	$3,650,275	Majesco
40.	Double Dragon	November 4, 1994	$2,341,309	Technos Japan
Total Revenues of Top 40 Videogame-Based Movies:			$5,260,496,926	

Source: Ret. 01-Jul-18 Wikipedia

Super Mario: The First Videogame to Be Made into a Movie

In 1993, the Super Mario franchise became the first videogame to become a movie. Another 34 games have followed. Super Mario made $21 million. World of Warcraft grossed $434 million in 2016.

IMAGE COURTESY: NINTENDO OF AMERICA INC.

Virtual Reality

Put on a virtual reality headset and look around. You'll immediately be spellbound by immersive 3D vistas. It's the most transformational experience you'll ever have, bar none.

It's extraordinary experiences like these that promise to vault virtual reality into a host of new markets, in the process creating a $61 billion market by 2023. [186] It has already taken a long time for VR to fulfill its promise, judging by its stop-and-start history.

The term virtual reality was popularized in the 1980s by Jaron Lanier, one of its modern pioneers. In 1991, Sega announced its trendsetting Sega VR headset, which used LCD screens in its visor, stereo headphones, plus inertial sensors to allow the system to track and react to user head movements. The 1990s also brought one of the first films to feature virtual reality, 1992's *The Lawnmower Man*.

But it wasn't until 2007 when Google introduced its 3D Street View feature that VR began to wake up from its long nap. In 2010, Palmer Luckey created the first prototype of the Oculus Rift VR platform. Luckey went on to raise $2.4 million on Kickstarter in August 2012 and subsequently sold Oculus to Facebook for $2 billion in March 2014, to the consternation of many of the company's early Kickstarter supporters. [187]

The Oculus Rift camp consists of owner Facebook plus Samsung, which launched its first Samsung Gear VR headset on November 27, 2015. Oculus Rift ($400) requires a powerful PC, but that requirement has been addressed in Oculus' latest headset, Oculus Go, which costs just $200 (sidebar). The second VR platform to launch was HTC Vive on April 5, 2016. Vive is a collaborative effort between HTC and game developer Valve Corp. Sony

Virtual Reality at Walmart

Walmart is adding 17,000 Oculus Go VR systems in approximately 4,700 U.S. locations. [1]

The virtual reality headsets use 45 modules that run employee training simulations, such as a Black Friday shopping rush. The Oculus systems will also familiarize employees with this leading-edge technology. Virtual reality at Walmart? Now I will totally enjoy my Walmart greeter training.

1. Adi Robertson, "Walmart is putting 17,000 VR headsets in its US stores for training," *The Verge*, 20-Sep-18.

---

186. "Virtual Reality (VR): Exponential Growth of 49.71% CAGR is Expected," *ResearchAndMarkets.com*, 03-May-18.
187. "Virtual reality," *Wikipedia*, ret. 04-Jan-19.

Google Cardboard Jolted the Virtual Reality Market Awake

There is no faster way to kickstart a market than to make an enabling tool available for free or nearly free. That's what Google did with Cardboard, its reference set VR headset, which was actually produced by Zeiss, Mattel, Dodocase, and even *The New York Times*.

IMAGE COURTESY: GOOGLE LLC.

joined the party on October 13, 2016, with its PlayStation VR platform, a headset add-on for its popular PlayStation 4 platform.

Last, but not least, is Google, which shipped its Daydream VR system in November 2016. Daydream is integrated into the Android operating system starting with the release of Android 7.1, aka Nougat.

Google kicked the VR market into high gear by releasing a fold-out cardboard viewer and matching VR platform, distributed to all attendees at its I/O 2014 developers conference.

Google Cardboard is a low-cost system designed to be used with a head-mounted smartphone. More than 10 million Cardboard VR headsets have been shipped as of early 2017. [188]

188. Adi Robertson, "Google has shipped over 10 million Cardboard VR headsets," *The Verge*, 28-Feb-17.

TechRadar: Oculus Go "Is the Headset That Will Take VR Mainstream"

One technology site believes the latest Oculus Go VR headset is the clear leader in the consumer virtual reality market today. A key advantage over the older but more powerful Oculus Rift is that Go is a stand-alone device, meaning it no longer requires a PC. TechRadar's Michelle Fitzsimmons and Gerald Lynch write that "Oculus Go marks a new era for VR, one in which anyone can simply slip on a headset and dive into virtual realms." They note that although not perfect, Oculus Go offers a comfortable fit and solid build, excellent visual quality and the promise of more content to come. For its $229 price, Oculus Go is a better value than the tethered Oculus Rift. Continuing their praise, "Oculus Go is, in many ways, the dawn of a new era in virtual reality (VR)." Despite its low price, Oculus Go has also done away with the smartphone, unlike Google Cardboard you just slip on the headset and you go. [1]

1. Michelle Fitzsimmons, Gerald Lynch, "Oculus Go Review," *TechRader*, 29-Jun-18.

Cyber Warfare

Friday, April 27, 2007 was a cool but dry Spring day with temperatures in the 50s (10 C). In Tallinn, Estonia's capital, the new defense minister, Jaak Aaviksoo, was trying to access the country's leading newspaper site, *Postimees*, to no avail. He tried a few other news sites, but they also generated an error.

> " This was the first time that a botnet threatened the national security of an entire nation."
>
> **Jaak Aaviksoo**
> Minister of Defense, Estonia

Then an aide rushed in to report that Estonia's leading bank was under attack. Worse, government communications were also about to go down. A so-called botnet had invaded the country's computer networks and was causing havoc among dozens of targets. It was the world's first real act of cyber warfare. [189]

As Aaviskoo tells *Wired*, "The attacks were aimed at the essential electronic infrastructure of the Republic of Estonia. All major commercial banks, telcos, media outlets, and name servers — the phone books of the internet — felt the impact, affecting a majority of the Estonian population. It was the first time that a botnet threatened the national security of an entire nation."

While Estonia fell victim to a brute force "denial of service" attack, a more sophisticated form of cyber warfare took place in Iran. In January 2010, inspectors with the International Atomic Energy Agency visiting Iran's Natanz uranium enrichment plant noticed that centrifuges used to enrich uranium gas were failing at an unprecedented rate. The cause was a complete mystery to both the visiting inspectors as well as their Iranian hosts. But when a Belarus computer security firm was called in five months later to

189. Joshua Davis, "Hackers Take Down the Most Wired Country in Europe," *Wired*, 21-Aug-07.

Cyber Warfare Videogame Redux

Norse is a U.S.-based company that monitors malware and spyware. It offers an interactive representation of actual worldwide cyber attacks by bad actors "based on a small subset of live flows against the Norse honeypot infrastructure." The Norse map resembles the vintage video game Missile Command.

troubleshoot computers that were constantly crashing and rebooting, the company discovered a handful of malicious files belonging to the world's first digital weapon, Stuxnet, which was unlike any other virus or worm known before. Rather than merely stealing data from computers or hijacking them, Stuxnet was designed to cause physical destruction of equipment controlled by the machines. [190]

The Stuxnet worm infecting Iran's nuclear facilities was considered extremely dangerous because it could shut down the entire national power grid. Cybersecurity experts labeled Stuxnet the world's first known cyber super weapon designed specifically to destroy real-world targets.

Gaming the System

The perpetrators of both of these first cyber warfare attacks were easy to ascertain. The Russians had objected strongly to Estonia's planned removal of a bronze statue the Soviets had built in 1947 to commemorate their war dead. The Russian government had warned ominously that removal of the statue would be "disastrous for Estonians."

Israel, meanwhile, was strongly opposed to Iran's ability to produce uranium. The middle eastern nation had succeeded in producing 839 kilograms (1,850 pounds) of low-enriched uranium — enough to build a nuclear weapon. Industry experts believe that Stuxnet was developed by the U.S. in concert with Israel. [191]

Fast forward to 2016. Evidence points to the Russians as the most likely culprits behind the hacking of the U.S. Democratic National Committee's computers, which lead to the release of confidential and very embarrassing

---

190. Kim Zetter, "An Unprecedented Look at Stuxnet, the World's First Digital Weapon," *Wired*, 03-Nov-14.
191. Ellen Nakashima and Joby Warrick, "Stuxnet was work of U.S. and Israeli experts, officials say," *The Washington Post*, 02-Jun-12.

documents. [192] Leaked information revealed that DNC chairwoman, Debbie Wasserman Schultz, schemed to undermine the presidential campaign of Senator Bernie Sanders, confirming the worst suspicions of the party's left wing. Schultz ended up resigning her post.

The government announced in 2016 that "The U.S. Intelligence Community is confident that the Russian Government directed the recent compromises of e-mails from U.S. persons and institutions, including from U.S. political organizations. These thefts and disclosures are intended to interfere with the U.S. election process." [193] This Russian intrusion sounds like something straight out of a cyber spy novel.

Evidence that the Russians and Chinese have been actively hacking U.S. institutions is so overwhelming that the Pentagon was forced to declare in 2011 that cyberattacks by foreign entities were an act of war. [194] As early as 1996, just *two years* after the mainstreaming of the internet, 42% of respondents to a survey by the Computer Security Institute and the FBI reported a breach. [195] That figure soared to 70% in 2000, some 18 years ago.

In February 2008, the Air Force posted a Cyber Command recruiting video on YouTube that shows the Pentagon's headquarters in Washington, D.C. and opens with this statement, "This building will be attacked 3 million times today." [196] Imagine the level of cyber warfare today if 10 years ago there were already *1 billion* cyber attacks on the Pentagon annually.

The Air Force needs all the help it can get. Cyber attacks are exploding, and the daily siege of the Pentagon is just part of today's cyber warfare landscape. If anything, attacks have become more brazen, as the Estonia and U.S. political hacks suggest. And more widespread too. From media sites to major corporations, hackers are proving that they're capable of infiltrating any organization's ostensibly secure computers.

Cyber snoopers broke into NASA's digital network in December 2005 and stole a mind-boggling 20GB of data, which was routed to a server in Taiwan. That country is widely acknowledged by U.S. security specialists to be a digital way station for the Chinese government. [197]

In January 2010, Adobe, Intel, Google and other companies were subject to a coordinated hacking campaign. Google said the attacks originated in China, leading the company to abandon the Chinese market. [198]

The following year, Morgan Stanley admitted that it too had been hit by the same China-based hackers who attacked Google, an operation that cybersecurity firm McAfee dubbed "Aurora." McAfee estimates that the number of companies known to be hit by Operation Aurora now exceeds 200. [199] *The New York Times* reported in 2013 that Chinese hackers were routinely attacking its computers. [200] The Chinese have been implicated in numerous hacking incidents dating as far back as 2005.

192. Eli Lake, "Cybersecurity Experts Say Russia Hacked the Democrats," *Bloomberg News*, 25-Jul-16.
193. "Joint Statement from the Department Of Homeland Security and Office of the Director of National Intelligence on Election Security," *Department of Homeland Security*, 07-Oct-16.
194. Siobhan Gorman and Julian Barnes, "Cyber Combat: Act of War," *The Wall Street Journal*, 31-May-11.
195. "CSI/FBI 2000 Computer Crime And Security Survey," *PBS FRONTLINE*, Feb-01.
196. "Air Force Cyber Command Recruiting Video," *YouTube*, 28-Feb-08.
197. Benjamin Elgin, "Network Security Breaches Plague NASA," *Bloomberg Businessweek*, 19-Nov-08.
198. Robert McMillan, "Google Hack Raises Serious Concerns, US Says," *PC World*, 22-Jan-10.
199. Michael Riley, "Morgan Stanley Attacked by China-Based Hackers Who Hit Google," *Bloomberg Businessweek*, 28-Feb-11.
200. Nicole Perlroth, "Hackers in China Attacked The Times for Last 4 Months," *The New York Times*, 30-Jan-13.

The United States' Power Grid Is Very Vulnerable to Attack.

The FBI has kicked off a nationwide program warning of the dangers faced by U.S. utilities from damaging cyber attacks like the brazen December 2016 hacking of Ukraine's power grid.

The startling cyber intrusion of Sony in late 2014 rattled corporate America. If tiny and relatively unsophisticated North Korea was indeed responsible for the Sony intrusion, and all indications are that it was, imagine the scale of attacks that Russia and China are already engaging in and the type of cyber terrorism they are capable of unleashing.

As I wrote in a 2013 ReadWrite article, "World War III is already here — And we're losing." [201] Many others share that worldview.

Government organizations and companies spend vast amounts of money on security precautions. But the situation has become so dire that the Defense Department, whose Advanced Research Projects Agency (DARPA) created the internet in the 1960s, "is beginning to think it created a monster," reports *Bloomberg Businessweek*. [202]

As Rand Corporation puts it: "Cyberspace is its own medium with its own rules. Cyber attacks are enabled not through the generation of force but by the exploitation of the enemy's vulnerabilities." [203] And weak spot exploration is a *forté* of hackers.

IMAGE COURTESY: SHUTTERSTOCK.

Hacking the Grid

If there's one big weak spot in this world today, it's our vast warren of power lines, collectively called the "power grid." Network security professionals believe that the threat of an attack on a nation's infrastructure is all too real, mainly because the power grid is so vulnerable to attacks.

On December 23, 2015, hackers invaded a utility control center in a western region of Ukraine and took nearly 60 substations offline, plunging more

201. Michael Tchong, "World War III is already here — And we're losing," *ReadWrite*, 05-Feb-13.
202. Chi-Chu Tschang, The New E-spionage Threat, *Bloomberg Businessweek*, 09-Apr-08.
203. Martin Libicki, "Cyberdeterrence and Cyberwar," *RAND Corporation*, Oct-09.

than 230,000 residents in the cold and dark. It was the first confirmed hack of a power grid. [204]

Experts believe that if hackers were to knock out 100 strategically located generators in the Northeast, the damaged grid would quickly overload, causing a cascade of secondary outages across multiple states. While some areas might recover quickly, others could be without power for weeks. That would mean no internet, no TV, no refrigerator, no burglar alarm, resulting in massive chaos. The U.S. got a preview of how destructive a power outage can be in 2003, when overhanging foliage downed a power line in Ohio, resulting in a blackout that quickly spread from the coastal Northeast into the Midwest and Canada, leaving 45 million Americans and 10 million Canadians without power. [205]

The University of Cambridge and insurer Lloyd's of London believe that a lengthy outage across 15 states and Washington, D.C., would leave 93 million residents in the dark. Damage to the economy would run into hundreds of millions of dollars, including a surge in hospital fatalities. [206]

In July 2018, the Department of Homeland Security announced the creation of the National Risk Management Center, a new cyber hub that will coordinate critical infrastructure protection measures against attacks and subversion by online adversaries.[207]

Hacktivism

In the 2006 movie, *V for Vendetta*, the protagonist "V," played by Hugo Weaving, is an anarchist freedom fighter who attempts to ignite a revolution through elaborate terrorist acts, while always wearing a Guy Fawkes mask. The story of *V for Vendetta* is essential because the movie plays a pivotal role in the birth of Anonymous, the world's most famous hacker collective.

V for Vendetta was directed by James McTeigue and is based on the 1988 DC/Vertigo Comics limited series of the same name written by Alan Moore and illustrated by David Lloyd. The screenplay was written by the Wachowski sisters, Lana (formerly Larry Wachowski) and Lilly (Andy Wachowski), who directed 1999's *The Matrix*. The Wachowskis were early fans of Alan Moore's graphic novel and wrote a draft screenplay In the mid-1990s before work began on *The Matrix*.

Unfortunately, Moore was unhappy with film adaptations of his other works, *From Hell* (2001) and *The League of Extraordinary Gentlemen* (2003) and asked not to be credited or paid royalties for *V for Vendetta*. He ended cooperation with the publisher, DC Comics, after its corporate parent, Warner Bros., failed to retract statements about Moore's supposed endorsement of the film. Moore felt that the script contained "plot holes" and ran contrary to the theme of his original work, which was to juxtapose

204. Kim Zetter, "Inside the Cunning, Unprecedented Hack of Ukraine's Power Grid," *Wired*, Mar-16.
205. James Scott and Drew Spaniel, "The Energy Sector Hacker Report," *ICIT Briefing*, 24-Aug-16.
206. Katie Bo Williams and Cory Bennett, "Why a power grid attack is a nightmare scenario," *The Hill*, 30-May-16
207. Devin Coldewey, "DHS launches a new cyber hub to coordinate against threats to US infrastructure," *TechCrunch*, 31-July-18.

two political extremes — fascism and anarchism. [208]

While Moore distanced himself from the *V for Vendetta* movie, his illustrator David Lloyd felt it had a positive effect: "The Guy Fawkes mask has now become a common brand and a convenient placard to use in protest against tyranny – and I'm happy with people using it. It seems quite unique, an icon of popular culture being used this way." [209]

What captivated David Lloyd was another unusual Digital Lifestyle phenomenon: the ability for the online world to propel ideas at internet speeds. Thanks to netizens, the Guy Fawkes mask quickly spread around the globe as a symbol of activism.

Anonymous, the hacker-activist group that traces its 2003 origins to the 4chan online community, shared images of the stylized Guy Fawkes mask of *V for Vendetta* in internet chat forums. In 2008, two years after the movie's release, Anonymous used the mask for the first time at a protest against the Church of Scientology.

Anonymous is a loose association of international activist hackers, called "anons." [210] The group is the driving force behind the "hacktivism" trend — the subversive use of computers and computer networks to promote a political agenda. [211] Few knew Anonymous in 2008, but its adoption of the Guy Fawkes mask dramatically raised its profile, leading to protest movements in places as far off as Egypt and Brazil. Anonymous focuses its attacks on high-profile organizations and causes, including city and state officials of Flint, Michigan; Harambe, the Cincinnati Zoo gorilla; the police force of Ferguson, Missouri; and even ISIS.

A parallel trend was the rise of the "ethical hacker" — defined as hackers who dedicate themselves to hacking tasks that do not victimize anyone. There is even an organization that now certifies ethical hackers.

Guy Fawkes Mask Gains Popularity After *V for Vendetta*

The dystopian 2006 political thriller *V for Vendetta* and its 1982 book namesake popularized the Guy Fawkes mask. It is now better known as the "Anonymous Mask," after being adopted by the activist group and becoming a widely recognized symbol of global activism.

Security Finance Dissonance

The U.S. plans to spend $700 billion on the military in its upcoming 2019 fiscal year. [212] Most of that money will be spent on resources and equipment designed for old-fashioned warfare, like $11 billion on the F35 Joint Strike Fighter. Unfortunately, the real spending priority should be on cyber warfare.

In 2017, venture capital firms funded cybersecurity startups to the fune of $7.6 billion, double the $3.8 billion invested in 2016. [213] Clearly, the U.S. cybersecurity market is woefully underfunded.

As Delaware Senator Thomas Carper puts it, "The issue of Cyber Warfare is not science fiction anymore. It's reality." [214]

208. Rich Johnston, "Moore Slams V for Vendetta Movie, Pulls LoEG From DC Comics," *CBR.com*, 23-May-05.
209. Rosie Waites, "V for Vendetta masks: Who's behind them?," *BBC News Magazine*, 20-Oct-11.
210. "Anonymous," *Wikipedia*, ret. 04-Jan-19.
211. "Hacktivism," *Wikipedia*, ret. 04-Jan-19.
212. Brad Lendon, "What the massive US military budget pays for," *CNN*, 28-Mar-18.
213. Becky Peterson, "Cybersecurity startups raked in $7.6 billion in VC money in 2017," *Business Insider*, 07-Jan-18.
214. "More Security, Less Waste: What Makes Sense for our Federal Cyber Defense," *Opening Statement*, 29-Oct-09.

Artificial Intelligence

Digital Lifestyle

The final Jeopardy answer was insane: "William Wilkenson's 'An Account of the Principalities of Wallachia and Moldavia' inspired this author's most famous novel." Realizing he was too far behind to catch IBM's Watson computer, Ken Jennings threw in the towel, writing on his video screen, "I, for one, welcome our new computer overlords," a line borrowed from an episode of *The Simpsons*. [215]

The Jeopardy win was a milestone for IBM's artificial intelligence, or AI, research. In 1997, another computer built by I.B.M., called Deep Blue, defeated Garry Kasparov, the world chess champion, in a six-game match. At the time, it was considered a monumental achievement and a significant leap forward in the field of AI. [216]

Jennings was no run-of-the-mill Jeopardy player. He achieved fame by winning 74 Jeopardy games in a row. Unlike Kasparov, Jennings was graceful in defeat, sagely commenting, "I had a great time, and I would do it again in a heartbeat. It's not about the results; this is about being part of the future."

Deep Blue's win stretched the limits of comprehension so much that Gary Kasparov suspected foul play. But these advances in

Kasparov Trash Talks Deep Blue

When IBM's Deep Blue computer defeated world chess champion Garry Kasparov on May 11, 1997, machine learning made history by becoming the first computer to beat a world champion in a six-game match under standard time controls. After Kasparov won the first game, lost the second and drew the next three, Deep Blue took the match by winning the final game. Unlike Ken Jennings (text), who accepted his Jeopardy defeat gracefully, Kasparov cried foul, accusing the computer of being controlled by a real grandmaster. Robot hate!

215. John Markoff, "Computer Wins on 'Jeopardy!': Trivial, It's Not," *The New York Times*, 16-Feb-11.
216. Dylan Loeb McClain, "First Came Deep Blue, Which Defeated a Chess Champion," *The New York Times*, 17-Feb-11.

Google Proselytizes the Benefits of Artificial Intelligence

DeepMind is the brains behind Google's research project AlphaGo, which is the first program to beat South Korean Go master Lee Se-dol in 2016 at the ancient game of Go, a feat considered impossible before the match.

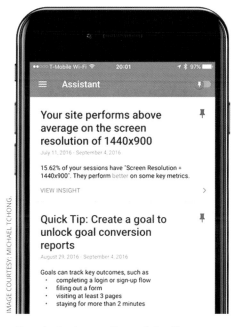

Google Assistant: One of the First Machine Learning Applications

Assistant, a feature of the Google Analytics mobile app, analyzes site traffic results, flags issues and makes recommendations based on Google Analytics' gathered intelligence on millions of site traffic data points. Interestingly, the machine learning feature launched in the mobile app first.

artificial intelligence were predicted as far back as the 1980s when companies such as Symbolics, Gold Hill Computers and others were hard at work developing the technology. Unfortunately, the science of AI imploded due to a few high-profile collapses and the field was set back some 20 years.

Today, IBM's advances with Deep Blue and Watson, and Google's DeepMind are pushing AI science forward. Google scored a feat when DeepMind's AlphaGo, stunned one of the world's top Go players, South Korean Go master Lee Se-dol, on March 9, 2016, defeating him in a three-and-a-half hour game. Go is believed to be the most complicated board game ever created.

The match was considered an important gauge of how far artificial intelligence, also referred to as the science of machine learning, had come in its quest to create machines smarter than humans. Observed Lee at a Seoul news conference, "I am very surprised because I have never thought I would lose. I didn't know that AlphaGo would play such a perfect Go." [217]

Machine learning is about to revolutionize many data-driven fields. Digital marketing, for example, is ripe for reinvention, judging by what Google has delivered as part of its Google Assistant feature in its Google Analytics mobile app (left). One day, artificial intelligence will become so adept at crunching massive amounts of data to provide tailored solutions that it will no longer be necessary to hire "experts" of any kind.

Many will say hooray to that.

217. Choe Sang-Hun and John Markoff, "Master of Go Board Game Is Walloped by Google Computer Program," *The New York Times*, 09-Mar-16.

E-commerce

The Digital Lifestyle is inundating retail, and shopping habits will never be the same again. The first telltale sign came in January 2016 when Walmart announced it would close 269 stores. [218] That same year, Macy's said it would shutter 100 stores. [219]

Hardest hit so far is Sears, which as recently as 2012 had 1,305 Kmart stores and 867 Sears stores in the U.S. [220] Today, it has fewer than 800 full-line stores nationwide. The latest announcements bring the total number of stores closing in 2018 to 3,800. Add to that the 6,403 stores that closed in 2017, and you have a sobering tally of 10,203 store closings in two years. By comparison, the previous all-time high was 6,163 store closings in 2008.

Real estate developers count on premium retail brands to anchor their shopping malls, but Amazon's 100 million prime members are siphoning off sales from brick-and-mortar stores (chart). [221] Not only do Prime members spend more money than non-members, $1,500 per year compared to about $625 per year for non-members, they also price-compare less, relegating the less desirable shoppers to the likes of JCPenney, K-Mart and Walmart. [222]

Walmart is trying to claw back market share from Amazon, acquiring four marketing and e-commerce optimization start-ups, Torbit, Inkiru, OneOps and Tasty Labs, after forking over $3 billion for e-tail startup Jet. [223] [224]

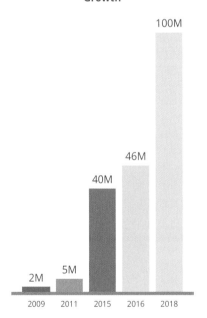

Amazon.com U.S. Prime Membership Growth

100M — 2018
46M — 2016
40M — 2015
5M — 2011
2M — 2009

19-Apr-18 Jeff Bezos, Amazon.com, CNN; 05-Oct-16 Recode/Cowen; 03-Feb-15 USA Today/CIRP; 16-Sep-11 Piper Jaffray/PracticalEcommerce

218. Krystina Gustafson and Courtney Reagan, "Wal-Mart to close 269 stores as it retools fleet," *CNBC*, 15-Jan-16.
219. Matt Egan, "Macy's is closing another 100 stores," *CNN/Money*, 11-Aug-16.
220. Nathan Bomey and Charisse Jones, "Does Sears have a future? Troubles mount with more Sears, Kmart store closures," *USA Today*, 23-Aug-18.
221. Jason Del Rey, "Amazon has 143 billion reasons to keep adding more perks to Prime," *Recode*, 05-Oct-16.
222. Elizabeth Weise, "Amazon Prime is big, but how big?," *USA Today*, 03-Feb-15.
223. Panos Mourdoukoutas, "Who Killed Wal-Mart's Business Model?," *Forbes*, 16-Jan-16.
224. "Walmart Agrees to Acquire Jet.com, One of the Fastest Growing e-Commerce Companies in the U.S.," *Walmart*, 08-Aug-16.

The Digital Lifestyle Has Claimed Many Iconic Retail Brands

At its peak in 2003, Borders operated 1,249 stores under its own and the Waldenbooks brands. On September 18, 2011, it liquidated its last store in Singapore, a victim of the "Amazon Factor."

Walmart is not only being squeezed in cyberspace, but its revenue model is also under attack from Costco, which skims off upscale shoppers, saddling Walmart with younger and less affluent customers. [225]

If there's a lesson that can be learned from the ongoing battle between Amazon.com and Walmart, it's that clicks are annihilating bricks. The trend is reflected in Walmart's market cap, which is nearly half that of Amazon's, despite Walmart generating almost five times Amazon's revenues (table).

Amazon.com Versus Walmart					
Retailer	Annual Revenues	Revenue Growth	Net Income	Employees*	Market Capitaliztion
Amazon.com	$178B	+30.8%	$3.0B	566,000	$803B
Walmart	$500B	+2.98%	$9.9B	2,200,000	$276B

Source: * Finance.Yahoo.com, Macrotrends ret. 11-Jan-19

The impact of the "Amazon Factor" is not limited to mass retailers. In its core markets of books, music and consumer electronics, Amazon has had a devastating impact on the retail landscape, contributing to the loss of such former stalwarts as Bebe, Blockbuster, Borders, Circuit City, Good Guys, RadioShack and Tower Records.

The decline in retail sales and the growing popularity of e-commerce has been a recurring theme of Wall Street investors these days. The pundits have focused *ad nauseam* on the large gulf that separates total U.S. retail sales, estimated at $5.3 trillion in 2018, and U.S. e-commerce sales, a puny $526 billion by comparison.

But the e-commerce trend is bound to gather momentum over the next decade. The acceleration will be fueled by Millennials and Digital Natives who mostly shun traditional retail. A study of Prime members reveals that 39% are aged 18-35, compared to 30% of the U.S population. [226]

By 2035, as much as 40% of U.S. retail sales, or more than $2 trillion will move through online channels. The chief driving forces behind this trend are AI and industrial robotics, which will optimize how products consumers buy are chosen, warehoused, packed and delivered...the same day.

225. "Wal-Mart Grocery Shopper less Affluent, Younger," *The Media Audit,* Nov-11.
226. "US Consumer Survey—Amazon Prime Members," Fung Global Retail & Technology, Apr-17.

Grayfields: The Future of Malls?

More than 500 deserted malls litter the landscape — part of a "grayfields" trend sweeping through suburbia. Many of these shopping malls were abandoned after anchor tenants left due to the "Retail Apocalypse" contagion. They leave behind hulking, gray skeletons, explaining the trend's name.

Grayfields

The U.S. is saddled with abandoned shopping malls, deserted wastelands dubbed "grayfields" by architects — malls and big-box stores surrounded by vast, decaying concrete parking lots whose initial use has run its course. [227] These grayfields were abandoned by store tenants who left, in part, due to the "Amazon Factor" or the "Retail Apocalypse," depending on your point of view.

The Retail Apocalypse has exacted an enormous human toll. The more than 10,000 stores that closed in the past two years took 66,500 U.S. retail jobs with them in 2017 alone. [228]

While the Digital Lifestyle is undoubtedly to blame for many of these exits, some store closings were due to extenuating circumstances. Sports Authority, once the nation's largest sporting goods retailer, had to shutter all its 450 stores after the retailer admitted to being swamped by debt. [229]

America's suburbs are now stuck with these grayfields. The number of American malls peaked at around 1,500 In the mid-1990s. Today, there are only about 1,000 left. [230] In a story about dying malls, CBS News' Mark Strassmann noted in 2014 that "no new enclosed mall has been built since 2006." [231]

The same report featured Robin Lewis, author of *The New Rules of Retail*, who predicted that "fully half of all our malls will close in the next 10 years." That suggests that about 500 are set to bite the dust. There are many reinvention concepts, some tied to the demographics of aging, like walk-in clinics and gyms. It remains to be seen whether those ideas will sell.

Consumers: I'd Rather Wash Dishes Than Shop in Stores

Some of the woes bedeviling retail could be self-inflicted. When one third, 32%, of consumers say they would rather wash dishes than visit your place of business, you may have an issue. Capgemini asked 6,000 people worldwide their opinions about brick-and-mortar stores and found that 71% find it difficult to comparison shop, 66% are annoyed by long checkout lines, while 65% can't find items they want. [1] Those shopper challenges are all addressed by online merchants. Pass the kitchen sponge.

1. "Future of bricks and mortar stores in question as a third of consumers would rather 'wash the dishes' than shop in-store," *Capgemini*, 13-Jan-17.

227. Kaid Benfield, "Reinventing the Big Box Store," *Citylab*, 12-Mar-12.
228. Chris Isidore, "Jobs everywhere! Except at stores," *CNNMoney*, 05-Jan-18.
229. Sharokina Shams, "Sports Authority among many retail chains to close stores," *KCRA 3*, 02-Mar-16.
230. Leanna Garfield, "Here's what could happen to America's hundreds of dead malls," *Business Insider*, 01-Jun-18.
231. Mark Strassman, "A dying breed: The American shopping mall," *CBS News*, 23-Mar-14.

Wearables

The thought was jarring. The founder of the Tumblr social media site, David Karp, wrote in a post that he and his girlfriend were going to "try wearing Fitbits during sex (with each other) to graph our physical exertion." [232] It was the most *outré* manifestation of a trend dubbed "the quantified self."

The quantified self refers to the science of self-knowledge gained through data generated by technology. [233] And the platform of choice for producing this type of data is "wearables" — digital gadgetry such as activity trackers by Fitbit, Garmin or Under Armour; smartwatches like the Apple Watch; or other devices, like the Oura ring sleep tracker (page 181), that can be worn in such a way as to measure pulse and other bodily vitals.

As Karp's post divulged, the wearables trend was about to engulf society, reshaping fashion and technology in a blistering maelstrom of machine-body convergence. Wearing a computer on one's wrist to monitor vital signs would one day become a common element of the quantified self.

Self-quantification or, as some like to call it, the self-surveillance trend, began in earnest with the introduction of the Fitbit Tracker in September 2008 (photo). [234] That device, a clip-on, has largely been subsumed by the popularity of Fitbit's bracelet-type trackers, such as the Fitbit Flex 2 ($59) and Fitbit Charge 2 ($121). Sure, athletes have had the benefit of wearable heart monitors since the 1980s, but those measured the pulse of but a tiny sliver of the market.

IMAGE COURTESY: FITBIT INC.

The First Mass-Market Digital Wearable: Fitbit Tracker

Launched in September 2008 and shipping in early 2009, the Fitbit Tracker provided Fitbit with a "first-mover advantage" in the emerging world of wearables. An innovator's most treasured benefit.

232. David Karp, "This is going to get competitive," *Tumblr*, 09-Feb-10.
233. "Quantified Self," *Wikipedia*, ret. 04-Jan-19.
234. Claire Cain Miller, "Fitness Gadget Aims to Help Users Lose Weight," *The New York Times*, 09-Sep-08.

Appearing next on the wearables scene was Pebble, which ignited the smartwatch trend with a record-setting $10 million Kickstarter crowdfunding raise in May 2012. [235]

Pebble's entry and the imminent arrival of the much-rumored Apple Watch began to shift the balance. In 2013, fully 61% of all wearable technology devices were fitness related sport/activity trackers. [236]

How big could the wearables market be? IDC predicts that wearables shipments will reach 222 million units worldwide by 2021 "as smartwatches and new product categories gain traction." [237]

While that is a rosy forecast, the impact of the quantified self would stretch far beyond mere shipment forecast numbers.

Perhaps the most extraordinary story involving a wearable fitness tracker is the story of Richard Dabate, who lived in Ellington, Conn. with his wife, Connie Dabate. On the morning of December 23, 2015, Connecticut police arrived at his home, and Dabate spoke of a violent struggle with a masked intruder who had zip-tied him to a chair, demanded his wallet and credit cards, cut him with a knife and then fatally shot his wife in the basement.

But a Fitbit on Connie Dabate's waistband told an entirely different story. It recorded that she had walked 1,217 feet (370 m) around the house during the time her husband said the intruder was allegedly attacking them. [238]

It was the fifth incident of a wearable featuring prominently into a legal case or police investigation. In 2014, a Calgary, Alberta law firm used a Fitbit device as part of a personal injury case to show that their client was far more active before a car accident injured her, according to *Canadian Lawyer* magazine. [239]

In March 2017, a Garmin device worn by Kelly Herron, a Seattle runner, tracked her ordeal as she fought off an attacker in a park restroom.

And in a case profiled on NBC's Today Show, a Fitbit showed that a 43-year old woman who claimed she was sexually assaulted during a break-in in Susquehanna Valley, Penn. was actually walking around at the time she told investigators she had been sleeping. [240]

It's not just the Digital Lifestyle Ubertrend that is behind the exceptional changes being brought about by wearables.

Other Ubertrends, such as the Fountain of Youth and Unwired, are also conspiring to accelerate the adoption of these devices, in particular, the Apple Watch Series 4.

Apple Watch: Wearables Market Innovation Leader

Apple has clawed its way to the top of the wearables industry, capturing a 15% share of the market. In the process, The company has battered the Swiss watch industry, which has seen its fortunes wane after a Silicon Valley smartwatch captured the world's timekeeping imagination.

IMAGE COURTESY: APPLE INC.

235. Jenna Wortham, "Pebble Smartwatch Tops Out at $10 Million on Kickstarter," *The New York Times*, 11-May-12.
236. "Wearable Computing Devices, Like Apple's iWatch, Will Exceed 485 Million Annual Shipments by 2018," *ABIresearch*, 21-Feb-13.
237. IDC Forecasts Shipments of Wearable Devices to Nearly Double by 2021 as Smart Watches and New Product Categories Gain Traction, *IDC*, 20-Dec-17.
238. Christine Hauser, "In Connecticut Murder Case, a Fitbit Is a Silent Witness," *The New York Times*, 27-Apr-17.
239. Jennifer Brown, "Data fit for the courtroom?," *Canadian Lawyer*, 02-Feb-15.
240. Jeff Rossen, "Here's how a FitBit helped police crack a case in Lancaster County, Pennsylvania," *WGAL*, 19-Apr-16.

Snap Spectacles Shoots Vids 4u

Snap, the public company best known for its Snapchat social network, launched Spectacles (Version 2: $150) — sunglasses capable of shooting 10-second video clips that can be shared on Snapchat and other social networks — in 2016. The short-lived Google Glass, a product that even at its lofty developer price of $1,500 garnered a tremendous amount of publicity, opened the doors for Snap's Spectacles. Long lines formed at vending machines in California and New York to buy the first version but despite intense initial interest, Snap lost nearly $40 million on the device, "primarily related to excess inventory reserves and inventory purchase commitment cancellation charges."

IMAGE COURTESY: SNAP INC.

Killer App: Health

It may sound like a *contradictio in terminis*, but health is the "killer app" of wearable devices. Judging by the market's early response, the new Apple Watch Series 4 with ECG monitoring represents the first step towards the consumerization of clinical healthcare.

In September 2018, Apple introduced the first wearable capable of producing electrocardiogram readings using an FDA-approved ECG app, a feature traditionally reserved for medical devices used for clinical purposes. [241]

While previous versions of the Apple Watch were able to track the wearer's heartbeats per minute, ECG heart monitoring is much more sophisticated. Using two skin-touching electrodes, it measures the natural electricity that powers your heart, providing a graph of the way your heart is beating.

Within days of the ECG app's launch, reports began filtering in that owners of the new Apple Watch had been alerted to underlying heart disease issues. When Ed Dentel, a 46-year-old communications consultant living in Richmond, Va. updated his Apple Watch Series 4 on the evening of December 6, 2018, he didn't expect it to immediately diagnose atrial fibrillation, or "AFib." [242]

After receiving an official EKG, Dentel's doctor concluded, "This thing may have just saved your life." Devices like the Apple Watch Series 4 and advanced apps could transform how we care for chronic diseases.

Now imagine a future where wearables will be completely integrated into the fabric of life. Chips embedded under your skin, glasses that record and display augmented reality, smart fabrics that make you feel better.

I have seen the future and I'm wearing it on my wrist.

> " The new Apple Watch Series 4 with ECG monitoring represents the first step towards the consumerization of clinical healthcare."
>
> **Michael Tchong**
> Ubertrends

241. Jeremy Horwitz, "Apple prepares to release ECG app for Watch Series 4," *VentureBeat*, 28-Nov-18.
242. Soo Youn, "An Apple Watch told a 46-year-old man he had an irregular heartbeat. It was right.," *ABC News*, 11-Dec-18.

Blockchain & Cryptocurrency

Digital Lifestyle

The history of Bitcoin is legendary and equally mysterious. On October 31, 2008, a white paper entitled *Bitcoin: A Peer-to-Peer Electronic Cash System* was posted to an e-mail discussion list focusing on cryptography by someone called Satoshi Nakamoto. [243]

To this day, Nakamoto's true identity remains a mystery, although quite a few attempts have been made to identify this celebrated individual, including, reportedly, a sophisticated stylometry text comparison by the NSA. [244] But even that supposedly successful attempt has not resulted in the public unmasking of Satoshi Nakamoto. Surely *someone* in the leaky U.S. government would have coughed up that information by now.

Newsweek took another stab. In a sensational article, the publication pointed its finger at model-train enthusiast Dorian Nakamoto suggesting he was the brains behind Bitcoin's. [245] That article was widely discredited and even lead to a lawsuit by the purported Mr. Nakamoto himself.

But the cryptocurrency crowd was hooked. One year after the publication of Nakamoto's groundbreaking white paper, Bitcoin launched as the world's first cryptocurrency. While there had been previous attempts at creating online currencies with ledgers secured by encryption, including B-Money and Bit Gold, these attempts never made it past the drawing table.

It took just three years for Bitcoin to become the intense focus of investment speculation. The first run-up in Bitcoin prices, symbol: BTC, happened in mid-2011. Another run-up took place in late 2013 and the most recent peak occurred in December 2017. Market interest in the cryptocurrency

243. Satoshi Nakamoto, "Bitcoin: A Peer-to-Peer Electronic Cash System," *Bitcoin Project*, 31-Oct-08.
244. Alexander Muse, "How the NSA Identified Satashi Nakamoto," *Medium*, 26-Aug-17.
245. Leah McGrath Goodman, "The Face Behind Bitcoin," *Newsweek*, 06-Mar-14.

hasn't abated since. And if imitation is the sincerest form of flattery, a host of imitators would soon laud their mentor.

The success of Bitcoin has resulted in an explosion of cryptocurrencies. The open-source architecture of most of these currencies means that it's relatively straightforward to make copies of the basis software, or "fork" its code in developer parlance.

Most of the forks are derived from Litecoin, which is based on Scrypt (pronounced "ess crypt") — a password-based key derivation function created by Colin Percival. The Scrypt algorithm was specifically designed to make it costly to perform large-scale custom hardware attacks by requiring large amounts of memory.

The number of cryptocurrencies listed on CoinMarketCap.com, the reference site for digital asset developers and speculators alike, has jumped from just seven on April 28, 2013, the first available historical snapshot, to a staggering 2,067 today. [246]

These dramatic developments provide ready evidence of the impact Bitcoin and other cryptocurrencies are having on the financial community today and, eventually, on the world at large.

A New Wave: ICOs

In 2016, one cryptocurrency platform, Ethereum, came very close to halting Bitcoin's momentum. Ethereum uses a cryptocurrency dubbed Ether to facilitate blockchain-based smart contracts and apps. What drew investor attention to Ethereum was the emergence of Initial Coin Offerings or ICOs.

Much like an initial public offering, an ICO is a method of raising capital that exchanges future crypto coins for cryptocurrencies of immediate, liquid value. Investors provide the ICO-offering organization Bitcoin or Ether, and they receive a set value of a yet-to-be-issued coin.

Most ICOs sell what basically amounts to IOUs for future tokens under the Simple Agreement for Future Tokens (SAFT) framework. And like IPOs, ICOs are speculative and their intrinsic value proposition depends entirely on the organization's mission.

In 2016, 52 ICOs raised $100 million (chart). These figures jumped to 454 ICOs and $6.6 billion, respectively, in 2017. [247] The 2017 ICO figure far exceeds the $900 million in venture funding raised by blockchain and blockchain-adjacent companies through traditional venture capital rounds. [248] In 2018, total funds raised exploded to a staggering $21.5 billion from 1,072 initial coin offerings.

The first ICO was orchestrated by Mastercoin, now called Omni, which raised 5,000 Bitcoin valued at $500,000 in July 2013. The second ICO was held in mid-2014 and raised 31,591 Bitcoin worth $18.4 million — a spectacular success for Ethereum inventor Vitalik Buterin and his Zug,

Initial Coin Offering (ICO) Trend: Funds Raised

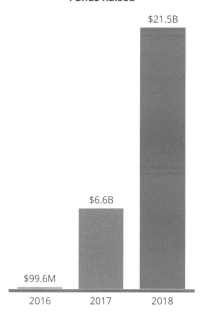

11-Jan-19 CoinSchedule

---

246. "Historical Market Snapshot," *CoinMarketCap*, 28-Apr-13.

247. "Cryptocurrency ICO Stats 2017," *CoinSchedule*, ret. 11-Jan-19.

248. Jason Rowley, "ICOs delivered at least 3.5x more capital to blockchain startups than VC since 2017," *TechCrunch*, 04-Mar-18.

Ethereum's Is the Platform for Crypto-Asset Entrepreneurs

Ethereum and its Ether cryptocurrency have become the platform of choice for ICOs due to its ease of development and built-in scripting language, which allows for the creation of smart contracts.

Switzerland-based nonprofit, the Ethereum Foundation. [249]

Ethereum has become the preferred platform for ICOs because, unlike Bitcoin, it launched with its own built-in scripting language, enabling the creation of complex smart contracts, decentralized autonomous organizations (DAOs), decentralized apps (DApps) and even other cryptocurrencies with relative ease.

By comparison, Bitcoin relies on a relatively bare-bones blockchain system that requires layers of protocols to be built on top of it to make it a usable platform for such utilities as smart contracts.

The ease of Ethereum development, combined with the rising price of Ether and a desire by early Ethereum adopters to re-invest their crypto fortunes in the Ethereum ecosystem, has made Ethereum the platform of choice for crypto-asset entrepreneurs.

The table on the facing page shows the top 25 ICOs of all time, ranked by amount raised. This table does not tell the whole story, however. Some notable ICOs have raised millions in Time Compression-worthy periods:

- **Aragon** – Raised $25 million in about 20 minutes.
- **Bancor** – Received an astonishing $140 million in just a few hours.
- **Brave** – Raised $34 million in roughly 30 seconds for its "Basic Attention Token."
- **Gnosis** – The originator of the Reverse Dutch Auction raised $12 million in about 12 minutes.
- **Tezos** – Raised $232 million in two weeks for its Zug, Switzerland-based foundation.

These financing trends demonstrate that the initial coin offering has had a major impact on the fundraising and investing communities. It's yet another lightning bolt from the Digital Lifestyle Ubertrend.

249. Pete Rizzo, "Ethereum: Bitcoin Price Decline Created $9 Million Funding Shortfall," *CoinDesk*, 28-Sep-15.

Blockchain Unleashed

Bitcoin has lead to yet another major upheaval, the blockchain revolution. While the financial sector's attention has focused mainly on the rollercoaster gyrations of Bitcoin's cryptocurrency value, it's Bitcoin's underlying blockchain architecture that is generating even more excitement in both financial and technology circles.

Blockchain promises to disrupt a host of industries, including advertising, banking, content, cross-border transactions, crowdfunding, e-commerce, healthcare, logistics, real estate and supply chain.

Blockchain uses a distributed ledger technology invented to support Bitcoin. This ledger monitors and verifies each Bitcoin transaction by relying on a decentralized network of thousands of volunteer-run "nodes" that, in effect, agree on the order in which transactions occur. The entire network deploys a sophisticated algorithm to ensure that each transaction is unique.

This algorithm plays a critical role in securing the blockchain. Because each new block contains the hash of a previous block, blockchains are immutable. If a hacker were to corrupt a block in the blockchain, all subsequent blocks would contain incorrect hashes. In fact, the record of transactions and balances remains secure as long as a simple majority, or 51% of nodes, remains independent.

Once a majority of nodes reaches "consensus" that all recent transactions are unique, they are digitally signed into a block. Each new block is linked to previously sealed blocks to create a chain of accepted history, thereby preserving a verified record of every transaction.

In its most basic form, blockchain is an alternative to the traditional database. But it differs from databases in many ways, with the biggest difference being the decentralized nature of blockchain. While a database requires a central "authority" to maintain and manage data, blockchain offers a decentralized approach to storage and data verification.

This architecture is radically innovative because it permits the secure sending of digital assets, without requiring trusted third parties, such as banks. Its ability to convey a shared truth that everyone agrees on without intermediaries, or centralized authority, is a major selling point.

These outstanding features have made blockchain one of the fastest-moving technology trends in enterprises, with 55% of companies monitoring, researching, or developing solutions on top of blockchain, according to The International Securities Association. [250] A survey by Juniper Research corroborates this finding: six of 10 large corporations are either actively considering or in the process of deploying blockchain technology.

The development of this breakthrough innovation is just getting started. For a disruptive technology, blockchain has managed to capture the imagination of investors remarkably early compared to other technologies. Fully three decades had to pass before entrepreneurs and investors were able to participate in the internet.

We will see the repercussions of blockchain in less than a decade.

Top 25 ICOs		
Rank	ICO Name	Amount Raised
1.	Filecoin [Futures]	$257,000,000
2.	Tezos	$232,000,000
3.	EOS	$180,000,000
4.	SIRIN LABS Token	$157,885,825
5.	Bancor	$153,000,000
6.	Status	$108,000,000
7.	QASH	$105,000,000
8.	Aragon	$73,000,000
9.	Bankex	$70,600,000
10.	TRON	$70,000,000
11.	DomRaider	$65,890,000
12.	WAX	$64,000,000
13.	Gnosis	$63,000,000
14.	Nebulas	$60,000,000
15.	MobileGo	$53,000,000
16.	Cosmos	$53,000,000
17.	LatiumX	$51,578,800
18.	TenX	$51,000,000
19.	NAGA	$50,020,960
20.	Paragon	$50,000,000
21.	Kyber Network	$48,960,000
22.	SALT	$48,500,000
23.	Loopring	$46,522,800
24.	Enigma	$45,000,000
25.	ICON	$45,000,000
26-Jul-18 Coinist		

250. "How Blockchain Could Disrupt Banking," *CB Insights*, 08-Feb-18.

Digital Lifestyle Timeline

1970
Sharp's EL-8 is first hand-holdable calculator.

1976

1984
William Gibson coins the term "cyberspace" in his book, *Neuromancer*, which foretells of a dark future filled with artificial intelligence, paranoia and viruses.

1972
Pulsar introduces the world's first digital watch.

Steve Jobs and Steve Wozniak establish Apple Computer Inc. The Byte Shop in Mountain View, Calif. orders 50 units of their first computer, the Apple 1.

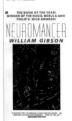

Gary Kildall develops the first commercially successful operating system (OS) for microcomputers, CP/M, which runs on a variety of computers built with eight-bit microprocessors.

1964

1954
IBM spent $5 billion on System/360. It paid off with sales of 1,000 units per month.

IBM ships Model 701, an "Electronic Data Processing" machine, and sells 19 units to organizations like the U.S. government.

1946

The first mini computer, DEC's PDP-8, sells for $18,000, one-fifth the cost of a small IBM System/360.

1974
Xerox PARC Alto is first computer with a "GUI," WYSIWIG Bravo word processor and built-in mouse.

Steve Jobs launches $2,495 Macintosh, which mainstreams the graphic user interface (GUI) and popularizes the mouse as an input device.

ENIAC computer is more than 1,000 times faster than previous mechanical computers. It weighs 30 tons and uses 18,000 vacuum tubes.

1958

1896
Herman Hollerith establishes the Tabulating Machine Co. — renamed IBM in 1924.

First Pizza Hut opens in Kansas City, Mo. Pizza becomes food of choice for techies around the world.

Magnavox Odyssey videogame console and Atari Pong arcade game debut.

1890	1940	1950	1960	1970	1980

Westinghouse's Elektro robot responds to voice commands with messages pre-recorded on 78 rpm records.

Remington Rand introduces first widely recognized commercial computer, the Univac, selling 46 units for more than $1 million each.

AT&T invents the first modem, which is the size of a small refrigerator and runs at the not-so-blinding speed of 110 bps.

HP becomes a dominant player in the handheld calculator market with the introduction of the HP-35, which introduces "RPN" — Reverse Polish Notation.

The January 1975 issue of Popular Electronics has a cover story on the MITS Altair 8800 computer kit.

Osborne 1, a 24-pound "luggable," is first mass-produced portable computer.

Nintendo releases Nintendo Entertainment System (NES) in the U.S.

1985

1951

1960

IBM launches Personal Computer, a $1,565 device with 16MB RAM, disk drives optional.

Nintendo has a big new hit on its hands, the handheld Gameboy.

1939

First Intel microprocessor, the Intel 4004, is released.

Bill Gates and Paul Allen launch Microsoft.

198

1975

1981

IMAGES COURTESY: ACE/BERKLEY BOOKS (PENGUIN GROUP), AMAZON.COM INC., AOL INC., APPLE INC., ASSOCIATED PRESS, ATARI SA, AT&T CORP. CANON INC., COMPUTER HISTORY MUSEUM, CROCK-POT/ THE RIVAL COMPANY, CTA DIGITAL, FORMLABS INC., GOOGLE INC., HEWLETT-PACKARD CO., HILTON HOTELS CORP., HONDA MOTOR CO. LTD., IBM CORP., INTEL CORP., IROBOT CORP., LOGITECH INTERNATIONAL S.A., MAGNAVOX, MICROSOFT CORP., NEST LABS, NINTENDO CO. LTD., PIZZA HUT INC., SEGA OF AMERICA INC., SEIKO WATCH CORP., 7-ELEVEN INC. SONY CORP., THE WALT DISNEY COMPANY, WESTINGHOUSE ELECTRIC CORP., XEROX CORP., ZIFF-DAVIS PUBLISHING COMPANY.

1971

Atari releases the Video Computer System AKA 2600.

Andy Grove, Robert Noyce and Gordon Moore create Intel Corp.

1968

1977

1990
█ Berners-Lee █nches the █orldWideWeb" █ the CERN █ysics laboratory █witzerland.

February 19, █be launches █toshop 1.0 █ the Mac █usively, it sets █ standard for █tal editing.

█itech intro-█es Fotoman, █ mass-market █tal camera.

█rosoft launches █ndows 3.0 █ndled with █taire, pro-█ing an instant █eogame hit.

Solitaire

1992
Apple CEO John Sculley introduces Newton Message-Pad, the world's first PDA (Personal Digital Assistant).

1994
The Netscape web browser officially ushers in the internet era.

N

1996
Palm Computing debuts Palm Pilot 1000 PDA, featuring a serial port and 128KB of memory. It's a cult phenomenon.

In May, Canon announces its first PowerShot digital camera. Sony follows in August with Cyber-shot priced at $849.

2000
Honda debuts a hu-manoid robot, ASIMO (Advanced Step in Innovative Mobility).

2004
Blizzard Entertain-ment launches World of Warcraft, a Massive Multiplayer Online Role Playing Game (MMORPG).

Faebook founded in Cambridge, Mass. on February 4, 2004 by Mark Zuckerberg.

2002
Friendster debuts, stoking a social revolution as the first social network of the aughts.

iRobot launches the Roomba In-telligent Floorvac, the world's first domestic robot.

2006
The Oxford English and Merriam-Webster dictionaries add "google" as a new verb.

First "unboxing" video of a Nokia E61 cellphone is uploaded to YouTube on June 12, 2006.

Amazon launches Amazon Web Services, which evolves into the world's largest cloud service.

Nintendo Wii goes on sale. It's the first videogame system to feature a haptic feedback interface.

2008
The iTunes Music store surpasses Walmart to become the largest music retailer in the U.S.

2012
Pebble raises $10.3 million on Kickstarter for its Pebble smart-watch, a record fundraise.

Facebook reaches 1 billion users in October 2012.

FormLabs raises $3 million for its high-precision 3D printer, the FormLabs 1.

2014
The Crock-Pot Smart Slow Cooker can be controled remotely via a mobile app.

Nearly half of Americans have cut back on travel, food and health care spending, in order to afford their technology.

U.K.'s Ofcom reports that six-year-olds understand digital technology better than adults.

Apple introduces the Apple Watch, which relies on an iPhone for a wire-less connecton.

Sleep Number debuts a "connect-ed bed" — the x12 with SleepIQ technology.

2016
Named after its founder, Hilton launches "Connie" robot at its Mc-Lean, Va. hotel.

In July, Pokémon Go, an augmented reality mobile game, draws 45 million users, less than two weeks after its debut.

Fisher-Price creates the Code-a-Pillar toy to teach children how to code.

Apple launches a MacBook with an innovative Touch Bar, aka the "emoji" keyboard.

1990 — 2000 — 2010

1991
Sega announces Sega VR headset featuring LCD displays, stereo speakers, plus sensors that track head movements.

1995
Amazon opens the virtual doors of its cyber book store in July 1995.

Sony launches the PlayStation, priced $100 less than the Sega Saturn at $299. It's a videogame sensation.

1997
IBM's Deep Blue supercomputer defeats world champion Gary Kasparov in a chess match.

1999
Sony introduces a pet robot dog, AIBO (Artificial Intelligence RObot), which responds to more than 100 voice commands and costs $2,000.

In September, Sergey Brin and Larry Page register a new domain, Google.com.

2001
Apple iPod, turns white headphones into a cool, global phenomenon.

65% of Americans spend more time with their computer than their spouse.

2007
Amazon releases Kindle book reader.

2009
Zynga's Facebook game FarmVille debuts and reaches 80 million players in a little over six months.

FarmVille ice cream by 7-Eleven.

The first Bitcoins, a virtual currency, are "mined" by its inventor in January 2009.

2011
Fueled by social media, the Arab Spring spreads throughout the Middle East.

Nest introduces first "learning" digital thermostat, an example of the "Internet of Things" (IoT) trend.

Oxford Dictionary adds OMG and LOL to its lexicon.

A Japanese man, Sal 9000, marries "Nene Anegasaki," a videogame character, in a cer-emony witnessed by thousands on the Web.

Amazon's e-book sales overtake print for the very first time during the holidays.

2013
Disney rolls out its MagicBand at Disney World, bringing RFID to the masses.

The Digital iPotty launches at CES in Las Vegas, because baby needs to multitask while she poops, LOL.

A social media angst, FOMO, the "Fear of Missing Out," is added to the Oxford English Dictionary in 2013.

2015
An Instagram analysis finds that the "LMAO" emoticon is the most frequently used emoji in social media.

During the summer of 2015, 17 million people lodge at Airbnb properties.

As people live longer, the Fountain of Youth Ubertrend is stimulating a need for innovative rejuvenation solutions. The prevailing forever young attitude owes its existence to a youth obsessed culture that tacitly ignores the old while readily flirting with the new.

2

Fountain of Youth

Rejuvenating Body, Spirit and Environment

More than half a 1900-era lifetime has been added to longevity. The average lifespan then was 49 years. Today, a typical U.S. adult lives to 79, an increase of *30 years*. And more years will be added still, with many living well beyond 100. As humans and the world they live in experience adverse change, caused by the vagaries of age and the toxicity of contamination, the Fountain of Youth Ubertrend gathers momentum. It breeds waves of reinvention that aim to rejuvenate body, spirit and environment. "Middle age" is now a moving target. For today's generation, middle-age might begin at 50. For the next, 60 is more appropriate. The Fountain of Youth thrives on a forever-young attitude, an outlook that has inspired a long series of symbiotic trends.

Age Management

Fountain of Youth

The scene is set in San Francisco's Museum of Modern Art, near Moscone Center. On stage are a group of *Wired* panelists discussing the future of life extension — the art of living longer. At one point an audience member asks the inevitable question, "Will we ever be able to live forever?" The answer startles everyone in attendance, "We will be able to turn off the genetic clock by 2080."

> 66 We will be able to turn off the genetic clock by 2080."
>
> **Wired Magazine Panel**
> San Francisco MoMA, 2000

That is music to the ears of Extropians, a group whose boundless belief and faith in science and technology fuels an expectation that life will carry on much longer than most could imagine. As Extropy Institute Founder Max More puts it, "This is the fourth revolution in our history — the ultrahuman revolution." [1] One way to prolong life is to replicate oneself, in other words, make a "backup copy" of yourself. [2] That requires recording all your thoughts, feelings and memories, an arduous task to say the least.

A number of entrepreneurs are trying to discover ways to facilitate such downloads. One is Russian internet millionaire Dmitry Itskov, who confidently promises, "Within the next 30 years, I am going to make sure that we can all live forever." [3] Itskov believes immortality can be achieved by enabling the upload of an individual's mind to a computer, thereby freeing humans from the body's biological constraints. "The ultimate goal of my plan is to transfer someone's personality into a completely new body," Itskov tells the BBC.

1. Brian Alexander, "Don't Die, Stay Pretty," *Wired*, 01-Jan-00.
2. Ed Regis, "Meet the Extropians," *Wired*, 01-Oct-94.
3. Tristan Quinn, "The immortalist: Uploading the mind to a computer," *BBC News*, 14-Mar-16.

Liquid Nitrogen Storage Tanks Used for Cryopreservation

Michigan-based Cryonics Institute cryopreserves its clients in liquid nitrogen at −196° Celsius, essentially halting physical decay. The hope is that someday future science will be able to revive and restore life.

IMAGE COURTESY: CRYONICS INSTITUTE.

CRISPR

If there is a life science that is generating excitement, and controversy, it's a technique that goes by its scientific name, CRISPR-Cas9, an abbreviation of Clustered Regularly Inter-spaced Short Palindromic Repeats. [1] CRISPR lets scientists directly edit genetic code. In April 2016, Chinese scientists used CRISPR to edit the genes of human embryos and make them resistant to HIV, the AIDS virus. [2] Although those embryos were quickly destroyed, another Chinese scientist, He Jiankui, announced in November 2018 that he had genetically edited twin girl babies, providing them with the ability to resist future HIV infections. [3] The announcement caused an uproar in the scientific community. The big question: Who will prevent the 10-15 million doctors practicing worldwide from editing genes using CRISPR?

1. "CRISPR," *Wikipedia*, 24-Dec-18.
2. Angela Chen, "Science panel okays one day editing human embryos," *The Verge*, 14-Feb-17.
3. Marilynn Marchione, "Chinese researcher claims first gene-edited babies," *AP*, 26-Nov-18.

Another technique that may harness potential eternity is to freeze either body or brain so that a future society may one day be able to revive or clone your defrosted remains. One organization that offers this service is the Alcor Life Extension Foundation, which operates a cryonics facility in Scottsdale, Ariz. [4]

Alcor charges $200,000 for a whole-body cryopreservation. Want to save some money? Just freeze your head, a "neuropreservation" costs $80,000. These are actually quite reasonable sums, given what's involved. Just think of how quickly food can spoil in your refrigerator. To qualify for an Alcor cryo- or neuropreservation, one has to become a member at an annual fee of $525 and maintain an insurance policy with Alcor as the beneficiary.

The mainstream scientific community regards cryonics with much skepticism. No one can guarantee that future science will ever be possible to revive a cryopreserved human being, but given the rapid advances in genetic engineering, CRISPR genome-editing and other related life sciences, anything is possible (sidebar).

That explains why cryonics followers firmly believe that clinical death is merely a prognosis rather than a diagnosis of the true end of one's life. Such views are speculative, to say the least. Still, four cryopreservation facilities exist worldwide as of 2018; three in the U.S. and one in Russia. As of 2014, about 250 people have been cryogenically preserved in the U.S., with approximately 1,500 more signed up for a liquid nitrogen bath. [5]

While cryonics requires a suspension of disbelief, one message from that *Wired* panel that resonates loudly and is, at least partly, verifiable, is the ability to slow down aging, and perhaps one day, even halt it. It's an elusive goal that fuels a rapidly evolving industry, anti-aging.

Here is a roadmap to the Fountain of Youth.

4. "Alcor Life Extension Foundation," *Alcor.org*, ret. 24-Dec-18.
5. "Cryonics," *Wikipedia*, ret. 04-Jan-19.

A4M 26th Annual World Congress on Anti-Aging in Las Vegas

More than 4,000 industry professionals attended the American Academy for Anti-Aging Medicine's December 2018 conference at the Las Vegas Sands Expo and Convention Center. They attended sessions delving into such topics as "Fasting Mimicking Diet and its Impact on Longevity" and "How Not to Die — The Power of Your Gut."

IMAGE COURTESY: MICHAEL TCHONG.

Troisième Age

A famous saying goes, "Youth is wasted on the young." But it's not wasted on the not-so-young. Our lengthening lifespan is leading to a new age of activity and consciousness. The French have a term for it, *Troisième Age* or Third Age. Normally, our youthful human phase is followed by middle age. But now we enter a third age, a stage in life that the Fountain of Youth will completely upend.

Evidence of this disruption surfaces each fall in Las Vegas where some 4,000 healthcare professionals attend the Annual World Congress on Anti-Aging, Regenerative and Aesthetic Medicine, which features such sessions as "Sexual Health in the Older Woman" and "Fat Grafting: The Natural Filler." The event's exhibit hall in the Sands Expo & Convention Center features nearly 400 exhibitors that cater to this fast-growing market. [6]

A4M stands for the American Academy for Anti-Aging Medicine, a Boca Raton, Fla.-based professional organization that bills itself as a "global medical education provider." The A4M launched with just 12 physicians in 1992. In 2006, the Academy told *BusinessWeek* that 1,500 doctors had sought board certification in anti-aging medicine since 1996. [7] As of 2011, approximately 26,000 practitioners have received an A4M certificate. [8]

It should be noted that the field of anti-aging medicine is not officially recognized by such organizations as the American Medical Association (AMA) and the American Board of Medical Specialties (ABMS).

These boards find allies in physicians like Dr. Thomas Perls, professor of medicine at Boston University School of Medicine, who says, "there

6. "The 26th Annual World Congress," *A4M*, ret. 24-Dec-18.
7. Arlene Weintraub, "Selling The Promise Of Youth," *BusinessWeek*, 20-Mar-06.
8. "American Academy of Anti-Aging Medicine," *Wikipedia*, ret. 04-Jan-19.

are no treatments that have been rigorously shown to reverse aging." [9] Perls maintains a site, called HGHWatch.com that collects information countering the broad claims of the anti-aging industry.

There is growing evidence that Perls may eventually be proven wrong. *The New York Times* reports that the La Jolla-based Salk Institute has reversed aging in mice by reprogramming their genome, rejuvenating organs and lengthening their life spans by as much as 30%. [10]

Salk's research revolves around findings of Japanese biologist Shinya Yamanaka who identified four genes that reset the clock of a fertilized egg. Dr. Izpisua Belmonte has partially reset the clock of the aging process by removing so-called "marks" from the epigenome — a network of proteins that envelopes a cell's DNA and controls which genes are active and which are suppressed.

South San Francisco-based Calico Labs, an abbreviation of the California Life Company, has a $1.5 billion budget to help decode the secret of aging. That infusion was supplied by Google's parent company, Alphabet, and drug company AbbVie. [11]

Oracle founder Larry Ellison has poured $430 million into his anti-aging research foundation, called the Lawrence Ellison Foundation. [12]

What Perls, the AMA and ABMS boards and other naysayers may also be missing is the strong tide they are swimming against. Boomers will live nearly two full generations longer than Americans did just 100 years ago. [13] Although U.S. life expectancy took a sudden step back in 2015 and 2016, it's still 78.6 in the U.S., or 76.1 years for men and 81.1 years for women. [14]

The biggest change coming to our world is the 65 and older population, which will represent 20% of the total population by 2030 and nearly double in size to 84 million by 2050, according to the U.S. Census Bureau. [15]

This population tidal wave will flood the world with lots of fearful flotsam. A large number of baby boomers have no safety net. According to a 2016 PWC study, 50% of boomers have $100,000 or less saved for retirement. [16]

Then there is the looming issue of social care programs for the aged running out of money worldwide. A 2015 report by the U.S. Social Security Administration predicts the trust will be depleted by 2034. The Congressional Budget Office is even more pessimistic, believing a shortfall could come as early as 2025. [17]

No wonder the pressure on boomers to keep working is relentless. Between May 2000 and May 2016, the number of Americans 65+ who reported being employed full- or part-time rose from 13% to 19%, according to a Pew Research Center analysis of employment data from the federal Bureau of Labor Statistics. [18] A 2015 Bankers Life study found that 41% of baby

U.S. 65+ Population Trend

2030

2050

66 The 65+ population will represent 20% of the total population by 2030 and nearly double in size to 84 million by 2050."

U.S. Census Bureau

9. Elizabeth O'Brien, "10 secrets of the anti-aging industry," *MarketWatch*, 13-Feb-14.
10. Nicholas Wade, "Scientists Say the Clock of Aging May Be Reversible," *The New York Times*, 15-Dec-16.
11. Antonio Regalado, "Google's Long, Strange Life Span Trip," *MIT Technology Review*, 15-Dec-16.
12. Paul Tullis, "Are You Rich Enough To Live Forever?," *Town and Country*, 30-Mar-17.
13. "Life expectancy in the USA, 1900-98," *demog.berkeley.edu*, ret. 29-Jul-18.
14. Ben Tinker, "US life expectancy drops for second year in a row," *CNN*, 21-Dec-17.
15. "An Aging Nation: The Older Population in the United States," *U.S. Census Bureau*, May-14.
16. Austin Smith, "Half of American baby boomers face a frightening retirement reality," *USA Today*, 09-Dec-16.
17. Sarah Max, "Will Social Security Really Run Out of Money?," *Money*, 21-Mar-16.
18. Drew Desilver, "More older Americans are working, and working more, than they used to," *Pew Research Center*, 20-Jun-16.

boomers still in the workplace expect to work beyond age 69, or *never* retire. And among those already retired, 69% of middle-income retirees would have liked to have been able to work longer. [19]

But finding employment uncovers another prickly state of affairs. Baby boomers are increasingly running into a brick employment wall because age discrimination in the U.S. is widespread. [20] The situation is particularly dire in tech startups, where 40 is considered old. [21]

As Carol Hymowitz claimed in a September 2016 Bloomberg TV report, the average age at a Silicon Valley startup is 22, compared to a median U.S. worker age of 42. That has led many an older tech worker to go to great lengths, including plastic surgery, to appear younger as they try to win over potential bosses younger than their kids.

This confluence of trends, combined with innovative advancements in anti-aging science and technology, will drive demand for anti-aging products and solutions to previously unseen levels.

In 2013, the global anti-aging market amounted to $122 billion, according to Transparency Market Research. [22] Market Research Engine predicts it will reach $216 billion by 2021. [23] OrbisResearch.com is more bullish, forecasting a global market for anti-aging products and services at $331 billion in 2021. [24]

Some experts resist the term anti-aging, instead preferring to call it "age management," the label used in this section. Despite the subtle skepticism, some treatments can positively impact the biological process of aging, both internally and externally, with reproducible results.

The anti-aging industry can be divided into six major segments, including Age Management, Body Contouring, Facial Rejuvenation, Cosmetic Dentistry, Eyesight Correction and Hair Restoration/Removal. The first three will be described in this and following sections, with each section describing specific anti-aging treatments and their upside potential in greater detail.

Age Management covers non-aesthetic treatments, including caloric restriction, hormone replacement therapy (HRT), memory therapy, stem-cell therapy, plus stress relief and exercise. With the exception of the latter two, many of these treatments are still in early development and should be considered experimental in nature.

Hormone Replacement Therapy

Aging is caused by a biochemical process that affects the body, both internally and externally. This process causes the body to degenerate over a period of time, affecting the wellbeing and physical appearance of the aged. HRT seeks to delay the aging process through a biochemical "tune-up."

"That's it, Mrs. Chalmers.
This is as young as I can make you look."

IMAGE COURTESY: THE WALL STREET JOURNAL, ROBERT LEIGHTON.
PERMISSION CARTOON FEATURES SYNDICATE.

19. Hal Bundrick, "Boomers' biggest retirement regret? They didn't work longer," *CBS MoneyWatch*, 15-May-15.
20. Rupal Parekh, "Aging in Adland: The Gray-Hair Phobia That's Hindering Older Execs," *AdAge*, 29-Jan-12.
21. Carol Hymowitz and Robert Burnson, "It's Tough Being Over 40 in Silicon Valley," *Bloomberg*, 08-Sep-16.
22. James Perdue, "Global Anti-Aging Market to be Worth USD 191.7 billion by 2019," *LinkedIn*, 08-May-14.
23. "Anti Aging Market is Supposed to Reach US$ 216 Billion By 2021," *MarketWatch*, 30-May-18.
24. "Global Anti-Aging Market 2017 is Growing Rapidly and Expected to Reach $331 billion by 2021," *Reuters*, 19-Jun-17.

As people age, the cells that make the human body lose their ability to repair themselves make people vulnerable to disease and other conditions directly linked to aging. These changes, called somatopause in medical jargon, are associated with loss of vitality, muscle mass and physical function, and are often accompanied by belly fat (central adiposity), cardiovascular complications, physical frailty and deterioration of mental function.

The pituitary gland, a pea-sized organ located near the base of the brain, is responsible for encouraging childhood growth and maintaining tissues and organs throughout life. By the time adults reach middle age, however, the pituitary gland slowly reduces the amount of growth hormone it produces.

In the past decade, there has been a notable increase in the use of hormone replacement therapies, including the administration of synthetic human growth hormone or HGH, which was initially developed to help children grow. The term synthetic is used here to denote that the hormone was created from non-human materials, such as yams, soy and even horse urine. That means that the synthetic's origin is still nature.

The interest for more "natural solutions" has given rise to "bioidentical hormones" — hormones that are identical in molecular structure to the hormones produced in the human body. The differences between HRT and Bio-Identical Hormone Replacement Therapy (BHRT) is shown in the table (left). Keep in mind that this comparison is provided by parties that mix and match drugs, called "compounding" to tailor-make solutions for specific therapies. Compounding labs have gained a lot of currency due to the popularity of BHRT.

HRT vs. BHRT		
Attributes	HRT	BHRT
Identical to human hormones	No	Yes
Customized dosage for each patient	No	Yes
Therapy goal: Hormonal balance	No	Yes
Overall goal	Prevent disease	Improve quality of life
Source: The Compounder's Forum 24-Feb-09.		

In 1958, HGH was extracted for the first time from cadavers. By the early 1980s, genetic engineering enabled mass-production of synthetic HGH, which eliminated the need for cadavers. The HGH hormone increases the height of hormone-deficient children, although they still typically remain shorter than average.

In 1989, National Institutes of Health researchers began to test HGH in children who were not deficient in growth hormone but were simply short. An FDA report found that non-hormone-deficient children gained an average of 2.8 to 5 cm (1 to 2 inches) beyond their predicted height at 19, after 4.4 years of treatment. In another study, a higher dose of six injections per week for an average duration of 5.3 years, resulted in a mean gain in adult height of 7 cm, or about 2.7 inches. [25]

In 2003, the FDA approved the use of HGH in non-hormone-deficient short children. The long-term risks of HGH injections in children who already produce adequate growth hormone are not known. Possible risks of such treatment relate both to the multiple injections the children receive and to the drug itself.

The good news is that Pfizer is in phase 3 trials of a new drug, currently called HGH-CTP, which would revolutionize patient treatment by reducing injections to once per week. [26]

While most HGH prescriptions were initially written for children, by 2004 74% went to people ages 20 and older. That year, sales of HGH totaled $622

25. "Concerns about Growth Hormone Experiments in Short Children," *The Physicians Committee*, ret. 04-May-17.
26. Todd Campbell, "Pfizer's Next-Generation Human Growth Hormone Takes a Step Forward," *The Motley Fool*, 11-July-15.

Genotropin Human Growth Hormone

Human growth hormone (HGH) therapy is an essential element of age-management techniques and is typically administered via easy-to-use syringes, which were originally designed for children, like Genotropin's MiniQuick.

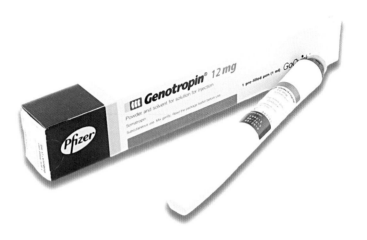

Injectable Testosterone

Testosterone replacement therapy (TRT) comes in many forms, including vials containing injectable hormones (shown above), gels and patches.

million for legitimate and non-legitimate uses, according to *BusinessWeek*. [27] Ten years later, global sales for the two top players alone, Pfizer Genotropin and Novo Nordisk, reached $1.7 billion in 2014. That year, Novo Nordisk generated more than 30% of market revenues ($973 million) followed by Pfizer ($723 million). [28]

Pfizer's Genotropin was one of the HGH drugs reportedly used by baseball's Barry Bonds, who morphed from a skinny Pittsburgh Pirates player into a muscular San Francisco Giants slugger, and who, at age 37, hit a record-setting 73 home runs in 2001. While Bonds' brawny physique was partially gained through intense physical training, BHRT is known to help shed fat and gain lean muscle mass. As with any medical treatment involving humans, some study subjects experience side effects including diabetes and glucose intolerance, which is why some experts hesitate to recommend using HGH to treat aging or age-related conditions.

Dr. Fred Sattler, Professor of Medicine and Biokinesiology at the Keck School of Medicine, University of Southern California, reports that "a limited number of controlled studies suggest that GH [growth hormone] supplementation in older men increases lean mass by ~2 kg with similar reductions in fat mass." [29]

In 2010, researchers at Garvan Institute of Medical Research in Sydney, Australia found that the use of HGH can provide as much as a 0.4-second improvement in a 10-second sprint, enough to turn a last-place Olympic athlete in either a running or swimming event into a gold medal winner. [30]

Professor Ken Ho, head of pituitary research at Garvan Institute and Chairman of the Department of Endocrinology at St. Vincent's Hospital in Sydney, conducted the research study in concert with Dr. Udo Meinhardt

27. Arlene Weintraub, "Selling The Promise Of Youth," *BusinessWeek*, 20-Mar-06.
28. "Hormone Replacement Therapy (HRT) Market," *Grand View Research*, Mar-16.
29. Fred Sattler, "Growth hormone in the aging male," *Best Practice & Research Clinical Endocrinology & Metabolism*, Aug-13.
30. Ken Ho, "First Scientific Study Showing Effects Of Growth Hormone On Athletes," *Garvan Institute*, 04-May-10.

At 85, Ed Whitlock is the oldest person to run the marathon in under four hours, "equivalent of a runner in his prime completing a marathon in 2:04:48." [1]

If the Rio Olympics proved anything, it's that "old" athletes have become a permanent fixture of mainstream sports.

Sure, older athletes have won the Olympics. One male athlete won silver at age 64 in 1912, and one female won gold at age 63 in 1904, but both participated in less demanding sports, shooting and archery, respectively. [2] Also, certainly in a less scientific era. After 42-year-old cyclist Kristin Armstrong won gold in Rio, she had a ready answer for reporters who always asked her why she kept competing despite her age and multiple hip surgeries, "Because I can." [3]

Kristin can, and so does Michael Phelps, who won five more gold medals at age 31, or Oksana Chusovitina, a 41-year-old gymnast for Uzbekistan, or Katherine Grainger, a 40-year-old rower from the U.K, plus many more. Then there's Peyton Manning, who at age 39 became the oldest quarterback to win a Super Bowl. [4]

After winning the 2016 U.S. Open, 28-year-old Angelique Kerber became the oldest player to achieve tennis' number one ranking for the first time. [5]

Then there's Barry Bonds who smashed a record 73 home runs at age 37 for the San Francisco Giants. Get ready, set, go for the age of the ageless athlete.

1. Jeré Longman, "85-Year-Old Marathoner Is So Fast That Even Scientists Marvel," *The New York Times*, 29-Dec16.
2. "Oldest and Youngest Olympians (Summer Games)," *Topend Sports Network*, ret. 04-May-17.
3. Rae Ellen Bichell, "Olympic Athletes Prove That Older Doesn't Have To Mean Slower," *NPR*, 16-Aug-16.
4. Alec Nathan, "Peyton Manning Becomes Oldest QB in NFL History to Win Super Bowl," *Bleacher Report*, 07-Feb-16.
5. "Angelique Kerber," *Wikipedia*, ret. 04-Jan-19.

and Dr. Anne Nelson. Their findings were published in the journal *Annals of Internal Medicine*. Observes Ho, "Athletes given growth hormone improved their sprint capacity by 4 to 5%." Another key finding: Sprint capacity nearly doubled in men who received testosterone injections in addition to growth hormones.

Testosterone is an androgenic anabolic steroid — a synthetic substance that produces such anabolic effects as the growth of skeletal muscle, and androgenic effects, like the development of male sexual characteristics in both males and females. Testosterone is a widely used hormone in both age management and sports and comes in a variety of form factors, including injectable fluids, gels, patches, creams, oral pills or pellets and powders.

Testosterone replacement is often used by geriatric male patients suffering from hypogonadism — defined as the diminished functional activity of the gonads, the testes in males or ovaries in females, that may result in diminished sex hormone biosynthesis. Like HGH, testosterone treatment can have undesirable side effects, including acne or oily skin, fluid retention, increased risk of prostate cancer and breast enlargement.

U.S. sales of testosterone drugs reached $2.4 billion in 2013, and are forecast to reach $3.8 billion by 2018, driven by the availability of new gel-based formulations and the aggressive direct-marketing techniques used by pharmaceutical companies. [31]

But it's menopausal women that are at the forefront of the hormone replacement trend. The loss of female hormones in aging women lead to the first estrogen drug in 1942 when Ayerst launched Premarin, an estrogen synthesized from the urine of pregnant mares, explaining its creative branding. [32]

31. "Annual testosterone drug revenue in the U.S. in 2013 and 2018," *Statista*, ret. 24-Dec-18.
32. Lynne Paige Walker and Ellen Hodgson Brown, "A Woman's Complete Guide to Natural Health," *Penguin Group U.S.A*, 2003.

Sir2 Activity in Mice Regulates Longevity

The lifespan of mice is dictated by Sir2 activity — the more active the gene is, the longer the animal lives. Mice play a major role in health science. The mouse shown here provided evidence that the blue dye contained in M&Ms, called Brilliant Blue G (BBG), can cure spinal injury, according to Rochester Medical Center researchers.

IMAGE COURTESY: UNIVERSITY OF ROCHESTER.

Hormone Replacement Therapy (HRT) began catching on in the mid-1970s when a mixture of estrogen and progesterone became the preferred treatment. The interest in a more natural approach to hormone therapy led to the creation of bioidentical hormones — hormones that are identical in molecular structure to those made in women's bodies. Bioidentical estrogens are 17 beta-estradiol, estrone, and estriol.

A growing female population ages 45 to 59, plus a median menopausal window of 7.4 years is propelling growth. [33] According to the American Congress of Obstetricians and Gynecologists, an estimated 6,000 U.S. women reach menopause every day, or more than 2 million each year in the U.S. alone. [34] And their ranks are growing. In 1998, about 477 million women worldwide were post-menopausal, a figure that will more than double to 1.1 billion by 2025.

In a product segment that includes human growth hormone, estrogen, testosterone and thyroid hormones, estrogen-based products, including both combination drug therapies and single doses of estrogen or progestin, contributed more than half of the revenue in 2014 while generating the largest number of doctor prescriptions. [35]

Estrogen drugs such as Premarin, Menest and Combipatch lead the category. Pfizer reports that Premarin was its seventh best-selling drug, generating sales of $1 billion in 2015. [36]

Still, some believe human growth hormone therapy will be the fastest growing segment due to the growing number of premature births globally. That, plus the market launch of such innovations as Pfizer's HGH-CTP, which requires only a weekly injection in children, will further stimulate growth.

33. Pam Belluck, "Up to 14 Years of Hot Flashes Found in Menopause Study," *The New York Times*, 16-Feb-15.
34. JoAnn E. Manson, "Overview of menopause. Menopause practice: a clinician's guide," *North American Menopause Society*, 2010."
35. "Hormone Replacement Therapy (HRT) Market," *Grand View Research*, Mar-16.
36. "Top 10 Pfizer products based on revenue in 2015," *Statista*, ret. 04-May-17.

Caloric Restriction

In 2006, two Cambridge, Mass.-based biotech start-ups, Sirtris Pharmaceuticals and Elixir Pharmaceuticals, created quite a stir for their research into drugs that mimic the beneficial aspects of reduced caloric intake. Their research data revealed that lowering the caloric intake of a mouse by 30% would make it live at least 30% longer than its normal two-year life span. [37]

A stressed body apparently produces protective substances that extend life. Just four years after being founded, Sirtris was acquired by GlaxoSmithKline for $720 million in April 2008. [38] Elixir Pharmaceuticals, which had received $99 million in funding from nine investors, quietly disappeared some time ago. [39] In 2013, GlaxoSmithKline unceremoniously shut down Sirtris, five years after its acquisition. [40]

To understand the history of longevity startups, one has to travel back to the 1990s, specifically the December 2, 1993 issue of *Nature*, which contained a paper entitled, "A C. elegans mutant that lives twice as long as wild type." [41] The article was a catalyst for startups searching for the Fountain of Youth because it described for the very first time a gene, daf-

37. Arlene Weintraub, "Biotech's Diet In A Bottle Could Extend Your Life," *Bloomberg Businessweek*, 19-Mar-06.
38. Mark Hollmer, "Sirtris Pharmaceuticals sold to GlaxoSmithKline for $720 million," *Boston Business Journal*, 22-Apr-08.
39. "Elixir Pharmaceuticals," *Crunchbase*, ret. 04-Jan-19.
40. Luke Timmerman, "GlaxoSmithKline Shuts Down Sirtris, Five Years After $720M Buyout," *Xconomy*, 12-Mar-13.
41. Cynthia Kenyon, Jean Chang, Erin Gensch, Adam Rudner and Ramon Tabtiang, "A C. elegans mutant that lives twice as long as wild type," *Nature*, 02-Dec-93.

HCG Diet: A Hormonal Scam?

In 1954, a British physician living in Italy, Dr. Albert Simeons, created the HCG diet, consisting of a daily regimen of 500 calories and 125-unit HCG injections. [1] Simeons described the diet in a self-published manuscript,

Pounds and Inches, in which he cited weight loss results of as much as ½ to 1 lb. per day.

HCG (Human Chorionic Gonadotropin) is a hormone made from the placenta of pregnant women, which mobilizes fat in women to supply nutrients for a developing fetus. It's nature's way of preparing for the eventuality of a mother's food supply being interrupted.

While quick weight loss usually causes an individual to feel tired and hungry, followers of the HCG diet report maintaining energy levels and decreased appetite.

The FDA has not approved HCG for weight loss. However, it has been used off-label in the U.S. since the 1970s.

Sheri Emma, the creator of "Dr. Emma's HCG Protocol," conducted a small-sample study of 12 patients that appears to support Simeons' findings. Her study results, which were aired on the March 14, 2012 Dr. Oz show, reported an average weight loss of 13 pounds in four weeks. [2] Since Emma has an active interest in promoting HCG for weight reduction, this is likely a biased study. Emma has also never formally published the study's findings only reinforcing that impression.

Joe Cannon, who runs the site Supplement Clarity, compiled the results of eight HGC studies conducted between 1963 and 1995 and found that only one 1973 study reported that HGC works. [3] That study by Asher and Harper, however, notes that Harper, who conducted the "clinical work" also "has an active practice using HCG for weight reduction."

Score: Two dubious HGC diet wins versus seven losses.

1. Richard Lipman, M.D., "Restaurants and Recipes for the HCG Diet," *eBookIt.com*, 2011.
2. Mehmet Oz, M.D., "Does the HCG Diet Work?," *DoctorOz.com*, 15-Mar-12.
3. Joe Cannon, "HCG Diet: Does It Really Work? Evidence Based Review," *Supplement Clarity*, 23-Feb-17.

2, that could cause an adult roundworm, *Caenorhabditis Elegans*, to live more than twice as long as its counterparts in the wild.

In 1999, Leonard Guarente, a professor in MIT's department of biology, co-founded Elixir Pharmaceuticals hoping to extend human life by developing a drug based on his research into a gene called Sir2. [42] Guarente had discovered that the lifespan in yeast, worms and mice is regulated by Sir2 activity — the more active the gene is, the longer the animal lives.

Sirtris Pharmaceuticals, co-founded by Harvard pathologist David Sinclair and a local entrepreneur Christoph Westphal in 2004, was also conducting research on drugs that could enhance the activity of Sir2-like genes in humans.

Like Elixir, Sirtris focused its research on genes that make enzymes called sirtuins, explaining the company name. Sirtris scientists were hoping to make sirtuins more active, thereby mimicking the effects of caloric restriction.

Guarente joined Sirtris as co-chair of its scientific advisory board in 2007, after a philosophical disagreement with Elixir management about company direction.

A 2013 article by Guarente revisits the role sirtuins play in calorie restriction and cites a number of studies, both pro and con. Observes Guarente, "Since [my] 2000 review, thousands of studies on sirtuins and activating compounds like resveratrol have been published along with some challenging data, and this large body of information now prompts a re-evaluation of the robustness of the original hypothesis." [43]

According to Dr. Liji Thomas, resveratrol is a phytoalexin molecule — a protective antibiotic produced in plants under stress, caused by either a fungal attack, drought, ultraviolet irradiation or inflammation — that helps plants fight back to maintain their health. [44]

Resveratrol piqued the interest of scientists due to its antioxidant properties, which could contribute to longevity because of anti-inflammatory and anti-cancer attributes. Found in many plant varieties, resveratrol is abundant in the skin of red grapes, peanuts and pistachios, and in such fruit as blueberries, cranberries, mulberries and raspberries, and cacao beans. Its abundance in red grape skins gives red wine its notable concentrations of resveratrol, a fact not lost on mass media, which helped propel its talking-head popularity.

It may also help explain the French paradox: despite a diet rich in bread, butter, cheese and pork, France has a relatively low incidence of coronary heart disease. The French eat four times as much butter, 60% more cheese and nearly three times as much pork, compared to Americans, based on data compiled in 2002 by the Food and Agriculture Organization of the United Nations. [45]

Although the French consume only slightly more total fat, 171 grams per day compared to 157 grams per day for the average American, the U.S. diet contains much more saturated fat due to a much larger proportion of vegetable oil fat, mostly soybean oil. According to 1999 British Heart

> " Due to all the positive red wine publicity, Americans now prefer red wine based on dollar volume sold at 51%, compared to white (46%) and rosé (6%)."
>
> Nielsen

42. Wade Roush, "Sir2 Roads Diverged: Elixir Co-founder Joins Rival Sirtris," *Xconomy*, 19-Nov-07.
43. Leonard Guarente, " Calorie restriction and sirtuins revisited," *Genes & Development*, 01-Oct-13.
44. Liji Thomas, "What is Resveratrol?," *News-Medical.Net*, 25-May-15.
45. "French paradox." *Wikipedia*, ret. 04-Jan-19.

Foundation data, the rate of death from coronary heart disease among U.S. males ages 35-74 was 115 per 100,000 people but only 83 per 100,000 in France. These statistics are outdated, but they do underscore the remarkable dichotomy of the French paradox.

And perhaps due to all the positive red wine publicity, Americans now prefer red wine, based on dollar volume sold, at 51%, compared to white (46%) and rosé (6%), according to 2014 Nielsen data. [46] However, this is an incomplete market snapshot, since white wines have historically been less expensive due to less demanding aging requirements. [47] Nielsen reports that the five most popular varietals are: Chardonnay, Cabernet Sauvignon, Pinot Grigio, Merlot and Pinot Noir. In other words, two of the first three top wines are white.

And while the jury is out on whether resveratrol can help prolong human life, there's no question that resveratrol mimics the lifespan-extending effects of very-low-calorie diets in flies, fish and mice — apparently by activating SIRT1, one of seven Sir2-like genes in humans that play a crucial role in anti-aging. [48]

Concludes Guarente, "This review addresses these challenges and draws from a great body of new data in the sirtuin field that shows a systematic redirection of mammalian physiology in response to diet by sirtuins. The prospects for drugs that can deliver at least a subset of the benefits of [caloric restriction] seem very real."

46. Liz Thach, "The state of wine drinking in America today," *The Week*, 24-Jan-15.
47. "Why is white wine cheaper than red?," *Quora*, 30-Jun-16.
48. Wade Roush, "Sir2 Roads Diverged: Elixir Co-founder Joins Rival Sirtris," *Xconomy*, 19-Nov-07.

Elysium Health

You can't fault Leonard Guarente for lack of trying. Guarente co-founded Elysium Health to launch a nutraceutical to help fight aging, called Basis. The problem, as Guarente tells *MIT Technology Review*, is that it's nearly impossible to prove, in any reasonable time frame, that drugs that extend the lifespan of animals can do the same in people. [1] Clinical trials plus FDA approval could take decades. That explains the thinking behind Elysium's unusual approach of packaging leading-edge R&D as a supplement in order to bring it to market faster. Then again, the $30 billion supplements market is growing at a 7% annual pace, according to Elysium Health COO Dan Alminana, and at twice that rate online.

Guarente's track record inspired believers to pony up $26 million at a $157 million valuation. [2] Basis, which sells for $40 on a prepaid annual subscription, or $60 one-time, contains two key ingredients: nicotinamide riboside (NR) and pterostilbene, which are naturally found in milk and blueberries, respectively. NR is a chemical precursor of nicotinamide adenine dinucleotide, or NAD, a compound that cells use to carry out metabolic reactions like releasing energy from glucose. NR has been shown to counteract aging. [3] Pterostilbene is considered a more powerful version of resveratrol, with a reportedly more convincing lab track record. [4]

In a business where one-third of herbal supplements contain no trace of plants listed on the label, Elysium may well succeed.

1. Karen Weintraub, "The Anti-Aging Pill," *MIT Technology Review*, 03-Feb-15.
2. Sarah Buhr, "Anti-aging pill startup Elysium Health inks at least $20 million in Series B funding," *TechCrunch*, 06-Dec-16.
3. Kathryn Ramsey et al., "Age-associated loss of Sirt1-mediated enhancement of glucose-stimulated insulin secretion in beta cell-specific Sirt1-overexpressing (BESTO) mice," *Aging Cell*, Jan-08.
4. Benjamin Wallace, "An MIT Scientist Claims That This Pill Is the Fountain of Youth," *New York Magazine*, 23-Aug-16.

Mount Tam Said To Be Developing Rapamycin Drug

Brian Kennedy, head of the Buck Institute for Research on Aging, is also chairman of Mount Tam Biotechnologies, located in Novato, Calif. As a grad student, Kennedy researched yeast aging with Leonard Guarante.

As Dr. Patricia Dimond observed in 2010, "One desirable outcome of research on SIRT1 modulation would be the discovery of a new treatment for currently untreatable neurodegenerative diseases like [Huntington Disease]. These diseases are generally related to the accumulation of an abnormal form of a protein in specific brain cells, which causes their destruction." [49] The key to combating that protein may lie in a special category of cells, so-called senescent cells. At the Mayo Clinic in Rochester, Minn., a research team led by Darren Baker and Jan van Deursen discovered that senescent cells tend to promote tissue aging while accumulating in cataracts, arthritic areas and the plaque that may line elderly arteries. [50]

These cells secrete agents that stimulate the immune system and cause low-level inflammation. Ridding the body of senescent cells could delay many aging diseases. Baker and Deursen reported in the journal *Nature* that mice that had these cells removed did not develop cataracts, avoided muscle wasting and could last much longer on a treadmill. And they retained skin fat layers that usually thin out with age and lead to wrinkles in people.

For his part, Guarente continues to push the age management envelope. His latest venture is Elysium Health, which has introduced a nutraceutical formulated with ingredients it says will keep you feeling young ("Elysium Health," page 85). Guarente's feelings about anti-aging are echoed by Sonia Arrison, the author of *100 Plus: How the Coming Age of Longevity Will Change Everything*, who claims that recently born babies could be the first generation to live to be 150 years old. [51]

The U.K. Office for National Statistics supports the notion that more human beings will reach 100, estimating that 35% of the 797,000 babies born in 2013 could still be alive in 2113. In the U.K., like elsewhere, the life expectancy of women is better than that of men, with 77,000 centenarian females expected by 2037, compared to just 34,000 centenarian men. [52]

49. Patricia Dimond, "Examining Both Sides of the Sirtuin Coin," *Genetic Engineering & Biotechnology News*, 22-Feb-10.
50. Nicholas Wade, "Purging Cells in Mice Is Found to Combat Aging Ills," *The New York Times*, 02-Nov-11.
51. Kamelia Angelova, "Peter Thiel: Death Is A Problem That Can Be Solved," *Business Insider*, 09-Feb-12.
52. "One third of babies born in 2013 are expected to live to 100," *Office for National Statistics*, 11-Dec-13.

Novartis Afinitor (Everolimus)

Novartis Afinitor, a proprietary drug based on rapamycin, is used to help fight breast and kidney cancer. A Novartis age management drug will likely be a derivative of Afinitor. Bloomberg reported in early 2015 that Novartis' rapamycin would be tested on dogs at the University of Washington.

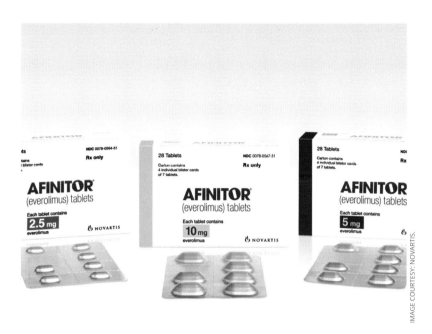

Rapamycin

Other approaches to age management are also beginning to show promise. In 1972, Suren Sehgal, then a scientist at Ayerst Laboratories in Montreal, identified a rare bacterium found in Easter Island soil, *Streptomyces Hygroscopicus*, that possessed potent anti-fungal properties. He named it rapamycin, inspired by Easter Island's native name, Rapa Nui. [53]

Sehgal eventually convinced Wyeth, which had acquired Ayerst in 1987, to let him continue his rapamycin research. He discovered that rapamycin not only had powerful antifungal qualities but was able to suppress the immune system, blocking the body from rejecting a new kidney or another vital organ. That ability lead the U.S. Food and Drug Administration to approve rapamycin for transplant patients in 1999.

Further research uncovered rapamycin capabilities that extend far beyond immune system suppression. The National Institutes of Health sponsored a major study in 2009 that confirmed that rapamycin and its derivatives helped mice live longer. The study discovered that rapamycin not only extends life by delaying the onset of such old age diseases as Alzheimer's, cancer and heart disease but apparently also postpones the effects of normal aging.

What excites scientists is how the drug delays aging. According to a University of Washington scientist, Matt Kaeberlein, a biology of aging researcher and another former grad student collaborator of Leonard Guarente, rapamycin appears to delay the "age-related decline in multiple different organ systems, which is something we would expect if we were fundamentally slowing the aging process."

---

53. Bill Gifford, "Does a Real Anti-Aging Pill Already Exist?," *Bloomberg*, 12-Feb-15.

Novartis, a $260 billion Swiss pharmaceutical giant, has begun to position a derivative version of rapamycin, called Afinitor, as the first true anti-aging drug. Like penicillin, rapamycin is a biological agent and therefore not patentable. But compound derivatives like Afinitor are.

How does rapamycin work? Scientists at Novartis' predecessor, Sandoz, discovered in the early 1990s that certain rapamycin molecules inhibit a key cellular pathway regulating growth and metabolism. This pathway is called "target of rapamycin," or TOR, and has been identified in a number of species. In humans and mammals, it's dubbed mTOR.

Rapamycin elicits a response in the human body similar to that of caloric restriction. Brian Kennedy, CEO of the Buck Institute for Research on Aging in Novato, Calif. and chairman of Mount Tam Biotechnologies, tells Bloomberg, "Really what rapamycin is doing is tapping into the body's systems for dealing with reduced nutrition."

Buck Institute also houses a colony of naked mole rats, which are used by Google's mysterious life-extension research and development company, Calico Labs. [54] Naked mole rats can live up to 30 years, which is much longer than a typical laboratory mouse. Calico scientists, including one of its first hires, Vice President of Aging Research Cynthia Kenyon, co-author of the paper published in the December 2, 1993 issue of *Nature* that kick-started the age management industry, are reportedly sequencing the genome of the mole rat. [55]

Google founders Sergey Brin and Larry Page launched Calico, which seeks to extend life through genetic research and drug development. Ex-financier Michael Milken is also working on new approaches to aging, as is Jeff Bezos who invested in a company called Unity Biotechnology that is "targeting cellular mechanisms at the root of age-related diseases."

Stem Cell Therapy

In the eternal quest to find solutions that slow, prevent or reverse the aging process, the scientific community often goes where no one has gone before. The latest leading-edge discoveries touch on the vast world of stem cells, which is not surprising given that stem cell research specializes in finding drugs and techniques that can help restore what nature took away.

The term "stem cell" was proposed in 1908 by Russian histologist Alexander Maksimov for scientific usage. [56] The first successful use of stem cell restoration happened in 1968 when the first bone marrow transplant was performed in Minnesota on two siblings who each suffered from severe immunodeficiency. [57]

Ten years later, in 1978, stem cells were discovered in human cord blood. In 1981 came another breakthrough, the first in-vitro stem cell line created

54. Rachel Becker, "Google wants to use naked mole rats to find the secret to slow aging ," *The Verge*, 15-Dec-16.
55. Cynthia Kenyon, Jean Chang, Erin Gensch, Adam Rudner and Ramon Tabtiang, "A C. elegans mutant that lives twice as long as wild type," *Nature*, 02-Dec-93.
56. Rainish Kumar et al., "Stem cells: An overview with respect to cardiovascular and renal disease," *Journal of Natural Science, Biology and Medicine*, Jul/Dec-10.
57. Theodore Moore, "Bone Marrow Transplantation," *Medscape*, 07-Nov-14.

First Stem-Cell Cloned Mammal: Dolly the Sheep

Professor Ian Wilmut of Roslin Institute, part of the University of Edinburgh, Scotland, whose team created the world's first mammal cloned from an adult cell, says stem cell research might still lag 20 years behind if Dolly the Sheep had never been born in 1997.

IMAGE COURTESY: ALAMY.

from mice. It took an additional 14 years to derive the first embryonic stem cell from a primate, a rhesus monkey. [58]

That was followed in 1997 by the first stem-cell cloning of a sheep. The lamb, called Dolly, was the first mammal cloned from an adult cell, using a process called somatic cell nuclear transfer. This process involves transferring a cell nucleus from an adult cell to an unfertilized, developing egg cell that had its nucleus removed. Dolly was cloned by Ian Wilmut, Keith Campbell and colleagues at the Roslin Institute, part of the University of Edinburgh, Scotland. [59]

In 1998, James Thomson and co-workers at University of Wisconsin–Madison isolated cells from the inner cell mass of early embryos and derived the first human embryonic stem cell lines. In 1999 and 2000, scientists discovered that bone marrow cells could produce nerve or liver cells, and that brain cells could also yield other cell types.

In a little more than two decades, the field of stem cell research had made quantum leaps, exciting the global scientific community. When President George W. Bush issued an executive order banning federal funding for new sources of stem cells developed from preimplantation human embryos in 2001, his short-sighted action froze U.S. stem cell research and discouraged scientists.

In 2006, a Kyoto University stem cell researcher, Shinya Yamanaka, and a graduate student, Kazutoshi Takahashi, revived the field by creating a way to induce any adult cell, such as a skin cell, to revert to its earliest "pluripotent" stage — an iPS cell. iPS stands for induced pluripotent stem cells. In the pluripotent stage, a cell has the ability to generate all cell types that make up the human body. [60] Embryonic stem cells are considered

58. J.A. Thomson et al., "Isolation of a primate embryonic stem cell line," *Proceedings of the National Academy of Sciences*, 15-Aug-95.
59. "Dolly (sheep)," *Wikipedia*, ret. 04-Jan-19.
60. "What is the difference between totipotent, pluripotent, and multipotent?," *New York State Stem Cell Science*, ret. 04-May-17.

pluripotent. These cells can become any type of cell, from a heart muscle cell to a neuron. The process of maturing stem cells from a pluripotent state to an adult tissue type is called differentiation.

Yamanaka cites a great example of the use of stem cells in disease management. At the Riken Center for Developmental Biology, Dr. Masayo Takahashi and her colleagues used iPS cells to treat macular degeneration in a 70-year-old patient, deriving adult retinal cells from skin cells and transplanting these iPS cells into the patient's eye to restore her vision.

As of January 2016, 10 stem cell therapies have been approved globally, including Parkinson's, retinal and corneal diseases, heart and liver failure, diabetes, spinal cord injury, joint disorders and some blood disorders.

Currently, the only widely used stem-cell-based therapy is bone marrow transplantation. Blood-forming stem cells in the bone marrow were the first stem cells to be identified and have helped thousands worldwide suffering from such blood cancers as leukemia. [61]

That pioneering treatment dates back to 2005 when stem cell researchers at the University of Minnesota were able for the first time to coax human embryonic stem cells to create cancer-killing cells in the laboratory, paving the way for future treatments for various types of cancers or tumors. [62]

The seductiveness of innovative stem cell therapies has propelled a new type of business: stem cell tourism. Many overseas clinics advertise miraculous stem cell therapies for a wide range of incurable diseases that have not been tested for safety or even for effectiveness. International, and even domestic, clinics are offering up unproven and untested stem cell therapies leading to the death of some patients.

Still, some notable case studies have surfaced that underscore the vast potential of stem-cell therapy. Take the case of New York Yankees pitcher Bartolo Colon.

In the summer of 2011, Colon was enjoying his best season since 2005, his last full season. At 3.10, his ERA was among the best in the league. On May 30, six days after his 39th birthday, he pitched his first shutout in five years, hurling his final pitch at 95 mph. Keep in mind that was after he sat out the 2010 season to rest his aging and injured right arm.

What was the secret behind Colon's remarkable comeback? According to Joseph Purita, founder of the Institute of Regenerative and Molecular Orthopedics in Boca Raton, Fla., it was an infusion of stem cells, which Colon received in the Dominican Republic before the baseball season began. [63]

As Purita tells *USA Today*, "Here's a guy who was fooling around for two years and not getting any better. All of a sudden, you do this procedure and a few weeks later he's dramatically better. There must be something going on here."

In June 2016, Dr. Gary Steinberg, professor and chair of neurology at Stanford University School of Medicine in Palo Alto, Calif., released the results of a stem cell study involving 18 individuals with an average age of 61, who had motor function disabilities as a result of a stroke suffered

> **"Here's a guy who was not getting any better. All of a sudden, you do this [stem cell] procedure and a few weeks later he's dramatically better."**
>
> Joseph Purita
> Founder, Institute of Regenerative and Molecular Orthopedics

61. "The Power of Stem Cells," *California Stem Cell Agency*, ret. 04-Jan-19.
62. "Researchers Use Human Embryonic Stem Cells To Kill Cancer Cells," *ScienceDaily*, 12-Oct-05.
63. Steve Sternberg, "Doctors offer unapproved stem cell therapies," *USA Today*, 29-Jun-11.

six months to three years before. Some patients were unable to move their arm, while others were unable to walk.

A hole was drilled in the skull of each patient and SB623 cells injected in the stroke-damaged areas of the brain. SB623 cells are mesenchymal stem cells (MSCs) — multipotent stromal cells that can differentiate into a variety of cell types. MSCs were taken from the bone marrow of two donors and induced to boost brain function. [64]

Within a month of the procedure, Steinberg's team noticed that the patients started to show signs of recovery, and their improvements continued over several months, lasting for more than two years in some patients.

As Steinberg notes, "This wasn't just, 'They couldn't move their thumb, and now they can.' Patients who were in wheelchairs are walking now."

Advances in stem cell therapy have given rise to a new type of healthcare discipline, called regenerative medicine, which is catering to an *avant garde* of athletes and intrepid sufferers. Therapies available treat all bodily zones prone to frequent breakdown: joints, like knees, shoulders and arms, plus that perennial health challenge, the back.

Early results like the ones described above point to the future promise for this young science and hold out hope for next-generation therapies that will fight age-related diseases, including macular degeneration, joint disorders like rheumatoid arthritis and heart disease.

But as Shinya Yamanaka cautions in *The New York Times*, "iPS cells are only 10 years old. The research takes time. That's what everybody needs to understand." [65]

> 66 iPS cells are only 10 years old. The research takes time. That's what everybody needs to understand."
>
> **Shinya Yamanaka**
> Stem Cell Researcher
> Kyoto University

Exercise

Research has shown that exercise can help stem the tide of aging. One study of 400,000 Taiwanese found that just 15 minutes of exercise each day was associated with a three-year increase in life expectancy plus a 14% reduction in risk of death by any cause, compared with a sedentary lifestyle.

Respondents to the study were defined as inactive if they exercised less than one hour per week. Compared with inactive individuals, those who participated in even small amounts of moderate activity each day lived longer. "The 30-minute-a-day for five or more days a week has been the golden rule for the last 15 years, but now we found even half that amount could be very beneficial," lead author Dr. Chi-Pang Wen tells ABC News. "Finding a slot of 15 minutes is much easier than finding a 30-minute slot in most days of the week." [66]

A Danish study of 20,000 men and women aged between 20 to 93 years sought to identify the benefits of jogging on longevity. The Copenhagen City Heart Study study compared the mortality of 1,116 male joggers and 762 female joggers with that of non-joggers in the main study population.

---

64. Honor Whiteman, "Stroke patients able to walk again after stem cell transplant," *Medical News Today*, 06-Jun-16.
65. Wallace Ravven, "The Stem-Cell Revolution Is Coming — Slowly," *The New York Times*, 16-Jan-17.
66. Meredith Melnick, "Just 15 Minutes of Exercise a Day May Add Years to Your Life," *Time*, 16-Aug-11.

First Gold's Gym Opens in Venice, Calif. in August 1965

From its humble beginnings near the beaches of Venice, Calif., Gold's Gym has helped transform a market that numbers some 201,000 gyms and fitness clubs worldwide. More than 60 million Americans now belong to a gym or fitness club.

Three data sets were collected between 1976 and 1978, from 1981 to 1983, 1991 to 1994, and 2001 to 2003. The Danish Central Person Register's unique personal identification number allowed researchers to track participants over time. The data shows that the risk of death was reduced by 44% for male and female joggers, extending life an additional 6.2 years for men and 5.6 years for women.

The study lead, Dr. Peter Schnohr, chief cardiologist at Bispebjerg University Hospital in Copenhagen, reports that between one and two-and-a-half hours of jogging per week at a "slow or average" pace delivers optimum longevity benefits. [67]

A 2008 study of 69 Swiss hospital workers, who had what researchers described as a sedentary lifestyle, were asked to skip elevators and take stairs instead for 12 weeks. After the three-month trial, tests showed study participants had more lung capacity, plus improved blood pressure and cholesterol measurements.

Their weight, body fat and waist measurements also dropped, and their capacity for doing aerobic exercise increased. According to Dr. Philippe Meyer, lead researcher of the University of Geneva team, these improvements translated to a 15% decrease in the chance of dying prematurely from any cause. [68]

A Harvard Alumni Health Study of 13,485 men with an average age of 57.5, published in 2000, found that climbing 35 or more flights of stairs a week significantly increased longevity when compared to people who climbed fewer than 10 stories a week. [69]

These and similar findings have been a boon to the exercise business. The gym industry, in particular, has come a long way since Adolph Spiess built the first indoor gymnasium in Hesse, Germany in 1852. [70] Incidentally, the Greek word gymnasium means "school for naked exercise" because that's how ancient Greeks did it. Thankfully, that's a practice most of us no longer adhere to.

67. Peter Schnohr, "Regular jogging shows dramatic increase in life expectancy," *EurekAlert*, 03-May-12.
68. "Climbing stairs can prolong life," *BBC News*, 01-Sep-08.
69. "Exercises That Can Add Years to Your Life," *Everyday Health*, 23-Jul-12.
70. "Gym," *Wikipedia*, ret. 04-Jan-19.

America's first gym was reportedly built in 1851 by the YMCA in Boston, a fact disputed by the Boston Young Men's Christian Union. Today, the U.S. gym, health and fitness clubs industry is a $30 billion business encompassing 94,956 locations, according to IBISWorld. [71] Worldwide, those figures are $87 billion and 201,000, respectively. [72]

That's a Bob Beamon-size leap forward from August 1965 when Joe Gold opened the first Gold's Gym in Venice, Calif. Gold's became a landmark gathering place for bodybuilders, including Arnold Schwarzenegger who joined in 1968. Joe Gold sold the chain in 1970 and later founded World Gym in 1977. [73]

It took an innovation breakthrough to make gyms what they are today, and that came in 1970 when Arthur Jones began selling his Nautilus machines. [74] Jones' invention made resistance training appealing to the general public, fueling the fitness boom of the 1970s and 1980s.

Today, Dallas, Tex.-based Gold's Gym ranks third in the U.S. with a 4.2% market share, behind 24 Hour Fitness (4.8%), a San Ramon, Calif.-based chain, and Chanhassen, Minn.-based Lifetime Fitness (4.7%). [75] After the top five, all other health and fitness clubs account for 81% market share, indicative of a highly fragmented industry.

The best news is that the health and fitness market continues to grow. According to the International Health, Racquet & Sportsclub Association (IHRSA), health club membership has increased more than 10% over the past three years, reaching 60.9 million, or more than 16% of the adult U.S. population. [76] That figure may overlap with 8 million personal trainers, suggesting a total health and fitness market well in excess of 61 million. In the U.K., the proportion of people that go to a gym is 12%. [77]

Yoga Culture

The rapid growth in gym and fitness club membership is partly fueled by the skyrocketing growth of the yoga market, which has zoomed from 4 million in 1990 to 21 million as of 2016, according to a National Health Interview Survey of 2,021 U.S. adults 18+. [78] [79]

Industry growth data has traditionally been provided by *Yoga Journal*'s "Yoga In America" study, as well it should. *Yoga Journal* began publishing in May 1975 with an initial print run of 300 copies. [80]

Over the years, the publication has changed its research firm several times, causing *Yoga Journal*'s estimates of U.S. yoga practitioners to vary significantly, even producing two dips during the particularly downward dog days of 2002 and 2008.

71. "Gym, Health & Fitness Clubs Market Research Report," *IBISWorld*, May-16.
72. "Statistics and facts on Health & Fitness Clubs," *Statista*, ret. 04-Jan-19.
73. "Gold's Gym," *Wikipedia*, ret. 04-Jan-19.
74. "Arthur Jones," *Wikipedia*, ret. 04-Jan-19.
75. "Market share of major fitness, health and gym club companies in the U.S. in 2016," *Statista*, ret. 04-Jan-19.
76. Melissa Rodriguez, "IHRSA 2018 Global Report: Health Club Industry Revenue Totaled $87.2 Billion in 2017," *IHRSA*, 29-May-18.
77. Eric Chaline, "The Temple of Perfection: A History of the Gym," *History Today*, 04-Apr-15.
78. Anne Cushman, "Yoga Today: Is Yoga Becoming Too Mainstream?," *Yoga Journal*, 28-Aug-07.
79. "2016 Yoga in America Study Conducted by Yoga Journal and Yoga Alliance," *Yoga Journal*, 13-Jan-16.
80. Robert Velarde, "Yoga," *Watchmen Fellowship*, 2014.

An analysis by Trisha Lamb for the International Association of Yoga Therapists raised further questions. [81] In 2003, *Yoga Journal* halted the practice of tracking entry and core practitioners, providing only an estimate of total practitioners (table). *Yoga Journal*'s most recent market estimate of 37 million practitioners in 2016 is up an astonishing 80% compared to 2012. It's highly unlikely that the yoga market grew that fast after having plateaued in previous years. A 2015 National Health Interview Survey found that 9.5% of U.S. adults, or 21 million, used yoga as a complementary health approach. The chart at left shows a more reasonable growth trajectory.

Yoga arrived in the U.S. in 1920, courtesy of the Los Angeles, Calif.-based Self-Realization Fellowship, an organization founded by Paramahansa Yogananda, who wrote *Autobiography of a Yogi*, released in 1946. But yoga really began its modern-day ascent during the 1960s with the publication of *Light on Yoga* in 1966 by B.K.S. Iyengar, founder of Iyengar Yoga, and The Beatles who helped popularize it.

Type	1990	1994	1998	2002	2003	2005	2008	2012	2016
Entry Practitioners	1.0M	1.2M	9.5M	10.0M	—	—	—	—	—
Core Practitioners	3.0M	5.0M	9.0M	18.0M	—	—	—	—	—
Total Practitioners	4.0M	6.2M	18.5M	28.0M	15.0M	16.5M	15.8M	20.4M	36.7M

Source: 1990, 1994 Roper Starch; Jun-98 Wall Street Journal/NBC Poll; 16-Jun-03, 07-Feb-05 Harris Interactive Service Bureau; 05-Dec-12 Sports Marketing Surveys USA; 13-Jan-16 IPSOS Public Affairs.

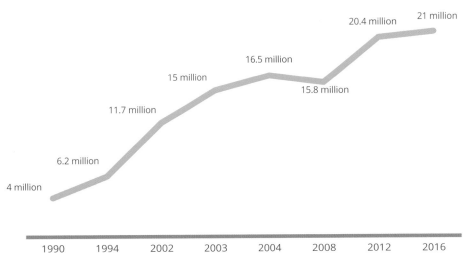

Yoga Market Growth 1990-2016

4 million — 6.2 million — 11.7 million — 15 million — 16.5 million — 15.8 million — 20.4 million — 21 million

1990 1994 2002 2003 2004 2008 2012 2016

Source: 1990, 1994 Roper Starch; Jun-98 Wall Street Journal/NBC Poll; 16-Jun-03, 07-Feb-05 Harris Interactive Service Bureau; 05-Dec-12 Sports Marketing Surveys USA; 13-Jan-16 IPSOS Public Affairs; 10-Feb-15 U.S. Department Of Health And Human Services; 04-May-17 Michael Tchong.

In 1965, The Beatles were in the Bahamas filming *Help!* when they met Swami Vishnu-Devananda, the founder of Sivandana Yoga. He presented them with signed copies of *The Illustrated Book of Yoga*. This chance meeting spurred George Harrison to begin studying yoga and Eastern religion. [82]

While Harrison was studying in India, his wife Pattie Boyd heard of Maharishi Mahesh Yogi, the founder of Transcendental Meditation (TM). The couple was struck by the Maharishi's teachings and flew him to London to meet the other Beatles. Much of the *White Album* was inspired by the Maharishi's words and The Beatles' TM experience. By the 1970s, more than five million people practiced Transcendental Meditation.

Despite being popular among *cognoscente*, yoga would take three more

81. Trisha Lamb, "Yoga Statistics and Demographics," *International Association of Yoga Therapists*, 27-Apr-06.
82. Janel Chatraw "Did the Beatles introduce yoga to the Western world?" *HowStuffWorks.com*, 08-Feb-08.

lululemon leverages the athleisure trend

Yoga fans who like to wear athletic leisurewear while shopping or traveling have buoyed the fortunes of yoga apparel maker lululemon, which sold $3 billion worth of trendy tops and pants during its last fiscal year.

IMAGE COURTESY: LULULEMON ATHLETICA INC.

decades to really take off. And its popularity would change its audience noticeably. In India, where 100 million participate in yoga, its practice has mostly been a male pursuit. [83]

Indra Devi, a Latvian-born Swede who moved to California in 1947 from China became yoga's first female ambassador. [84] In her 1959 book, *Yoga for Americans* Devi notes, "A great many people seem to have taken up the study of yoga simply because Gloria Swanson, Greta Garbo, Jennifer Jones, Marilyn Monroe, Olivia de Havilland, and also the world-famous beautician Elizabeth Arden are known to have been devotees."

Another major female factor was Lilias Folan, whose 1970s PBS series *Lilias, Yoga and You* brought yoga into millions of North American living rooms. The third female force was Geeta Iyengar, B.K.S. Iyengar's eldest daughter, whose book, *Yoga: A Gem for Women*, was published in 1983.

Their influence brought many women into the fold, so much so that *Yoga Journal*'s Yoga In America study found that U.S. women now make up 72% of yoga practitioners, while men constitute just 28%.

83. Charu Sudan Kasturi, Yoga gets biggest science thumbs up yet," *Hindustan Time*, 25-Jan-13.
84. Anna Dubrovsky, "In Loving Gratitude: A Tribute to Four Women Who Revolutionized Yoga, *Yoga International*, 28-Nov-13.

The ascendancy of a female-dominated sport provided an opening for Canadian entrepreneur Chip Wilson, who opened the first lululemon store in Vancouver in 1998. His timing was impeccable, as the "athleisure" trend was kicking in high gear. Yoginis eagerly wore trendy lululemon Groove pants and tops to yoga class, and everywhere else. lululemon's obsessive groupies helped drive sales to $1,675 per square foot, placing the popular retailer in fourth place behind Apple, Tiffany's and Michael Kors. [85]

When lululemon athletica made its stock market debut on July 27, 2007, its shares rose 56% to $28 on the first day of trading, giving the company a market value of nearly $2 billion. With 415 stores now open, lululemon shares currently trade around $131, making it worth $17 billion today. [86]

Yoga has much upside potential due to its mostly unexplored therapeutic value. A recent study by Meera Balasubramaniam found that yoga can be beneficial for people suffering from depression, sleep disorders, and as a way to augment the effectiveness of other therapies. [87]

Stress Relief

The Time Compression Ubertrend chapter will examine the origins of stress more closely, but suffice it to say that the business of stress relief has seen a decided up-tick over the past 60-plus years since the term "stress" first surfaced.

There are numerous effective ways to blow off steam, including exercise and yoga, but one stress therapy has grown exponentially since the 1980s, the spa business. Not too long ago, the only people who visited spas regularly were the Germans.

And that's because Germany has one of the most advanced spa cultures in all of Europe, with more than 900 spas registered across the country. [88] The German healthcare system lets doctors prescribe a spa treatment as a reimbursable medical expense. The Romans discovered that spas had medicinal properties, able to contribute to both mental and physical health.

That age-old thinking combined with new-age treatments has propelled the spa industry to dizzying new heights. Spas are now an integral aspect of the "wellness" industry, a word that traces its roots to a little-known book published by Dr. Halbert Dunn in 1961, called *High-Level Wellness*. [89]

Research firm SRI International was commissioned by The Global Wellness Institute to quantify the "global wellness economy," which the research firm estimates at $4.2 trillion. [90] The spa market, an integral part of wellness, grew from $94 billion in 2013 to $119 billion in 2017.

The Global Wellness Institute reports that the number of spa locations around the world soared from 105,591 in 2013 to 121,595 in 2015. Since

85. Phil Wahba, "Apple extends lead in U.S. top 10 retailers by sales per square foot," *Fortune*, 13-Mar-15.
86. "Lululemon Athletica Inc.," *Yahoo! Finance*, ret. 11-Jan-19.
87. Meera Balasubramaniam, Shirley Telles, Murali Doraiswamy, "Yoga on Our Minds: A Systematic Review of Yoga for Neuropsychiatric Disorders," *Frontiers in Psychiatry*, 25-Jan-13.
88. Rachel Bale, "The German Spa Experience: Warning Nudity Expected," *Department of Wandering*, 22-Oct-14.
89. "Spas and the Global Wellness Market: Synergies and Opportunities," *Global Spa Summit, SRI International*, 20-Aug-10.
90. "Global Wellness Economy Monitor 2017," *Global Wellness Institute*, ret. 04-Jan-19.

Azul Beach Offers Customers Beachfront Massages

Like any self-respecting major hotel or resort these days, Azul Beach Resort Riviera Maya, operated by Karisma Hotels, offers a full range of spa services, including a "Beachfront Sky Massage." Azul Beach is one of nearly 122,000 spas that now dot the globe.

IMAGE COURTESY: KARISMA HOTELS & RESORTS.

The Male Spa Factor

In 2009, ISPA reported that men made up just 24% of spa clientele. That was 15 years after term "metrosexual" was coined, and the trend started to rear its handsomely coiffed head. [1] While men are a minority among spa clientele, a growing number of men are visiting these temples of relaxation. In June 2015, Mashable reported the share of men "increased over the past few years from 31% to 47%, according to ISPA, nearly half of all spa-goers." [2] ISPA President Lynne McNees believed the trend was being propelled by the primary reason people go to spas — to manage stress. Yet, the notion that half of spa visitors are men is not supported by anecdotal evidence, as in "my eyes can't deceive me." The "mankini" and "boyzillian" trends may be catching on, but it's difficult to believe that the share of male visitors to spas nearly doubled in six years.

1. "Metrosexual," *Wikipedia*, ret. 24-Dec-18.
2. Kathleen Wong, "More men are going to spas, because getting pampered is awesome," *Mashable*, 26-Jun-15.

2013, the spa industry has added about 16,000 spas and more than 230,000 workers, reaching a workforce of 2.1 million.

The stresses of modern living are driving record numbers of people to spas. The International Spa Association (ISPA) recorded 187 million U.S. spa visits in 2017. [91] The association uses PricewaterhouseCoopers (PwC) to conduct its industry research. Between 1999 and 2016, U.S. spa revenues more than tripled, zooming from $5 billion to $17.5 billion, while the number of spa outlets jumped from 5,300 in 1999 to 21,770, a 310% increase.

In a May 2006 article, since removed, Frommers.com estimated that the spa business was the fourth-largest U.S. leisure industry, taking in more revenue than ski resorts, amusement parks and box office receipts combined, which was incorrect. That comparative total, about $31.4 billion, would be nearly double the spa market's size.

Consumers no longer see spa visits as "pampering," which explains why some spas have also begun adding such services as Botox injections, chemical peels, collagen and dermabrasion to their regular regimen, leading to the emergence of "medspas."

ISPA reported in 2004 that 471 U.S. spas offered medical treatments, ranging from day spas that sold Botox shots to destination resorts providing diagnosis and treatment by board-certified physicians.

In December 2012, *USA Today* quoted International Medical Spa Association Executive Director Allan Share stating that there were about 4,500 med spas in the United States, up from about 800 five years earlier. [92] That would suggest a five-year growth rate of 463%. According to the American Medical Spa Association (AmSpa), the total number of U.S. medspas in 2017 stood at 4,200. [93] AmSpa projects that medical spa revenues in the U.S. would reach $3.97 billion in 2017.

91. "U.S. Spa Industry Study's 'Big Five' Sets New Records," *ISPA*, 14-Aug-18.
92. Jayne O'Donnell, "Cosmetic surgery laws often aren't enough," *USA Today*, 10-Dec-12.
93. John LaRosa, "Medical Spa Industry Overview," *Modern Aesthetics*, May/June 2017.

Body Contouring

Fountain of Youth

Imagine for a moment that you could leave work for lunch, undergo a simple procedure and return to your desk having shed an inch from your waist. You may consider that a wild fantasy but technology to instantly shape the body has already arrived.

This is the magic of body shaping, a set of minimally invasive procedures that have revolutionized plastic surgery. The technology has enabled so-called "lunchtime procedures" — treatments that are more convenient and preferred by consumers. Body shaping falls under the treatment category of body contouring, which encompasses all non-surgical *and* surgical techniques that can be used to reshape the body, as described in this section. Together with facial rejuvenation, the subject of the next section, body contouring falls under the rubric of aesthetic medicine.

Body Shaping

Body shaping describes a new wave of innovative contouring technologies that require little or no downtime and are minimally invasive. Research firm Medical Insight, based in Aliso Viejo, Calif., reported in 2006 that total fees for body-shaping treatments alone were $4.2 billion worldwide in 2005, and were projected to rise to $7.5 billion by 2010. [94]

94. Rhonda Rundle, "Doctors Question Therapies For Sagging Skin," *The Wall Street Journal*, 15-Jun-06.

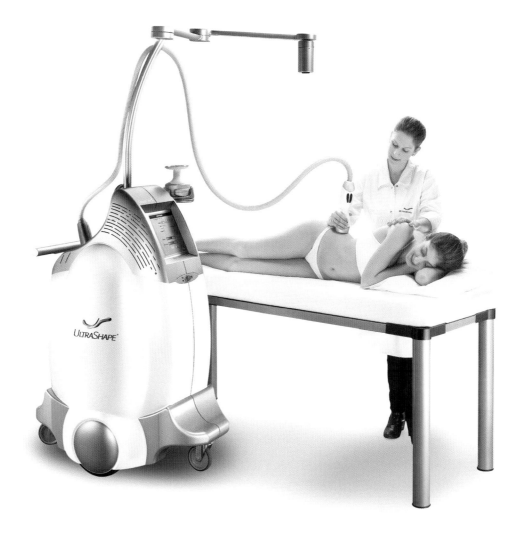

Body Shaping With UltraShape Body Contouring Device

UltraShape, made by Israel-based Syneron Candela, uses ultrasound technology to destroy fat cells. It received FDA clearance in mid-2016 and features a lighter transducer for improved maneuverability, which lets practitioners cover an entire abdomen in about 30 minutes.

IMAGE COURTESY: SYNERON CANDELA.

In 2008, Medical Insight estimated that the entire aesthetic industry was $5.2 billion, and projected that body shaping would grow from $384.5 million in global supplier sales to $809.6 million by 2012. Note that the 2005 forecast was for treatments and the 2008 forecast was for supplier sales. [95]

In its September 2017 Energy-Based Aesthetic Devices study, the researcher reported that in 2016 practitioners earned fees of more than $7.4 billion based on "more than 97,000 energy-based aesthetic treatment systems" installed worldwide and close to 28 million procedures performed during the year. [96]

A June 2018 from the American Society of Plastic Surgeons (ASPS) study found that the top five minimally-invasive, cosmetic procedures were botulinum toxin (Botox), soft tissue fillers (dermal or and facial filler injections), chemical peel, laser hair removal and microdermabrasion. [97]

The ASPS reports that Americans spent $16.7 billion on surgical and non-surgical procedures in 2017, a 2% increase, over 2016. As the chart on the next page shows, spending on surgical procedures was noticeably

95. "Body Shaping Fuels Growth of $5.2 Billion Global Medical Aesthetic Market," *PR Newswire*, 04-Aug-08.
96. "Energy-Based Aesthetic Devices," *Medical Insight*, 22-Aug-17.
97. "2017 Plastic Surgery Report," *American Society of Plastic Surgeons (ASPS)*, 13-Jun-18.

impacted by the 2007-9 recession.

Body shaping procedures available today rely either on low-level laser therapy (LLLT), suction massage, radio-frequency energy or high-frequency focused ultrasound and are designed to treat these symptoms of aging:

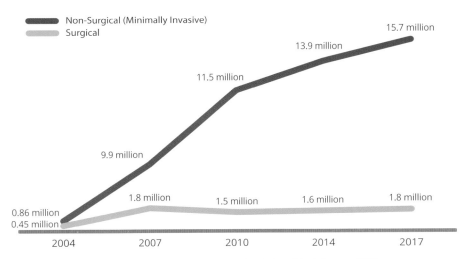

Cosmetic and Reconstructive Procedure Trend 2004-2017

— Non-Surgical (Minimally Invasive)
— Surgical

15.7 million
13.9 million
11.5 million
9.9 million
1.8 million
1.5 million
1.6 million
1.8 million
0.86 million
0.45 million

2004   2007   2010   2014   2017

Source: 2005, 2008, 2011, 2015, 2017 American Society of Plastic Surgeons (ASPS).

•**Cellulite reduction** – Cellulite is a common affliction that gives women's legs a dimpled, uneven appearance. The newest devices use a laser or other energy source to induce fat cells under the skin to release some of their contents, leading to a smoother surface appearance. The market for cellulite-fighting equipment was expected to reach $200 million by 2012, up from $80 million in 2007, according to the Millennium Research Group. [98]

• **Circumference reduction** – As YouTube user "the basicblond" tells it, her VelaShape treatments let her lose 2 centimeters (0.8 in.) around the waist each time, did not hurt and cost her $650 for three treatments. [99] It should be noted that the procedure is not always painless. On the site RealSelf, 87% of members rate the procedure as "worth it," based on 121 reviews.

• **Fat removal** – There are two basic body-shaping techniques that are used to fight body fat, one uses heat the other cold. Heating fat (adipose) tissue via radio frequency (RF) energy waves has been found to work best. The Exilis Ultra, marketed by Framingham, Mass.-based BTL Aesthetics, uses RF waves. Pleasanton, Calif.-based ZELTIQ Aesthetics offers CoolSculpting, which relies on a technology that freezes fat cells.

• **Skin laxity** – A 2015 study sought to quantify the effect that radio-frequency (RF) devices may have on wrinkles or facial and body laxity — the loose skin common in people who have lost a lot of weight. [100] The reviewed literature concluded that RF promotes a change in dermis tissues, specifically the reforming of collagen. Although a majority of the studies (96%) reported positive results in treating skin laxity using RF, only 44% showed statistical significance. The main physiological effect observed in

98. Rhonda Rundle, "The Latest Cellulite Treatments Sound Too Smooth to Be True," *The Wall Street Journal*, 19-Aug-08.
99. the basicblond, "Ultrashape & Velashape Experience, Body Contouring 101," *YouTube*, 10-Feb-16.
100. Angélica Rodrigues de Araújo et al., "Radiofrequency for the treatment of skin laxity: myth or truth?," *Anais Brasileiros de Dermatologia*, Sep-15.

the reviewed studies was a contraction of collagen in the short term, and the stimulation of collagen synthesis through tissue repair in the long-term.

Market interest in the field of aesthetic healthcare is rising quickly. That is evident from the explosive growth in body-shaping equipment aimed at the beauty and anti-aging markets around the world. Expect continued market growth, and confusion, as options proliferate without adequate treatment standards.

Allergan NATRELLE INSPIRA SoftTouch Breast Implant

These Allergan implants offer three gel firmness levels for better form stability and also come in 243 sizes. The implant uses a "cohesive gel" — a derivative of the same silicone gel that has made NATRELLE a "popular silicone implant since 1993."

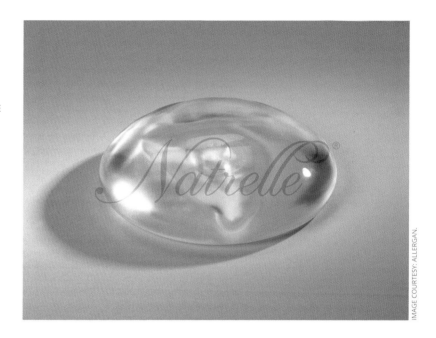

IMAGE COURTESY: ALLERGAN.

Breast Augmentation

You might be inclined to believe that after watching an episode of *The Bachelor* or any *Housewives of...* TV series that everyone is enhancing their breasts. Nothing could be further from the truth. About 300,000 breast augmentation procedures were recorded in the U.S. in 2017, a decline of 47,500, or 14%, from a decade earlier, when pocketbooks were clearly deeper. [101]

That means that every year a city the size of Pittsburgh parades their new big breasts in front of boob tube America. The actual breast augmentation procedure figure is somewhat higher when medical breast tourism is included. A 2010 *BBC News* report noted that 1.5 million underwent the procedure worldwide. [102] Breast augmentation remains the most popular U.S. cosmetic surgical procedure performed in 2017, ahead of liposuction.

The first breast enhancement operation occurred some 57 years ago, when Timmie Jean Lindsey, a mother of six, received the first silicone implants at Jefferson Davis Hospital in Houston, Tex. in Spring 1962. The intervening

101. "2017 Plastic Surgery Report," *American Society of Plastic Surgeons (ASPS)*, 13-Jun-18.
102. Claire Bowes & Cordelia Hebblethwaite, "A brief history of breast enlargements," *BBC News*, 29-Mar-12.

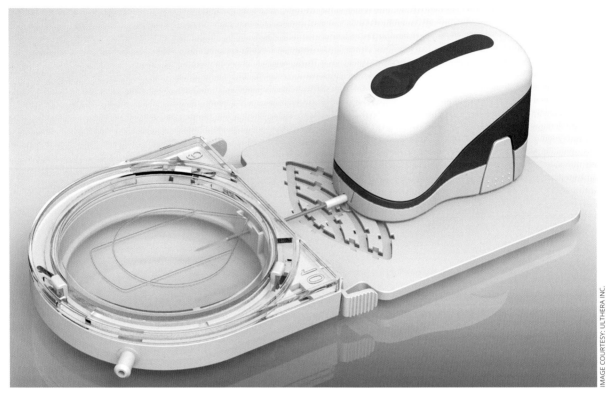

Cellfina Handheld Device Used to Reduce Cellulite

Cellulite is caused by connective bands that are woven throughout fat in thighs and buttocks. These bands pull down the skin, creating skin surface puckering. Cellfina breaks these bands in a minimally invasive treatment that usually lasts an hour.

decades have ushered in 3D-imaging and rupture-proof implants, but the biggest innovation may well be the level of customization available in today's breast implants.

In January 2017, now Ireland-based Allergan announced that it had received approval from the Food and Drug Administration (FDA) to market NATRELLE INSPIRA SoftTouch breast implants, which boast three levels of cohesive gel, including a medium firmness gel, and which are available in 243 sizes. [103]

The ultimate in breast customization may well be offered by Irvine, Calif.-based Mentor Worldwide, which manufactures the fully customizable MENTOR SPECTRUM saline implants. SPECTRUM implants are inserted in the patient without fluid and then filled to a predetermined size. When the fill-tube is removed, the implant automatically seals itself. [104]

Another trend in breast augmentation is the use of fat grafting, while the technique has been around for some years, it is now used by 62% of plastic surgeons for breast reconstruction and by 28% for aesthetic procedures. [105]

Lest you think that we are not beauty-oriented, and celebrity-obsessed enough, how about the unsettling phenomenon that has teenagers getting breast implants? [106]

While most surgeons will not operate on women younger than 18, between 18 and 21 anyone is apparently fair game.

103. "Allergan Announces FDA Approval of NATRELLE INSPIRA® SoftTouch Breast Implants," *PR Newswire*, 03-Jan-17.
104. "Why choose saline breast implants?," *Mentor Worldwide*, ret. 04-May-17.
105. Karan Chopra et al., "Fat Grafting Breast Augmentation Mammaplasty," *Eplasty*, 2013.
106. Susan Kreimer, "Teens Getting Breast Implants for Graduation," *Women's eNews*, 06-Jun-04.

Tummy Tuck

To use a well-worn cliché, there is no bigger battle than the battle of the bulge. And with mounting evidence that carrying a spare tire is a bad health sign, you have two options. [107] You can either exercise, practice yoga, or you can cheat and have your stomach reduced the twenty-first century way.

The good news is that the traditional tummy tuck operation, or abdominoplasty in medical *parlance*, has been complemented by innovative liposuction and body shaping techniques.

The reason why is simple: surgical tummy tuck operations are very invasive procedures. This type of abdominal plastic surgery involves removing excess fat, skin, and in some cases, reestablishing weakened or separated muscles. But the end result, an overall abdominal profile that is both firmer and smoother, is well worth it.

Abdominoplasty is often combined with a panniculectomy, which removes any overhanging "apron" of skin and tissue from below the belly button. This excess skin is typically the result of significant weight loss through diet and exercise.

There is also a less intrusive surgical approach, the mini tummy tuck, which requires smaller incisions in the patient's abdominal area to remove fat and skin from muscle fascia, the fibrous connective tissue that is present throughout the entire body.

The number of liposuction and tummy tuck procedures in the U.S. more than tripled between 2004 and 2017 to 376,107 procedures, most likely due to the influence of television shows like FX' *Nip/Tuck* (2003-2010) and NBC's *The Biggest Loser* (2004-2016). This happened despite the number of liposuction procedures, also known by their medical terms lipoplasty or lipectomy, actually declining from their pre-recession high of 354,015 procedures in 2007 to about 246,354 in 2017, the result of heightened competition from innovative body shaping or body sculpting procedures.

Despite the declining number of liposuction procedures, there have been many market innovations:

- **Smartlipo** – Cynosure, located in Westford, Mass., offers Smartlipo, which uses a laser-assisted lipolysis procedure to break down fats and other lipids through hydrolysis to release fatty acids. A laser fiber is inserted into the body through a thin hollow tube, called a cannula. The laser ruptures fat cell membranes and destroys them, after which the liquefied fat is suctioned out via the same cannula, which is also initially used to administer a numbing fluid.

- **VASERlipo** – Marketed by Hayward, Calif.-based Solta Medical, VASERlipo uses ultrasound technology to melt fat before it's removed through the cannula. The device is able to eliminate stubborn fat from some regions of the body, such as the stomach or love handles.

VASERlipo System

Depending on patient needs, VASERlipo can remove either small or larger volumes of fat for rapid contouring. Fat removed during a VASERlipo procedure can be treated for a subsequent fat transfer procedure.

IMAGE COURTESY: SOLTA MEDICAL INTERNATIONAL INC.

107. Steven Reinberg, "Belly Fat Is Bad, Even at a Normal Weight," *WebMD*, 09-Nov-15.

CoolSculpting Fat Freezing Body Contouring System

CoolSculpting is an FDA-cleared, non-surgical fat-reduction treatment that uses controlled cooling to reduce fat bulges in the area under the chin, thigh, abdomen and flank (love handles).

But the biggest star in the firmament of fat reduction is body shaping, which zoomed from 76,612 treatments in 2012, the first year they were reported separately by the American Society for Aesthetic Plastic Surgery, to more than 180,833 procedures in 2017. [108]

Yet, the market is still in the early stages of the body shaping revolution:

- **CoolSculpting** – ZELTIQ Aesthetics offers a technology that freezes fat cells, marketed under the brand CoolSculpting, which is one of the most popular aesthetic procedures on Real Self with 71% reporting it's "worth it," confirming the results obtained by YouTube user "the basicblond." [109]

- **Exilis Ultra** – BTL Aesthetics makes the Exilis Ultra, which uses RF waves to stimulate collagen and melt body fat. BTL also markets Vanquish, an FDA-cleared body contouring procedure that uses RF energy to heat and kill fat cells in a non-invasive way. The treatment is not intended for significant weight loss but for the temporary reduction of the abdomen and thighs. The procedure is virtually painless and requires zero downtime. Results are typically achieved in four to six treatments.

- **i-Lipo Xcell** – U.K.-based Energist says its multi-disciplinary approach, which includes intelligent body fat analysis and measurement, laser diode fat reduction, infra-red-based IR Vacuum massage and RF skin tightening is the "most advanced" body shaping system. The Xcell is an upgraded i-Lipo system from Energist that achieves laser lipolysis through the use of pads placed on the abdomen of patients.

- **UltraShape** – Israel-based Syneron Candela, which has offices in Irvine, Calif., markets UltraShape, a non-invasive ultrasound-based body contouring procedure that's FDA-cleared to treat stomach, hips and thighs areas of fat that are resistant to diet and exercise. The device causes fat cells to burst, which are eliminated through the body's natural metabolic process.

108. "Cosmetic Surgery National Data Bank Statistics," *American Society for Aesthetic Plastic Surgery* (ASAPS), 28-Mar-18.
109. "CoolSculpting," *RealSelf*, ret. 04-Jan-19.

Facial Rejuvenation

As Victoria Moran writes, "Just because you're grown up and then some doesn't mean settling into the doldrums of predictability. Surprise people. Surprise yourself." [110] Indeed, surprise yourself with a rejuvenated face, for if the eyes are the windows of our soul, our face is the business card of our being.

Now that the economy is humming and with the Dow Jones in record-high territory, it's as good a time as any to start planning a big comeback for the brand of "you." In a little under two decades, the science of facial rejuvenation has taken a quantum leap forward — advances that are nothing short of breathtaking, if not wrinkle reducing.

There have been at least three significant innovations in facial rejuvenation: Botox, facial fillers and the fractional CO2 Laser. The *Archives of Dermatology* notes that three anti-aging treatments are clinically proven effective: topical application of retinol; carbon-dioxide laser resurfacing; and injection of hyaluronic acid, a moisture-retaining acid that occurs naturally in the skin. [111]

Botox

When the Food and Drug Administration approved botulinum toxin injections, better known under the brand name Botox, for cosmetic use in 2002, it helped spark a cultural phenomenon, which included

---

110. Victoria Moran, "Younger by the Day: 365 Ways to Rejuvenate Your Body and Revitalize Your Spirit," *HarperOne*, 06-Sep-05.
111. Nicholas Bakalar, "Wrinkle Removers, Backed by Science," *The New York Times*, 18-Aug-08.

Botox: An Aesthetic Procedure Becomes a Cult Hit

Botox humor surfaced in the early part of the last decade and, like Botox parties, is a cultural manifestation of the Fountain of Youth Ubertrend.

IMAGE COURTESY: DAN PIRARO.

Botox parties, Botox gift cards and, of course, Botox humor.

The injectable muscle relaxant category, which includes Botox, is the top non-surgical procedure performed in the U.S., with 7.2 million procedures in 2017, according to the American Society for Plastic Surgery. [112]

Botulinum toxins, including Botox competitors Medicis Pharmaceutical's Reloxin, known in the U.S. as Dysport, and Xeomin, from Germany-based Merz Pharma, are the only FDA approved treatments to treat the "11s" — lines that form on the glabella, the skin that sits between the eyebrows and above the nose. Botox and its competitors can also be used off-label to treat horizontal forehead lines, crows feet, and the tiny "bunny lines" on each side of the nose.

Other than for its originally intended purposes, treatment of blepharospasm (eye spasm) and *strabismus* (misalignment of the eye), Botox has also been approved to treat a number of other ailments, including excessive sweating, weak bladder symptoms, migraine headaches and muscle stiffness. [113]

This growing list of approved applications, paired with its aesthetic popularity has boosted Botox revenues for the maker, Allergan, to nearly $3 billion in 2017, double the $1.4 billion recorded in 2008. Not bad for a drug named after the Latin word for sausage, *botulus*, because the toxin was first discovered in poorly prepared sausages during the 18th century. [114]

GlobalData Facial Aesthetics predicts that the U.S. market for Botox and other wrinkle fillers will grow from $2.5 billion in 2013 to $4.7 billion in 2018, equal to compound annual growth of 13.5%. [115]

A new vanguard of topical botulins is being developed by Newark, Calif.-based Revance. The company is currently in phase III clinical trials for a next-generation highly purified botulinum toxin, daxibotulinumtoxinA. Referred to internally as RT002, it has the potential of becoming the first long-lasting botulinum toxin type A injectable.

Approval of the RT002 injectable would represent the first major innovation to hit the neurotoxin market in 30 years.

112. "2017 Plastic Surgery Statistics Report," *American Society for Plastic Surgery*, 01-Mar-18.
113. "Botox Medication Guide," *U.S. Food & Drug Administration*, Jan-16.
114. "The drugs derived from deadly poisons," *BBC News*, 18-Oct-13.
115. Martine Geller and Alice Baghdijian, "Nestle boosts skincare business with $1.4 billion Valeant deal," *Reuters*, 28-May-14.

Facial Fillers

Botox effects are good for 3-4 months but facial fillers can last much longer, causing procedures to jump from 23,070 in 2004, the first year soft tissue fillers were identified separately by the American Society of Plastic Surgeons (ASPS), to 2.1 million in 2017, an 8,966% increase in 13 years.

Unfortunately, many cosmetic surgery and aesthetic treatments do not have a long-lasting effect. Even the most skillful procedure will need maintenance work at some point. That explains why a facial filler called Bellafill has created such a buzz among rejuvenation *aficionados*.

Bellafill is a collagen-based facial filler, formerly known as Artefill in the U.K. and Australia, and approved by the FDA for correction of "smile lines," also dubbed nasolabial folds, which run from the nose to the corners of the mouth.

Like all facial fillers, Bellafill adds volume below the surface of the skin, but unlike most, Suneva Medical, its maker, claims Bellafill can last as long as five years, based on a study released in September 2015. [116] Earlier that year, Bellafill was initially approved by the FDA for treating atrophic acne scars. [117] Atrophic indicates a loss of tissue, which happens when acne leaves a deep scar.

Botox, or botulinum toxin, injections are mostly used to correct the "11s," or glabellar lines (the vertical lines shown in 1), and also horizontal forehead lines (1). Bunny lines, which some people show when they wrinkle their nose, not shown here, are also treatable with Botox. Crows feet, the branching wrinkle at the outer corner of each eye (2), can also be addressed with Botox.

Smile lines next to the nose that extend to the corners of the mouth, called nasolabial folds (3), are best treated with facial fillers, such as Bellafill or Juvederm. The same goes for so-called "marionette" lines (4) and above the lip smoker lines (not shown).

The facial filler revolution began in earnest in December 2003 when the FDA approved the use of Medicis Pharmaceutical's Restylane for smoothing wrinkles and lip enhancement. That move, combined with the approval of Botox a year earlier, helped ignite the facial rejuvenation market.

The FDA refers to facial fillers as soft tissue or dermal fillers and describes them as "medical device implants for use in helping to create a smoother and fuller appearance in the face, including nasolabial folds, cheeks and lips and for increasing the volume of the back of the hand." Besides being used to treat smile lines, wrinkles and thin lips, facial fillers can be used to treat the sides of the mouth, which tend to show "marionette lines,"

116. "Suneva Medical Announces Landmark Clinical Study Confirming Long-Term Safety and Effectiveness of Bellafill Through Five Years," *Suneva Medical*, 10-Sep-15.
117. "Bellafill Receives FDA Approval for Treatment of Acne Scars," *Suneva Medical*, 06-Jan-15.

and wrinkles above the lips, called "smoker lines."

Most facial fillers, like Restylane, consist of a gel made of an organic material that eventually breaks down, usually hyaluronic acid, which is found in roosters' combs or produced by bacteria in the laboratory. [118]

Laval, Québec-based Valeant Pharmaceuticals acquired Medicis in 2012 for $2.6 billion. Valeant subsequently sold U.S. and Canadian marketing rights to Restylane, Perlane, Emervel, Sculptra and Dysport to Nestlé for $1.4 billion in May 2014. [119] Yes, the same company that makes KitKat chocolate bars, Gerber baby food and Nescafé now offers anti-aging treatments. The first four brands are facial fillers, while Dysport is a Botox competitor. Marketing will be handled by Forth Worth, Tex.-based Nestlé subsidiary Galderma, which markets such brands as Cetaphil and Differin.

Allergan, best known for its Botox anti-wrinkle serum, received FDA approval for its facial filler Juvéderm in June 2006. [120] In December of that year, another player, Radiesse made by BioForm Medical, also received FDA approval. [121]

Connective tissue cells, called fibroblasts, secrete a complex group of polysaccharides and proteins that create collagen, which gives skin its shape and elasticity while supporting blood vessels that permeate it. A mechanical tension with fibroblasts maintains collagen tissue.

While skin naturally deteriorates as it ages, sunlight exposure inhibits the ability of fibroblasts to produce collagen. That explains why hands, face, neck and the upper chest area suffer more than unexposed skin, and also why light-pigmented people wrinkle more readily than others.

In 2005, David Steinberg, an equity researcher in specialty pharmaceuticals at Deutsche Bank in San Francisco, estimated that the U.S. facial filler market was then already worth about $250 million a year, up from about $100 million in 2003. [122]

In 2005, the American Society of Plastic Surgeons reported 489,554 hyaluronic acid procedures. Based on the 2.1 million procedures performed in 2017, the facial filler market has more than likely quadrupled to about $1 billion in the U.S. alone.

That figure excludes other soft tissue fillers, such as calcium hydroxylapatite (66,182 Radiesse procedures), collagen (220,632 procedures), fat (48,960) and polylactic acid (46,732 Sculptra procedures). Adding those procedures would nearly double the facial filler's market dimensions.

And more facial fillers are on the way. Two of the latest hyaluronic acid fillers include Volift and Vobella, both of which are still in clinical trials in the U.S. and not yet FDA-approved but are currently being used in Europe where they're showing promising results.

With demand for anti-aging injectables already booming, as doctors, aestheticians and patients become more familiar with the art of dermal filling, facial remodeling is destined to become a major market force.

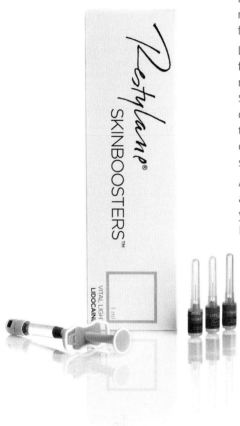

Restylane Facial Filler

Facial fillers, like Restylane, are mostly comprised of hyaluronic acid, a type of sugar (polysaccharide) that is present in body tissues, such as in skin and cartilage. Restylane does not contain any bird or bovine hyaluronic acid. Instead, it uses a patented ingredient known as non-animal hyaluronic acid or NASHA.

IMAGE COURTESY: GALDERMA LABORATORIES L.P.

118. "Hyaluronic Acid," *WebMD*, ret. 04-Jan-19.
119. Martine Geller and Alice Baghdijian, "Nestle boosts skincare business with $1.4 billion Valeant deal," *Reuters*, 28-May-14.
120. "Juvederm Approval History," *Drugs.com*, ret. 25-Dec-18.
121. "Radiesse," *Drugs.com*, ret. 04-Jan-19.
122. Natasha Singer, "Skin Deep; Wrinkle Rivals Go to War," *The New York Times*, 09-Nov-06.

Retinoids

Many products claim they will turn back the hands of time, but only one category truly shines when it comes to anti-aging, retinoids. Over-the-counter retinol and prescription retinoid counterparts Avita, Retin-A or Renova are all derived from vitamin A and promote faster skin cell turnover. They're some of the most effective and proven options available for treating skin issues ranging from acne to signs of aging.

In cosmetic products, retinoid forms of vitamin A are used as anti-aging chemicals, because once absorbed by the skin, retinoids cause new collagen to form in aged skin and in skin damaged by ultraviolet light, which promotes a more youthful appearance. While it was initially used to get rid of acne, blackheads and dead cell buildup in pores, retinol was also found to be an effective anti-aging agent.

Over-the-counter retinol products are available in various forms and strengths. Concentrations of 0.2% to 2.5% are typical, but stronger preparations can produce an undesirable rash called retinoid dermatitis.

Procter & Gamble, the maker of the popular Olay line of cosmetics, has sponsored a number of research studies on its anti-aging products. One such study compared Olay Pro-X Deep Wrinkle Treatment, which uses a combination of niacinamide (vitamin B3), peptide and retinyl propionate with a "0.02% tretinoin" (Renova) and found that after four weeks patients reported noticeably improved skin smoothness and texture, while after eight weeks 58% had noticeably reduced wrinkles. [123]

Procter & Gamble, which rarely discloses its proprietary formulas, uses a 0.3% concentration of retinyl propionate in its Olay Pro-X Deep Wrinkle Treatment (left), which is about "20 times less effective than retinol," according to one observer. [124] That observation is partially supported by a number of research studies that conclude that retinyl propionate is "less well-tested." [125]

The best-selling retinol-based beauty product on Amazon.com is Radha Beauty Retinol Moisturizer, which features "2.5% active Retinol, hyaluronic acid, vitamin E and green tea." Radha Beauty's moisturizer has more than 3,600 customer reviews and 4.3 out of five stars rating.

Olay Pro-X Anti-Aging Deep Wrinkle Treatment

Well-known for its moisturizing and anti-aging cosmetics, Procter & Gamble markets Olay Pro-X Deep Wrinkle Treatment, which contains a "pro retinol" — 0.3% retinyl propionate — plus niacinamide, a key ingredient that helps skin retain its water content.

IMAGE COURTESY: PROCTER & GAMBLE INC.

Laser Resurfacing

The carbon dioxide laser was invented by Kumar Patel in 1964 at Bell Laboratories. A series of inventions followed, culminating with the single most significant advance in medical lasers in the 1990s: the "pulsing" laser beam, which selectively destroys abnormal or

123. Fu et al. "A randomized, controlled comparative study of the wrinkle reduction benefits of a cosmetic niacinamide/peptide/retinyl propionate product regimen vs. a prescription 0·02% tretinoin product regimen," *The British Journal of Dermatology*, Mar-10.
124. Taylor Barbieri, "Olay Age-Defying Eye Cream Ingredient Analysis: Will It Really Reduce Wrinkles?," *FutureDerm*, 07-Mar-13.
125. "Retinyl Propionate," *Wisderm*, 24-Sep-14.

Clear + Brilliant Non-Ablative CO2 Fractional Laser

Clear + Brilliant is a next-generation CO2 laser that helps brighten skin, reduce pore size and improve the overall texture of the face. While Clear + Brilliant is a fractional laser, there is little downtime.

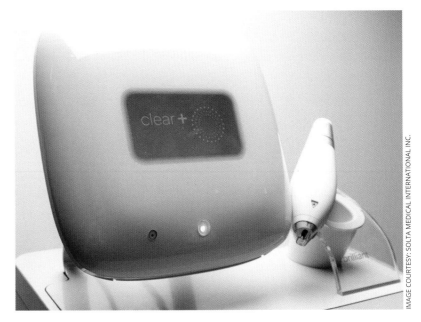

IMAGE COURTESY: SOLTA MEDICAL INTERNATIONAL INC.

undesired tissue while leaving surrounding tissues undisturbed.

In the early 1990s came another major step forward, the introduction scanning devices that offered precise, computerized laser beam control. Scanned, pulsed lasers revolutionized the practice of cosmetic and plastic surgery by making safe and consistent laser resurfacing possible. [126]

When lasers emit a very short-pulsed light energy at skin imperfections, including age spots, acne scars, blemishes, hyper-pigmentation and stretch marks, they remove thin layers of skin while minimizing heat damage to surrounding structures. The treated area heals in two to three weeks, and new collagen is produced. The treatment works by first inducing high levels of matrix metalloproteinase, or MMP, an enzyme that destroys fragmented collagen. Then it reduces MMP and increases production of new, undamaged replacement tissue.

Laser skin resurfacing is widely considered the anti-aging breakthrough of the 21st century. Each new generation improves the ability to target certain skin conditions. While carbon dioxide lasers create more lasting and noticeable results than any other laser, CO2 lasers are also associated with higher risk and potential for skin damage. That's because they're considered "ablative," which literally means "wounding."

Because the Fountain of Youth stakes are so high, the medical devices industry continues its relentless quest to develop breakthrough laser technologies. Below are just a few of the most notable developments:

- **Fraxel** – No laser technology has created a bigger stir than fractional skin resurfacing, using a fractionated CO2 laser, like Fraxel from Solta Medical, a division of Valeant Pharmaceuticals. Fractional lasers are non-ablative and less invasive, requiring less downtime. Candidates can expect to be pink and puffy for approximately 4-5 days but are able to wear makeup after 24 hours and resume

126. Albert Poet, "History of Medical Lasers," *American Medical Aesthetics*, ret. 04-May-17.

normal activities.

- **Erbium** – Like CO2, erbium lasers are ablative so they can remove anything on the skin's surface down to moderately deep wrinkles and lines. Erbium produces fewer side effects, which results in faster recovery times than carbon dioxide lasers. They also work better for people with dark skin.

- **Clear + Brilliant** – Solta Medical's Clear + Brilliant is a new fractional laser that is gentle but requires three to five sessions to see complete results.

Overall, 75% of people who have undergone a fractional laser treatment report that the procedure is worth it. [127] Driven by an aging population and a beauty-obsessed culture, the global aesthetic laser market is projected to reach $1.8 billion by 2024, according to Grand View Research. [128]

Allow us to set our lasers on stun(ning beauty).

Medical Tourism

If the medical spa business is the wave of the future, then a closely related trend, medical tourism cannot trail far behind. Medical spas are promising due to a fundamental societal value change. Today, consumers seek convergence in everything they do and that means multitasking treatments.

Spas that can perform the multiple services needed by waves of aging Baby Boomers and Generation X-ers will do well if they also put on a tourist hat. Medical tourism presents a significant opportunity because it combines the benefits of good healthcare with cost savings. And that means choosing a location where labor and material costs are lower than in the U.S.

In 2016, about 1.4 million Americans traveled abroad to seek healthcare, which is nearly double the number, 750,000, who went abroad in 2007. [129] [130]

Based on approximately 14 million cross-border patients worldwide, who spend an average of $3,800 to $6,000 per visit, according to Patients Beyond Borders, medical tourists were projected to spend between $46 and $72 billion in 2016, including medical costs, air travel and local transportation, plus in-patient stay and accommodations.

A hip replacement in a U.S. hospital costs $33,000 or more. The same procedure at Thailand's Bumrungrad International Hospital costs $16,500, plus $6,600 for airfare and postoperative stay. [131] That's a savings of about 30% compared to the U.S. Bumrungrad is a state-of-the-art facility that served 522,423 international patients in 2012, contributing to the hospital's total revenue of approximately $400 million that year.

With 75 million aging Baby Boomers, there is a lot more hip surgery to come.

127. "Fractional Laser," *RealSelf*, ret. 04-Jan-19.
128. "Aesthetic Lasers Market Size To Reach $1.8 Billion By 2024," *Grand View Research*, 30-Aug-16.
129. "Medical Tourism Statistics & Facts," *Patients Beyond Borders*, ret. 04-Jan-19.
130. Christina Madden, "Medical tourism causes complications," *Asia Times*, 07-Nov-08.
131. "Building for the future," *Bumrungrad Investor Presentation*, Nov-13.

Environmental Sustainability

Fountain of Youth

Delving into aesthetic beauty and the Fountain of Youth without discussing the preservation of our precious environment is inappropriate. Our world is under ceaseless attack from emissions, pollution, waste and other by-products of a convenience-craving culture.

It was the hippie movement of the 1960s that heightened ecological awareness, exemplified by the debut of the *Whole Earth Catalog* in 1968. [132] This back-to-nature movement had a significant impact on the 1970s. As Pew reports, "Congress passed the Clean Water Act and the Endangered Species Act, President Richard Nixon established the Environmental Protection Agency, and the nation observed its first Earth Day, created by Wisconsin Sen. Gaylord Nelson, on April 22, 1970." [133]

The greening of America is reflected in a 2016 Pew Research study, which found that 74% of U.S. adults say "the country should do whatever it takes to protect the environment." But going green is not easy. A Forrester Research study of nearly 61,000 U.S. and Canadian residents found that while 63% recycled paper, bottles and cans, and 57% bought energy-efficient light bulbs, just 14% took toxic materials to a community recycling center, while only 11% recycled their last TV or PC. [134]

In other words, consumers are choosing the road less hassled. Yet as the automobile industry has discovered, social pressure can induce consumers to buy more expensive hybrid or electric vehicles, such as the Toyota Prius or Tesla.

132. "Whole Earth Catalog," *Wikipedia*, ret. 04-Jan-19.
133. Monica Anderson, "For Earth Day, here's how Americans view environmental issues," *Pew Research*, 20-Apr-17.
134. Matt Nauman, "Research: Hassles, negative feedback affect green actions," *San Jose Mercury-News*, 27-Aug-08.

Eye Sore: East Beach, Henderson Island in the South Pacific

As much as 18 million tons of debris lies scattered on Henderson Island, estimates Jennifer Lavers, a research scientist at the University of Tasmania in Australia. Sadly, the world produces that amount of plastic every two seconds, according to a study by Lavers and her colleagues.

IMAGE COURTESY: JENNIFER LAVERS/INSTITUTE FOR MARINE AND ANTARCTIC STUDIES.

Healthier Eating

There is a growing interest in eating healthy. Nielsen found that 88% of consumers are willing to pay more for healthier foods. [1] Millennials are leading the way to healthy eating, with 47% of 18-34-year-olds in the U.K. reporting they changed their diet, compared to just 23% of those aged over 55. [2] This interest explains why the number of U.S. farmer markets has exploded from 120 in 2004 to more than 7,175 today. [3] And it's not just food, soda consumption in the U.S. fell to a 31-year low in 2016. [4] That was due to the growing popularity of bottled water, which outsold soda for the very first time in 2016. [5]

1. Nancy Gagliardi, "Consumers Want Healthy Foods--And Will Pay More For Them," *Forbes*, 18-Feb-15.
2. Eleanor Scott, "Healthy eating is increasingly on consumer's agendas," *PwC*, 26-Aug-16.
3. David Riley, "Growth of local farmers markets brings opportunity, challenge," *The Enterprise*, 18-Aug-11.
4. Leo Sun, "American soda consumption plunges to a 31-year low," *The Motley Fool/USA Today*, 01-Aug-17.
5. Jennifer Kaplan, "Bottled Water to Outsell Soda for First Time This Year," *Bloomberg*, 02-Aug-16.

Another area that is experiencing booming growth is solar energy. And that's primarily due to a decline in the price of solar photovoltaic (PV) systems, which saw their most meaningful drop, nearly 20%, in 2016. [135] In September 2017, South Miami became the second U.S. city to impose mandatory solar panels on all new real estate and large additions. San Francisco passed a similar ordinance in 2016. [136]

Wind power is another bright spot. In 2016, America's first offshore wind farm, built by Deepwater Wind, began operating off the coast of Rhode Island providing 30 megawatts of capacity. [137] Surprisingly, Texas leads all states in wind power, with more than 20,000 MW of capacity. [138]

The biggest challenge facing the world, besides global warming, is plastic. Since the 1950s, humans have produced more than 18 trillion pounds of plastic, equal to 25,000 Empire State buildings. [139] Since most plastic is not biodegradable, 80% of it now resides in landfills or the natural environment.

As much as 70 million tons of plastic waste has settled in our oceans, with some of it washing ashore in distant places like Henderson Island, pictured above. Worse, another 27 trillion pounds will be produced worldwide by 2050. It will take a major innovation or a fundamental change in consumer behavior to stop this miserable plastic tidal wave.

The plastic problem is starting to sink in. Kroger has announced that it will eliminate plastic bags by 2025. [140] Of course, that still means that the company will dump 738 million pounds of plastic waste in landfills between now and then. Plastic straws have also become a focal point, with the cities of Los Angeles, Portland, and the state of California restricting their use. [141]

135. "U.S. Solar Market Has Record-Breaking Year, Total Market Poised to Triple in Next Five Years," *SEIA*, 09-Mar-17.
136. Emily Bohatch, "More cities require solar as prices fall and sea levels rise," *USA Today*, 10-Aug-17.
137. Bill Loveless, "Offshore wind farm a green-energy milestone," *USA Today*, 21-Aug-16.
138. "Wind power in the United States," *Wikipedia*, ret. 04-Jan-19.
139. Doyle Rice, "Humans have produced 18.2 trillion pounds of plastic since the 50s," *USA Today*, 19-Jul-17.
140. Alexander Coolidge, "Kroger to kill plastic bags by 2025, will transition to reusable bags," *USA Today*, 23-Aug-18.
141. Jeff Daniels, "Los Angeles moves forward on plan banning plastic straws, going further than California state law," *CNBC*, 04-Dec-18.

Generation X-tasy is warping society's norms. Oscar Wilde's 1893 observation that "nothing succeeds like excess" has become par for the course. This experiential Ubertrend is the driving force behind a popular expression that says it all: "Been there, done that."

3

Generation X-tasy

Been There, Done That

Hair-raising roller coaster rides, leaps off tall buildings, skydiving, it's called "extreme entertainment." It's not fun unless you suffer a minor heart attack. Don't do that? How about movies with brutally explicit violence or nerve-wracking car chase scenes? Restaurants with outrageous decor or beguiling staff? How does a $190 Wagyu beef burger laden with truffles sound? Generation X-tasy brings thrilling new experiences to the easily distracted masses who use a phrase that puts it bluntly, "been there, done that." The masters of experience are ready for the challenge. They create ever-more grandiose buildings. Ever higher roller coasters. Ever more daring circuses. Ever larger homes. Ever hotter peppers. Ever more extreme ships. Generation X-tasy, it's all about your experience.

The Experience Economy

Generation X-tasy

They stand in long lines eager to gain entry into one of the city's celebrated nightclubs. Once they slip by the over-sized, 350-pound bouncers, they line up again at the bar, where they wait three-deep for a chance to scream their orders to bartenders making hundreds of $18 cocktails hourly. Welcome to Tao Las Vegas. Welcome to Generation X-tasy.

While the origin of the Generation X-tasy Ubertrend can be traced as far back as the Bible, a modern-day milestone was Nevada's 1931 legalization of gambling. Today, Las Vegas is the global hub of the experience generation.

Generation X-tasy substantially changed the fortunes of Las Vegas, twice. First came gambling, once considered a vice. Then came dining, shopping and clubbing. In 1990, 61% of Las Vegas revenues were generated by its casinos. Now, more than 64% of Las Vegas' total revenue mix is derived from non-gaming activities. [1]

Tao Asian Bistro, the restaurant that funnels dinner guests into the Venetian Hotel's Tao nightclub generates some $65 million in revenues each year. [2] That makes Tao the highest grossing, independent restaurant in America. Materially exceeding Bob Chinn's Crab House in Wheeling, Ill., which was the top-grossing restaurant in 2011 in a list that excludes venues like Tao, which convert into nightclubs, according to CHD Expert, a Chicago food industry research company. [3]

1. Sam Ro, "Las Vegas Hasn't Been About Gambling Since 1999," *Business Insider*, 08-Mar-13.
2. Chris Schonberger, "The Top-Grossing Independent Restaurants in America," *First We Feast*, 17-Oct-14.
3. Dorothy Pomerantz, "How Bob Chinn's Crab House Became The Highest-Grossing Restaurant In The U.S.," *Forbes*, 18-Jul-12.

MGM's CityCenter: Las Vegas' Extravagant New Strip Nexus

Built at a staggering cost of $8.7 billion and almost resulting in a (then-named) MGM-Mirage bankruptcy, CityCenter exudes *nouveau riche* Las Vegas, featuring such tony properties as ARIA, Cosmopolitan, Vdara and Waldorf Astoria, in addition to an appropriately opulent mall, The Shops at Crystals.

IMAGE COURTESY: MGM RESORTS INTERNATIONAL.

But those figures pale in comparison to the money involved in Las Vegas' largest clubs. The XS Nightclub, which Steve Wynn opened at his Encore hotel property in 2008, secured its top spot on the annual Nightclub & Bar Top 100 list for the third consecutive year after generating about $105 million in 2014, the last year the organization released data. [4] Securing its status as the "entertainment capital of the world," Las Vegas is now home to seven of the 10 top grossing nightclubs. Hakkasan at the MGM Grand is ranked second with an estimated take of $103 million. Marquee at the Cosmopolitan is third at $85 million (see table, next page). Together, the top 10 generate some $500 million in annual revenues.

The dollars lavished on these megaclubs is nothing short of astonishing. After its initial success with XS, Wynn Resorts spent $68 million on Surrender, which turns into the Encore Beach Club during the day. Together with Intrigue, formerly known as Tryst, Wynn Resorts now operates three of the top 20 Nightclub & Bar venues.

Trying to catch up to Wynn, Hakkasan Group lavished $200 million in partnership with MGM Grand on its namesake restaurant and nightclub. [5]

4. "Nightclub & Bar Releases 2014 Top 100 List," *Nightclub & Bar*, 05-Feb-15.
5. Robin Leach, "Hakkasan, the new 'king of clubs' at nearly $200 million, opens at MGM Grand" *Las Vegas Sun*, 18-Apr-13.

But it was the Palms that ignited the megaclub trend when it opened the 26,000-square-feet (2415 m²) Rain in 2001. [6] Caesars Palace followed in 2004 with the 36,000-square-feet (3345 m²) Pure. Wynn Resorts' XS is 40,000 square feet (3718 m²). The Cosmopolitan one-upped that in 2010 with the 60,000-square-feet (5574 m²) Marquee, only to upstaged by Hakkasan, which debuted on April 18, 2013 with an 80,000-square-feet (7443 m²) facility.

The meteoric rise of the clubbing culture, propelled by the Digital Lifestyle sub-trend Electronic Dance Music (see page 30), has turned superstar DJs into "electronic cash kings," as *Forbes* calls them. And sitting atop the cash pile is Scottish DJ Calvin Harris who made an astonishing $63 million between June 2015 and June 2016, according to *Forbes*. [7] Harris makes more than $400,000 for each Las Vegas gig at Hakkasan and then flies home to Los Angeles in a private jet after each performance. In second place is Dutch-born DJ Tiësto, who earned $38 million over the same year period (table).

The experiential tentacles of the clubbing culture extend far beyond Las Vegas. The trend has given rise to such specialized terminology as "turntablist" for the DJ and "mixologist" for the bartender. The experiential aspects of clubbing have transcended all aspects of evening entertainment. Gone are the days when bartending and drinking cocktails were formal affairs, as the photo comparison below shows.

Rank	DJ	Las Vegas Club(s)	Earnings
1.	Calvin Harris	Hakkasan	$63.0M
2.	Tiësto	Hakkasan	$38.0M
3.	David Guetta	XS	$28.0M
4.	Zedd	Hakkasan, OMNIA	$24.5M
5.	Steve Aoki	Jewel Nightclub	$23.5M
6.	Diplo	XS, Intrigue	$23.0M
7.	Skrillex	PC	$20.0M
8.	Kaskade	Hakkasan, OMNIA	$19.0M
9.	Martin Garrix	OMNIA	$16.0M
10.	Dimitri Vegas & Like Mike	XS, Intrigue	$15.5M
Total			$270.5M

World's Highest-Paid DJs: June 2015-2016

Source: 16-Aug-16 Forbes; 01-Jul-18 Michael Tchong, Ubertrends

Bartender Then, Mixologist Now

Having cocktails used to be a formal affair with bartenders and customers dressing up. The modern mixologist and her clientele have no time for such frivolities, even though cocktails often cost at least 10 times as much (a martini at San Francisco's iconic Tadich Grill restaurant cost just 90 cents in 1976). [1]

1. Brent Cox, "How Much More Do Martinis Cost Today?," *The Awl*, 05-Jun-12.

IMAGES COURTESY: TIME-LIFE, 2NITE VODKA.

Traditional drinking establishments have been hit hard by the changing preferences of the experiential generation. In Chicago, taverns, once popular

6. Tovin Lapan, "Nightclubs are the new cash registers at Strip casinos," *Las Vegas Sun*, 28-Mar-12.
7. Zack O'Malley Greenburg, "World's Highest-Paid DJs: Electronic Cash Kings 2016," *Forbes*, 16-Aug-16.

neighborhood watering holes, have plummeted from 7,000 in 1947 to less than 1,321 today. [8] While that trend is partially influenced by changing lifestyles, the absence of Millennials and Gen-Z is a contributing factor.

Changes are also noticeable in the types of drinks popular then and today. In the 1950s, gin was the preferred mixer and popular cocktails included the Dry Martini, Gimlet, Tom Collins, Gin Rickey and Singapore Sling. Today, the spirit of choice is more likely to be vodka, and the cocktail of choice either a Cosmopolitan, Margarita or Apple Martini. [9] [10] Because vodka is flavorless, it's an ideal mixer for the more sophisticated cocktails preferred by Generation X-tasy. U.S. sales of vodka exceeded gin in 1967 and surpassed whiskey to become the country's biggest-selling spirit by 1976. [11] Gallup reports that 26% of consumers now name liquor as their beverage of choice, the highest in 25 years of tracking. [12]

The Las Vegas gambling scene was about to experience a vodka-infused

8. Patrick Reardon, "Tapped Out," *Chicago Tribune*, 13-Jun-04.
9. Brent Rose, "The Five Most Mathematically Essential Bottles of Booze," *Gizmodo*, 06-Apr-12.
10. Craig Keolanui, Top 10 Most Popular Cocktails in the World, *The Richest*, 10-Jun-14.
11. Paul Clarke, "Vodka Makes A Comeback," *Imbibe*, 10-Feb-10.
12. Justin McCarthy, "Beer Remains the Preferred Alcoholic Beverage in the U.S.," *Gallup*, 19-Jul-17.

Las Vegas: The Capital of Generation X-tasy

Thursday, March 19, 1931 went by largely unnoticed. Yet it would turn out to be one of the most monumental days in America's history. It was on this day that the Nevada legislature voted to legalize gambling. [1]

As with any profound trend, the impact of this vote would not be felt for decades.

By the 1950s, Las Vegas' casinos had become a celebrity magnet. One particularly influential circle was The Rat Pack — Joey Bishop, Sammy Davis Jr., Dean Martin and Frank Sinatra — who would sing, drink and smoke their way into history, drawing attention to that neon-lit oasis in the desert. It wasn't until Steve Wynn opened The Mirage in 1987 that the very definition of experiential entertainment would change forever. Wynn single-handedly put Las Vegas on its current course of palatial excess.

From the dust of the Dunes rose his second *oeuvre*, The Bellagio, which features a multi-million-dollar art collection, including chandeliers of hand-blown glass by artist Dale Chihuly. Las Vegas has since witnessed  a dizzying array of grandiose visions, which have transformed this once dusty road stop of 800 souls into the "entertainment capital of the world." What Wynn did with The Mirage was not unique. Circus Circus had preceded the grandmaster of flash a decade earlier. It was Wynn's mastery of pomp that helped Las Vegas become home to seven of the top 10 largest

hotels in the world. [2] The world's largest, The Venetian/Palazzo, boasts a mind-boggling 7,092 rooms. In 2017, 42 million visitors stayed in Las Vegas, up from 30 million in 1997. [3] That was five years after Las Vegas adopted its now world-famous tagline, "What happens here, stays here," which was designed to lure adults.

Some say the slogan encourages raunchy behavior. In 2012, U.K.'s Prince Harry was caught exposing his royal jewels in grainy cellphone images. [4]

Visitors are now greeted by billboards that promote hotel pool parties with the headline, "Toptional." It's a clever play on words to draw attention to the latest Sin City trend, "European sunbathing" parties, where bikini tops are deemed frivolous. [5]

What happens in the capital of Generation X-tasy is guaranteed not to stay there.

1. "Nevada legalizes gambling," *History*, ret. 25-Dec-18.
2. John Hutchinson, "Bigger is better! Infographic reveals the 20 largest hotels in the world," *Daily Mail*, 18-Jun-15.
3. "Historical Las Vegas Visitor Statistics," *Las Vegas Convention and Visitors Authority*, ret. 25-Dec-18.
4. Gina Serpe, "Prince Harry Naked Vegas Photos: Anatomy of a Royal Scandal," *E! Online*, 24-Aug-12.
5. Kitty Bean Yancey, "Adult and topless pools make a splash in Vegas," *USA Today*, 10-Jun-10.

Top 10 Countries Ranked By Casinos		
Rank	Country	Casinos
1.	United States	1,511
2.	France	189
3.	Russian Federation	169
4.	Netherlands	167
5.	United Kingdom	140
6.	Canada	110
7.	Argentina	79
8.	Estonia	75
9.	South Africa	45
10.	Czech Republic	43
Source: Oct-11 Global Gaming Bulletin		

> "Neither Laliberté or Ste-Croix could ever have imagined that Generation X-tasy would one day make Cirque du Soleil the world's largest theatrical producer."
>
> **Michael Tchong**
> *Ubertrends*

stumble. That trend surfaced in 1998 when a survey by the Las Vegas Convention and Visitors Authority discovered that for the first time in its history, Las Vegas was perceived by more visitors as an "entertainment" (50%) than a "gaming" destination (48%). [13]

A survey of 8,000 leisure travelers conducted that year by Plog Research of Reseda, Calif., confirmed that finding with 67% of respondents listing shopping as their major activity, while 40% mentioned fine dining. Only 18% were interested in gambling.

That was a wake-up call for Nevada stakeholders. Casino gambling, once identified mainly with Las Vegas and Monte Carlo, had spread like a brush fire to other U.S. states and countries. In 1976, New Jersey became the second state to legalize "casino-style" gambling in Atlantic City. On Valentine's Day 1992, Connecticut's Foxwoods became the first tribal casino to open its doors. Within a few years, the number of states with legalized gambling had grown to six. [14] Today, either commercial or tribal gaming is legal in 39 states plus the Northern Mariana and U.S. Virgin Islands. [15] Only Arkansas, Georgia, Hawaii, Kentucky, Maine, New Hampshire, Rhode Island, South Carolina, Tennessee, Utah, Vermont, Virginia and the District of Columbia allow neither form of gambling.

Globally, the story is much the same (table). Gambling is now legal in 152 countries and territories, including the most populous market, China's private playground, Macau. [16] In 2006, Macau surpassed Las Vegas, as measured by total gambling revenue, with $6.95 billion. [17] The Special Administrative Region reached an all-time high of $45.2 billion in 2013, up 4,300% from the $2 billion recorded in 2001. [18] Due to a lengthy anti-corruption campaign by the Chinese government, Macau gambling income fell 27% to $33 billion by 2017. [19] Even that depressed figure is five times the $6.5 billion Las Vegas generated in 2017. [20]

Despite its lower gambling revenues, Las Vegas has proven beyond a shadow of a doubt that when it comes to immersive experiences, Sin City is the capital of Generation X-tasy.

Experiential Entertainment

In 1984, in a small village in Québec, Canada, called Baie-Saint-Paul, two street performers, Guy Laliberté and Gilles Ste-Croix put the finishing touches on a modest new venture, Cirque du Soleil. Neither Laliberté or Ste-Croix could ever have imagined that Generation X-tasy would one day make Cirque du Soleil the world's largest theatrical producer.

To attract generation *ennui*, one has to use every trick in the book. That's why

13. Robert Macy, "Survey says shopping, dining replace gaming as Vegas' top attractions," *Las Vegas Sun*, 16-Jul-98.
14. Matt Villano, "All in: Gambling options proliferate across USA, *USA Today*, 26-Jan-13.
15. "Gambling in the United States," *Wikipedia*, ret. 04-May-17.
16. "Worldwide Casinos, Horse Tracks and Other Gaming," *Casino City*, ret. 04-May-17.
17. David Barboza, "Macao Surpasses Las Vegas as Gambling Center," *The New York Times*, 23-Jan-07.
18. Howard Stutz, "Macau's 34.3% decline in 2015 was just the beginning," *Las Vegas Review-Journal*, 05-Jan-16.
19. Todd Prince, "Macau gaming revenue rose 19% in 2017, first gain since 2013," *Las Vegas Review Journal*, 02-Jan-18.
20. "Nevada Gaming Revenues, 1984-2017," *UNLV Center for Gaming Research*, Mar-18.

Cirque du Generation X-tasy

There are seven Cirque-like productions in Las Vegas, counting the ex-Cirque Director Franco Dragone-produced Le Rêve at Wynn. These multiple permanent Las Vegas shows play to more than 9,000 people each night or about 2% of the city's average nightly occupancy. The first Cirque du Soleil production in Las Vegas, Mystère, debuted on December 25, 1993 at the then Wynn-owned Treasure Island. At the Bellagio, Wynn built a $70 million aquatic theater for Cirque's O. New York New York spent $66 million on Zumanity, which premiered on September 21, 2003. For Kà, which opened at the MGM Grand on November 26, 2004, MGM reportedly spent $220 million, including $30 million for costumes and $135 million on the theater. It remains the largest and most expensive production Cirque du Soleil has created to date. Above photo is from the Varekai production in Lima, Peru. All qualify as Generation X-tasy experiences.

IMAGE COURTESY: REUTERS/ENRIQUE CASTRO-MENDIVIL.

Las Vegas boasts not one, not two, not three, but *six* concurrent productions of Cirque du Soleil. [21] It's the ultimate expression of a Generation X-tasy entertainment production, it's bold, it's different, and it's very dangerous.

That danger was tragically underscored by the June 29, 2013 death of Sarah Guyard-Guillot, a French acrobat and aerialist who fell to her death during a performance of the Cirque du Soleil show Kà at the MGM Grand in Las Vegas. [22] There is even video online showing the performer falling, which is part of the Voyeurgasm Ubertrend covered in a later chapter.

Not only are Cirque du Soleil productions perilous, so is setting them up. In November 2016, the son of co-founder Gilles Ste-Croix, Olivier Rochette, was killed In San Francisco after being hit by a telescopic aerial platform. [23] It should be noted, however, that no Cirque du Soleil performer had ever died during an actual performance in its 30-year history before Guyard-Guillot's fatal accident.

Big stage productions are not the only businesses buoyed by Generation X-tasy, the hospitality industry, including both hotels and restaurants,

21. "Cirque Du Soleil's Events in Las Vegas," *Cirque du Soleil*. ret. 25-Dec-18.
22. Dean Schabner, "Cirque du Soleil Performer Killed in Fall During Las Vegas Performance," *ABC*, 30-Jun-13.
23. Joseph Serna, "Son of Cirque du Soleil founder killed in preshow accident in San Francisco," *Los Angeles Times*, 30-Nov-16.

have been directly influenced by this Ubertrend.

In 1984, former Studio 54 nightclub owners Steve Rubell and Ian Schrager opened a nondescript hotel on New York's Madison Avenue, called Morgans. The hotel was designed by noted French interior and product designer Andrée Putman. Her design choices, constrained by a small budget, were simple but elegant. [24] Morgans launched an entirely new category of hotels, referred to as either design or boutique hotels. The concept of

Ian Schrager's Hotel Design 2.0: Gramercy Park Hotel Roof Club

For his own latest venture, Ian Schrager did not rely on a famous French designer but instead chose Julian Schnabel, a painter, sculptor and film director, to design the Gramercy Park hotel, which auspiciously re-opened its doors in August 2006.

IMAGE COURTESY: GRAMERCY PARK HOTEL.

these hotels is to cater to the avant-garde crowd, influentials who can help spread the word for new ventures, such as Rubell and Schrager's Royalton and Paramount hotels, which were both designed by another famous French designer, Philippe Starck.

In 2003, Smith Travel Research tallied 213 U.S. design hotel properties, including Starwood's W Hotels, the Kimpton chain, Joie de Vivre (now Commune), as well as Schrager's hotels. Today, an accurate design and boutique hotel count is simply impossible. There must be thousands of these types of hotels, with all the major hotel groups introducing their own brands, including Sheraton's Aloft, Hilton's Canopy and Indigo, Hyatt's Centric, Marriott's AC Hotel and EDITION, Best Western's Vib, and Commune's Tommie. All feature a similar focus on smaller rooms with sophisticated design and more active public spaces.

In some restaurants, the story is much the same. Since 1990, Amsterdam's supperclub has deftly combined dining with theatrical performances. Its servers are all accomplished artists, and you can enjoy immersive art, music and food from the comfort of your bed, but shoes off, please! The inspiration clearly wafted over from Montreal's Cirque du Soleil, but as this section explores later on when it comes to wafting, Amsterdam holds its own.

The outlandish can also take on other forms. In Taiwan, the Modern Toilet

24. "Andrée Putman," *Wikipedia*, ret. 05-Jan-19.

Modern Toilet Restaurant, Taiwan

Taipei's Modern Toilet restaurant is decorated in a theme befitting its utilitarian name. Besides toilet chairs, urinal sconces and even commode-shaped serving pieces, there's potty humor galore as customers take in the "scenic view."

restaurant is known more for its curvaceous scenery than for food, and we're not talking Hooters here. Chairs are made from toilet seats, and food is served in mini toilet bowls. Unfortunately, the food is not particularly good, so experience alone cannot make amends for a so-so product. Generation X-tasy demands a great experience all around.

Concept restaurants have been around since the early 1970s. Isaac Tigrett

Singapore: An Experiential Newcomer

Singapore wants to muscle in on the experience economy, as part of its Research, Innovation and Enterprise 2020 plan. [1]
The city-state already boasts the Marina Bay Sands, a three-tower hotel and casino property topped by a boat-like SkyPark, which was billed as the world's most expensive standalone casino property at $5.9 billion when it debuted in 2010.
Singapore also leads the underground urbanism movement by locating such projects as the world's largest district cooling system and a water reclamation system underground. [2]
That's critical in a city projected

to reach 6.9 million inhabitants by 2030, all living on an island just three-fifths the size of New York City.
Another innovative idea, VIRTUAL

Singapore, a digital map of the city-state rendered in virtual reality and based on real-time dynamic data, was scheduled to debut by the end of 2018. [3]

1. "RIE2020," *National Research Foundation*, 08-Jan-16.
2. Gregory Scruggs, "To Keep Up With Its Growth, Singapore Has a Grand Plan To Expand Underground," *Smithsonian*, 21-Feb-18.
3. Leila Lai, "Virtual Singapore project to be ready by end-2018: Tharman," *The Business Times*, 10-Jul-18.

Palm Jumeirah Island, Dubai

Designed by Orlando, Fla.-based Helman Hurley Charvat Peacock/Architects, Palm Jumeirah is an artificial island that opened to residents in October 2007. Today, 28 hotels occupy the island's outer crescent, including Atlantis The Palm, Dubai shown in the upper center.

IMAGE COURTESY: ZYZZL!NG.

and Peter Morton opened the first Hard Rock Cafe in London on June 14, 1971, but didn't cover its walls with rock-and-roll memorabilia until 1979. [25] Other experiential restaurants soon followed. Chuck E. Cheese's Pizza Time Theatre debuted in San Jose, Calif. in May 1977. [26] Planet Hollywood launched in New York City in October 1991, with the backing of Sylvester Stallone, Bruce Willis, Demi Moore and Arnold Schwarzenegger. [27] Rainforest Cafe first opened in the Bloomington, Minn.'s Mall of America on February 3, 1994.

While some of these have succeeded financially, they fail to execute when it comes to offering both quality food *and* immersive surroundings.

Dubai

When it comes to architectural eye candy, no city can match Dubai. This Muslim city-state of 3.1 million people has built what amounts to the world's largest oil-fueled mirage in the midst of the desert,

25. "Hard Rock Cafe," *Wikipedia*, ret. 25-Dec-18.
26. "Chuck E. Cheese's," *Wikipedia*, ret. 25-Dec-18.
27. "Planet Hollywood," *Wikipedia*, ret. 25-Dec-18.

proving that imagination, lots of money and cheap labor can create amazing structures.

The startling edifices of Dubai offer much appeal to the experiential longing of Generation X-tasy. It also helps Dubai stand out from the also-ran crowd. While the Ubertrend has a long history of being identified with unusual places, think Madonna Inn in San Luis Obispo or Hearst Castle not far from that, this phenomenon continues to morph rapidly.

The Emirate of Dubai is a tiny place, stretching just 45 miles (72 km) along the western shore of the Persian Gulf. But it has Texas-size ambitions. It already boasts the world's tallest skyscraper, the Burj Khalifa, which rises some 2,717 feet (828 meters) with 160 floors, counting the antenna. [28] It has fashioned two islands from reef sand, one in the shape of a palm tree, naturally dubbed "The Palm."

You can marvel at Palm Island from the luxury of the Burj Al Arab hotel, where each room comes with a butler, and which features an underwater restaurant. And where else can you find a 22,500-square-meter indoor ski resort, the size of three football fields, Ski Dubai, where skiers can enjoy snow in the desert year-round? [29]

Then there is the world's largest shopping center based on square footage, Dubai Mall, which has a staggering 1,200 retail outlets, more than 160 food and beverage outlets, plus a vast aquarium, the Dubai Aquarium with the world's largest single pane of glass. In front of the mall is Dubai Fountain, the largest dancing fountain in the world, illuminated by 6,600 lights and 25 color projectors. Is it any wonder that Dubai Mall attracts more than 750,000 visitors each week?

Then there is Dubai Marina, which is, wait for it, the world's largest human-made marina. And so on, and so on. While the current ruler, Sheikh Mohammed Bin Rashid Al Maktoum, Vice President and Prime Minister of the United Arab Emirates and Ruler of Dubai (yes, that's his title) is often credited with the explosive growth Dubai has experienced, it was his father, Sheikh Rashid Bin Saeed Al Maktoum, who in the early 1970s envisioned a town, seaport and airport focused on developing an industrial region in the emirate. [30] But there can be no doubt that both of his sons took some inspiration from the Palace of Versailles that Louis XIV of France, the Sun King, built, and created their own *fata morgana* on the shores of the Arab peninsula. In 2009, Abu Dhabi had to lend Dubai $20 billion in the aftermath of the global financial crisis to rescue it from inevitable collapse. [31]

But don't expect that lesson to go heeded. Our world is locked in a never-ending battle of one-upmanship. It's a fire stoked by a consumer culture that increasingly seeks more experiential adventures. And once they find them, it's on to the next. Been there, done that.

World's Tallest Building: Dubai's Burj Khalifa

Designed by Chicago-based Skidmore, Owings & Merrill, Burj Khalifa is the world's tallest building, standing 2,717 feet (828 m) tall and boasting 154 floors. It was originally called Burj Dubai, but after a $20 billion bailout by Abu Dhabi, it was tactfully renamed after its neighboring ruler.

IMAGE COURTESY: EMAAR PROPERTIES.

28. "Burj Khalifa," *Wikipedia*, ret. 25-Dec-18.
29. 10 - Ski Dubai, *Word Top Top*, 03-Jun-13.
30. Samir Salama, "Shaikh Rashid, the father of modern Dubai," *Gulf News & Government*, 07-Oct-15.
31. Andrew Torchia, "UAE, Abu Dhabi roll over $20 billion of Dubai's debt," *Reuters*, 16-Mar-14.

Nothing Succeeds Like Excess

Generation X-tasy

In a classic episode of *The Dick Cavett Show*, author Truman Capote once remarked that many prisoners he interviewed for his book *In Cold Blood* sported tattoos. That was in the early 1970s, when only one in a hundred Americans had a tattoo, according to the Alliance of Professional Tattooists. [32] Today, three (29%) in 10 Americans have tattoos. [33]

And the figure is much higher for Millennials, 47% of whom report having at least one. In a world of anonymity and conformity, tattoos are viewed as a way of expressing individuality, or, to put it in marketing lingo, "personal branding." The word branding itself stems from the practice of identifying cattle with an ownership "stamp," a tattoo of sorts. A word that has also made it into tattoo vernacular as the "tramp stamp."

A Harris poll confirms the heed of individuality, with 32% of tattooed adults saying it makes them more attractive, and 33% reporting that having one makes them feel sexy. Of course, one is often not enough. Among those with any tattoos, 69% have two or more. And as the image, right, of "Prince Albert" — Guinness World Records' Most Pierced Man of 2008 — suggests, two is often so not enough.

Truman's observation of the uncanny relationship between criminals and tattoos was confirmed by a study of Florida state prisoners, which found that three quarters, 75%, had at least one tattoo, nearly triple that of the

WE ALL WALK IN DIFFERENT SHOES.

THEO HOGAN, SINGER, ACTOR, ENTREPRENEUR AND FEMINIST.

KENNETHCOLE.COM
25 YEARS OF NON-UNIFORM THINKING.

Kenneth Cole Ad Shows Off Tattoos

Plenty of tattoos are on display in this Kenneth Cole shoe ad. As marketers, major celebrities and sports figures legitimize the look, the number of Americans sporting tattoos has grown 187% in the past five decades.

32. Mielikki Org, "The Tattooed Executive," *The Wall Street Journal*, 28-Aug-03.
33. "Tattoo Takeover: Three in Ten Americans Have Tattoos, and Most Don't Stop at Just One," *The Harris Poll/Cision*, 10-Feb-16.

general population. [34] More worrisome was the fact that tattoos were useful predictors of recidivism: 75% of the inmates who have been re-incarcerated had tattoos while just 30% of former convicts who managed to stay out of prison were noted as having tattoos.

Spring Break 2009 in Florida's Panhandle

Kendra Wilkinson, who played a starring role in E!'s *The Girls Next Door* uses a water hose to drench a college student during a "Wet & Wild" wet t-shirt contest at Club La Vela, Panama City Beach, Florida.

IMAGE COURTESY: SHANE BABIN/ZUMA PRESS.

Spring Break

If passing out is what you have in mind, there's no better time to do so than during the annual rite of spring break. Every year, half a million students used to descend on the "Spring Break Capital of the World," Panama City Beach, Fla. in the Redneck Riviera, for a bacchanalian fest that knew few limits. [35] That's all in the past now that local authorities have banned alcohol consumption on the beach during March.

After a video of a rape that took place on Panama City Beach went viral in 2015, the city council decided to crack down on spring break festivities. As a result, business has suffered, with bookings down as much as 90% in 2016. [36] The city is home to Club La Vela — the world's largest nightclub at 100,000 square feet (9290 m²), able to accommodate 6,000 people — that was often featured on *MTV Spring Break*. La Vela's owners are sure to feel the impact of the council's decision.

The spring break market is sizable. The National Center for Education Statistics estimates that 21 million U.S. students attended college in 2017. [37] Of those students, 55% were planning to go on spring break, according to Orbitz. Projecting this data, an estimated 11.3 million students went on spring break in 2017, with 31% using student loan money to fund their trip.

34. "A statistical analysis of the art on convicts' bodies," *The Economist*, 24-Dec-16.
35. Jane Reynolds, "10 most popular spring break destinations," *USA Today*, 17-Feb-16.
36. Connor Sheets, "Panama City Beach's Spring Break is 'dead' as beach drinking ban drives partiers away," *AL.com*, 17-Mar-16.
37. Mike Brown, "Spring Break Student Loan Study, " *Lendedu.com*, 08-Mar-17.

Ted Baker Party Animal Tuxedo

The term "party animal" was elevated to a new cultural stature when apparel maker Ted Baker launched its "Party Animal Tuxedo" — a spill-resistant tux lined with Teflon — that was perfect for Cancun spring break parties.

IMAGE COURTESY: TED BAKER PLC.

Each year, some students choose to venture farther away. While *MTV Spring Break* was in Cancun in the early part of the aughts, some 100,000 spring breakers turned Cancun into a wanton love fest each year. The latest port of call? Punta Cana, Santo Domingo. As with anything dependent on consumer whim, spring breakers will move on, ready to find a community that will embrace their alcohol-and-drug-fueled merriment. After all, drinking bans have been a recurring theme among past spring-break gathering spots.

Fort Lauderdale, Fla., once popularly known as "Fort Liquordale," began to see an influx of spring breakers in 1960, their number growing after the 1961 movie, *Where The Boys Are*, drew attention to the area. By 1985, almost 400,000 students packed Fort Lauderdale's beaches each year. [38] But when city fathers began a crackdown on alcohol consumption, the action moved to Daytona Beach, Fla. The very first *MTV Spring Break* show aired from Daytona Beach in 1986. [39] By the late 1980s, as many as 350,000 spring breakers converged on Daytona Beach, until local authorities there introduced a beach alcohol ban in the late 1990s.

That's when the scene shifted to Panama City Beach. *MTV Spring Break* broadcasts from Panama City Beach inspired a far more controversial series, the 1997 debut of Joe Francis' *Girls Gone Wild*. Francis ended up in jail due to his exploits, and as a court put it in 2011, "Francis has made millions of dollars by going to places crowded with young, enthusiastic, and often-intoxicated women and filming them exposing their breasts, fondling each other, kissing each other, and sometimes engaging in more explicit sexual acts." [40]

Francis exploited a well-known human weakness — mores tend to loosen when lubricated with alcohol. It's a trait the U.S. tried to put a stop to with Prohibition, which banned the production, importation, transportation

38. Sanika Dange, "The History of Spring Break," *WJHG.com*, 29-Apr-14.
39. Louise Hart, "MTV's First Spring Break VJ Remembers What Spring Break Was Like Before Camera Phones," *GQ*, 30-Mar-16.
40. Emily Bazelon, "May Joe Francis of Girls Gone Wild Rot in Jail," *Slate*, 08-May-13.

and sale of alcoholic beverages from 1920 to 1933, in order to cure an "ill society." [41]

But ridding society of illicit behavior is a practically impossible task. Alcohol-fueled wet t-shirt contests date back to the 1970s and were first observed by the *Palm Beach Post* in 1975. [42] It's just one artifact of modern era debauchery that makes spring break a challenge for law enforcement. In Panama City Beach, there were only 217 sworn-in deputies to maintain order among a spring break crowd of 500,000. [43] The surge in springtime violations in U.S. seaside communities even led to new legal expertise — lawyers who specialize in bailing out arrested party animals.

Of course, partying has long been an accepted part of modern culture. But with the Generation X-tasy firmly taking hold, it is leading to far more remarkable displays of excess, like those decadent teen parties featured on MTV's *My Super Sweet 16*, which is set to make

a comeback after nearly a decade off the air. The MTV show chronicled a typically wealthy teen's epic party that exemplified our age of overindulgence.

And speaking of teen overindulgence, who could forget that 11-year-old girl, who was charged with drunken driving in Alabama after leading police on a 100-mph chase that ended when she flipped her car over? These formerly remarkable outbursts are becoming more common as mainstream values evolve. [44]

Generation X-tasy also rules that other world of excess: over-eating. Who could ever have imagined that one person would be able to consume 74 hot dogs, including buns, or 21,000 calories, in 10 minutes? [45] Nathan's Hot Dog Eating Contest draws participants from all over the world who vie for the world's most absurdly gluttonous title. The contest is an unqualified signpost of excess because the event itself is so disgusting, it's virtually unwatchable.

What may also be a stomach-churning, but for a different reason, is cheerleaders performing hair-raising stunts. Due to a significantly raised ante of acrobatic maneuvers, cheerleaders have turned into true daredevils. Since the early 1990s, emergency room visits for cheerleading injuries nationwide have more than doubled, far outpacing

Ohio State Cheerleaders Practicing Stunt

Emergency room visits due to injuries sustained during dangerous cheerleading stunts have more than doubled since the early 1990s. It ranks number one for catastrophic injuries among female sports.

Parkour Runner Sebastien Foucan

Also known as "free running," Parkour is an urban sport designed for Generation X-tasy. It involves racing through the urban landscape and using any obstacle as a springboard.

41. "Prohibition in the United States," *Wikipedia*, ret. 30-Jul-18.
42. "Wet T-Shirt Contests Pack Pubs," *Palm Beach Post*, 11-Nov-75.
43. Sanika Dange, "The History of Spring Break," *WJHG.com*, 29-Apr-14.
44. "11-year-old charged with driving drunk," *Reuters*, 06-Jul-07.
45. "Nathan's Hot Dog Eating Contest," *Wikipedia*, ret. 25-Dec-18.

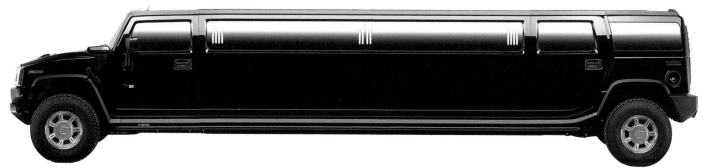

Stretch Hummer Holds 20 Partying Passengers

There is no need to go to a party in a boring car when you can party your heart out in an ostentatious stretch Hummer 2 limo that features a bar, stereo, television, light show and sometimes even a hot tub.

growth in the number of cheerleaders, according to the National Center for Catastrophic Sports Injury Research. [46]

Based at the University of North Carolina, the sports researcher ranks cheerleading first in catastrophic injuries among female sports and second overall, only American football ranks higher. [47] Nearly two thirds, 65%, of all catastrophic injuries in youth sports occur in cheerleading. It appears that pushing the limits of peril is now part of the entertainment experience.

Experiential diversions abound in sports. One recent arrival is Parkour — an acrobatic sport that originated in the streets of Paris and that was featured in Madonna's *Jump* music video. Participants run and vault through the urban jungle equipped with nothing more than a pair of running shoes, bouncing off walls, jumping over roofs and using any human-built obstacle as part of their concrete *parcours*. Words are not enough to describe Parkour stunts; they should be watched on YouTube.

Another symbol of too much? Those stretch Hummer limousines that transport partygoers to the prom or nightclub. It's an outsize American ego trip that has found converts in such faraway places as Paris and Australia.

46. Bill Pennington, "As Cheerleaders Soar Higher, So Does the Danger," *The New York Times*, 31-Mar-07.
47. "Cheerleading Ranks First in Catastrophic Sport Injuries," *United States Sports Academy*, 08-Apr-11.

924 Bel Air Road: A Humble $250 Million Abode

Developer Bruce Makowsky was baffled that no one was developing luxury real estate to match the mega yachts and private jets that sell anywhere from $50 to $500 million each, so he created 924 Bel Air Road, which also features a much-needed helipad.

IMAGE COURTESY: BRUCE MAKOWSKY.

Ultra Premium

The real estate listing created quite a stir. The home even had its own web address. [48] And why not? When you're asking $250 million for a home, the sky is truly the limit. That's what real estate developer Bruce Makowsky wants for the *second-most* expensive home ever offered for sale in the U.S., 924 Bel Air Road, which is located in beautiful Bel Air, Calif., near Los Angeles.

The amenities befit the price. The 38,000-square-feet (3530 m²) home is equipped with 17,000 square feet (1579 m²) of entertainment decks to take in 270-degree views of L.A., stretching from the snow-capped San Gabriel Mountains to Malibu. There are two master suites, 10 guest suites, and 21 bathrooms because we don't want to keep anyone waiting. There is no waiting at the five bars either. A massage room and spa; 40-seat Dolby Atmos theater with advanced home tech system, plus an 85-foot infinity pool take care of the entertainment. The home is turnkey, so it also comes with 100 "curated" artworks and $30 million worth of cars, all ready to drive you to Beverly Hills for a shopping trip worthy of a billionaire.

How big is Makowsky's target audience? According to the Wealth-X 2018 Billionaire Census, there are 2,754 billionaires in the world, up 15% from the year before. [49] *Forbes* reports that their combined net worth is a record $9.1 trillion. [50] The world's youngest self-made billionaire is John Collison, who, at age 27, is two months younger than Snapchat's Evan Spiegel. Collison and his brother are Irish citizens who co-founded Stripe, the online payment service.

The Digital Lifestyle increasingly influences the fortunes of the *nouveau*

48. "924 Bel Air Road," *Bruce Makowsky*, 19-Jan-17.
49. "The Wealth-X Billionaire Census 2018," *Wealth-X*, 15-May-18.
50. Luisa Kroll and Kerry Dolan, "Meet The Members Of The Three-Comma Club," *Forbes*, 06-Mar-18.

Showcase Symbols of "Ultra Premium" Pricing Excess

When you're worth billions what does a trifling $62,000 lipstick matter? Why not get a six-pack of $100 bottles of water, sheathed in crystal, of course. What started as a harmless "pricing war" in the opposite direction in the consumer electronics industry, has spilled over to all product categories.

IMAGES COURTESY: GUERLAIN INC., FILLICO JAPAN CO. LTD

riche. Wealth-X notes that of the 143 tech billionaires around the globe, 74 live in Silicon Valley, a telltale predictor of future wealth creation.

Boston Consulting Group notes that there are 18.5 million millionaire households around the world, 8 million in the U.S. alone, followed by 2.1 million in China, which has five times the U.S. population. [51] These households control 47% of the world's wealth and will control 52% by 2020, a genuinely frightening trend.

But what may be even scarier is that Makowsky's house is not ostentatious enough. A 100,000-square-feet (9290 m²) property with a $500 million asking price is being readied for sale. [52] Also located in Bel Air, "The One" as it's called, boasts 20 bedrooms, including a 5,500-square-feet master bedroom with its own pool and kitchen plus seven separately located bedrooms for the staff, a private nightclub, five elevators, and a wall made of jellyfish aquariums. If that's not enough, there are also four swimming pools, plus a moat that surrounds the castle, er, home.

In the past decade, the egregiousness of the luxury market has gone where no one has dared to thread before. You could not be faulted for suffering a bout of delirious tremors upon learning that a London Burger King would offer a $190 burger made from Wagyu beef, topped with white truffles and Pata Negra ham, and served on a bun finished with organic-white-wine-and-shallot-infused mayonnaise, pink Himalayan rock salt, and Iranian saffron. [53] Could that be true or was that a Whopper of a lie?

Similarly, you may have seen red reading that Guerlain was accepting appointments for you to acquire a KissKiss Gold and Diamonds lipstick made of 110 grams of 18-carat yellow gold and paved with a "rain of 199 diamonds" equal to 2.2 carats. [54] Price tag: $62,000. But if you have to ask,

51. Robert Frank, "By 2020, half the world's wealth will be controlled by millionaires," *CNBC*, 07-Jun-16.
52. Candace Jackson, "Who Wants to Buy the Most Expensive House in America?," *The New York Times*, 23-Dec-17.
53. Emma Hall, "Is BK's $190 Burger Worthy of a King?," *Ad Age*, 30-Jun-08.
54. Helen Lee, "Guerlain's $62,000 Kisskiss Gold and Diamonds Lipstick," *SASSYBELLA.com*, 09-Nov-07.

you can't afford it, dear.

The price infection trend has spread to every corner of the economy. Cars, like the Koenigsegg CCXR Trevita, now top $4.8 million. [55] Even zero-cost water has been dressed up in $100 crystal bottles thanks to Japanese "jewelry water" maker Fillico, proving that the top end of the market knows no upper limits when it comes to prices the 1% will happily pay. [56]

That type of pricing of ordinary liquids is a spillover of the "super-premium" or "ultra-premium" alcoholic beverage market, where a bottle of whiskey, like John Walker & Sons Diamond Jubilee, a 2012 release made to honor Queen Elizabeth II, can fetch a price of $200,000. [57]

In the audio business, they're referred to as "Golden Ears" — people who ostensibly are able to hear to the difference between an ordinary pair of $10 cables and Music Interface Technologies ACC 268, which cost $80,000 for a pair of "interfaces." [58]

And it's not just items made from new and exotic materials that have captivated the imagination of the filthy rich. Rarities ranging from art to ocean creatures have broken records at an unrelenting pace, culminating in the $450 million purchase of a Leonardo da Vinci by a Saudi Arabian prince. [59] That handily broke the previous record for a painting sold at auction, Pablo Picasso's *Les Femmes d'Alger*, which sold for $179 million in 2015. That makes paying $1.8 million for a 222-kilogram bluefin tuna seem like chump change. [60] When you say jump, I say "how high?"

55. Andrew Hard, Stephen Edelstein, "The 10 most expensive cars in the world," *Digital Trends*, 06-Dec-17.
56. Paula Forbes, "$100 Hello Kitty Crystal-Encrusted Luxury Water," *Eater*, 02-Aug-10.
57. Jake Emen, "Inside the World of Ultra-Premium Spirits," *Eater*, 04-Dec-15.
58. Alexander Lamascus, "9 of the Most Wildly Expensive Speaker Cables Available," *Robb Report*, 06-Apr-17.
59. David Kirkpatrick, "Mystery Buyer of $450 Million 'Salvator Mundi' Was a Saudi Prince," *The New York Times*, 06-Dec-17.
60. Patrick Boehler, "Japan: World's Most Expensive Fish Sold for $1.8 Million," *Time*, 07-Jan-13.

All Chiefs, No Indians

There was a time in America when most large corporations were headed up by someone with a truly impressive title, "President."
In 1955, only one Fortune 200 company boasted a "chief executive officer." [1] Twenty years later, almost all were led by chief executive officers.
Researching the acronym "CEO," Louis Galdieri discovered that Webster's believed it emerged in 1975. [2] In fact, the March-April 1972 *Harvard Business Review* featured this line, "a technician in his early forties who joined the company three years ago as president but not CEO." The Ivy League magazine had decided that business was ready for a new titular acronym.
So came to be a title fit for Generation X-tasy. One that has resulted in a dizzying array of chiefs: Chief Operating Officer, Chief Information Officer, Chief Technology Officer, Chief Marketing Officer, Chief Innovation Officer, Chief Strategy Officer and, soon, Chief Outsourcing Officer. Not only has there been an explosion of corporate chieftain titles, but CEO salaries have expanded commensurately with their inflated authority.
In 1965, chief executives were paid on average 20 times what workers earned. By 2012, the ratio was 273-to-1. [3]
Yet between 1973 and 2015, the productivity of American workers rose 73%, while their hourly pay increased by only 11%. [4]
By comparison, CEO compensation, increased 875% between 1978 and 2012.
Hail to the Chief!

1. Anonymous, "What is the origin of the title 'Chief Executive Officer'?" *Quora*, 01-Aug-13.
2. Louis Galdieri, "The First CEO," *lvgaldieri.com*, 06-Apr-12.
3. Natalie Sabadish, Lawrence Mishel, "CEO Pay in 2012 Was Extraordinarily High Relative to Typical Workers and Other High Earners," *Economic Policy Institute*, 26-Jun-13.
4. "The Productivity–Pay Gap," *Economic Policy Institute*, Aug-16.

The Carolina Reaper Looks Ominous and Packs Lethal Heat

Most of today's hottest peppers, like the ghost and scorpion peppers, have been cross-bred to boost their already spectacular heat index. The Carolina Reaper, which registers 2.2 million on the Scoville Heat Unit gauge, was created by PuckerButt Pepper Co. owner Ed Currie.

IMAGE COURTESY: PUCKERBUTT PEPPER COMPANY.

Hot Peppers

This heated scene takes place in Long Beach, Calif. Thousands have gathered for the annual California Hot Sauce Expo ready to indulge their favorite passion, freaking out on fiery food and punishing their palates by sampling savagely spicy sauces. One contest even involves trying to ingest the hottest known pepper on earth, the appropriately named Carolina Reaper.

Why do people want to singe mouths and throats, and break out in sweat for sheer entertainment? Remember "been there, done that?" Not only is it an experience but foodies are becoming immune to such common condiments as Cholula Hot Sauce, Sriracha and Tabasco and are continually ratcheting up their tolerance for heat. The trend is catching fire due to the intermingling of global ethnicities and the growing popularity of such spicy ethnic cuisines as Cajun, Hunan, Indian, Mexican, Szechuan and Thai. Case in point: Four in five Americans now regularly eat ethnic food. [61]

The ethnic trend is best illustrated by 41,000 Chinese restaurants in the U.S., more than McDonald's, Burger King and Wendy's combined. [62]

According to the American Spice Trade Association, Americans downed more than 1 billion pounds of spices in 2000, up 87% from the 544 million pounds consumed in 1981, and up 485% from 1961's 171 million pounds. [63] The fastest growing category: "hot spices" — including black and white pepper, red pepper, ginger and mustard seed, which now comprise 41% of U.S. spice usage, up 71% since the late 1970s. The use of spices doubled between 1970 and 1990 and will double again between 1990 and 2020,

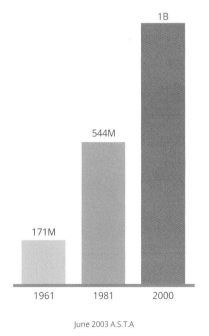

U.S. Spice Consumption Trend 1961-2000 (Pounds)

1B

544M

171M

1961   1981   2000

June 2003 A.S.T.A

61. "4 in 5 consumers eat ethnic cuisines regularly," *National Restaurant Association*, 23-Sep-15.
62. "Chinese Cuisine in the United States," *Life in the USA*, ret. 06-Aug-17.
63. Martha Masterman, "The Case of Spices," *University of Michigan Business School*, 1998.

when the market will top $16 billion, up from about $12 billion in 2014. [64]

The best proxy for the market's interest in hot food may well be the race to create the world's hottest peppers and sauces. In 2017, Tabasco debuted Tabasco Scorpion Sauce — a sauce that was 20 times hotter than the original. Marketed as a "small batch" with pre-orders starting on July 31, it sold out within a few hours. [65]

Tabasco claims that Scorpion Sauce, made from what else, scorpion peppers, registers 50,000 Scoville Heat Units (SHU) on the pungency heat scale, compared to 2,140 SHU for the Original Red Sauce. [66] That's nothing compared to the 16 million SHUs claimed by Blair's 16 Million Reserve, which is, thankfully, only sold in 1-milliliter vials.

The blow-your-brains-out trend started, where else, in San Francisco where Dave's Gourmet, founded in 1993 by Dave Hirschkop, sells as many as 1 million bottles each year of Dave's Insanity Sauce, a sauce that lives up to its billing.

Hirschkop invented his sauce out of necessity. After launching an offbeat taqueria in Maryland, called Burrito Madness, Hirschkop needed a way to fend off unruly, drunk kids who insisted on frequenting his burrito joint and who were very annoying. So he created the "hottest hot sauce in the universe" to return the favor, but the kids actually liked it. Hirschkop started bottling his sauce and named it "Insanity Sauce" after people told him the sauce was "insane."

A wave of competition emerged, including the PuckerButt Pepper Co., owned by Ed Currie, who is responsible for growing the Carolina Reaper monstrosity pictured on the previous page. Boasting 2.2 million SHUs, it currently holds the Guinness record for the world's hottest pepper. [67] Like other cultivated peppers, including ghost, naga and scorpion peppers, the Carolina Reaper targets young males who drive category growth.

Pushing the limits of what can be eaten is not unique to the hot food category. *Fear Factor*, which originally aired on NBC from 2001 to 2006, was famous for its vomit-inducing eating stunts, starting with worms and progressively getting worse, even forcing contests to drink donkey semen in a segment NBC wisely decided not to air. [68]

If you have any lingering doubts that people will be eating far hotter foods in the future, despite today's often-heard protestations, perish the thought.

Hot peppers are here to stay and ready to incinerate your palate and Indian food may well influence the progress of this trend.

IMAGE COURTESY: MCILHENNY COMPANY.

Tabasco Scorpion Sauce Is 20x Hotter Than the Regular One

McIlhenny's Tabasco has been under fire, pardon the pun, from far hotter sauces. Its Scorpion Sauce, with 20x the burning power of the leading brand, sold out quickly in July 2017.

IMAGE COURTESY: DAVE'S GOURMET.

A Hot Sauce Trailblazer: Dave's Insanity Sauce

Boutique hot pepper brands, like Dave's Insanity Sauce, are on fire, pardon the pun, as consumer palates adapt to ever hotter foods due to the popularity of spicy ethnic cuisines.

64. "Global Seasonings and Spices Market to Witness 5% CAGR During 2015 - 2020," *P&S Market Research*, 10-Nov-15.
65. Claire Reid, "Tabasco Made A Sauce 20 Times Hotter Than Its Original," *LAD Bible*, 23-Jul-17.
66. "The Hottest Sauces In the World," *Chez-Williams.com*, ret. 05-Aug-17.
67. Alex Scola, "22 of the world's hottest peppers (and where to eat them)," *Matador Network*, 08-May-14.
68. Melissa Leon, "'Fear Factor' Donkey Semen, More Gross Things Eaten on TV," *The Daily Beast*, 03-Feb-12.

India Style

The wedding dress was a stunner. Designed by Ralph Lauren, it was adorned with 2.4 million mother-of-pearl sequins and featured an over-the-top 75-foot-long (23 m) veil. [69] That was just one of six outfits Priyanka Chopra wore during her three-day wedding celebration, including one that took 110 embroiderers 3,720 hours to make. It was a showcase Generation X-tasy wedding.

India-born Chopra rose to U.S. fame when she starred from 2015 to 2018 as Alex Parrish in the ABC crime drama *Quantico*, becoming the first South Asian to lead an American network drama series. [70] She is part of the India Style wave, which is poised to turn India into a cultural and style trendsetter.

Anecdotal evidence suggests that people of Indian origin have vaulted to the most significant ethnic minority on U.S. television. In 2011, they trailed only Spanish-speaking actors on TV, but if IMDB is any indication, its 30-member list of Hispanic/Latino actors has been trumped by the "Indian actors in Hollywood" list, which now numbers 39. [71] [72]

That's in stark contrast to U.S. demographics. Indians make up less than 1% of the U.S., with an estimated population of 2.4 million, while Hispanics number 58 million, or 18% of the U.S. total. [73] [74] Compare that figure to 1960, when just 12,000 Indian immigrants lived in the U.S.

And unlike the earliest groups of Indians, who entered the U.S. workforce as taxi drivers, farmers or small business owners, newer arrivals include professionals or recent graduates, many on high-skilled H-1B visas. Indians now own 50% of all economy lodges and 35% of all hotels in the U.S., with a combined market value of nearly $40 billion, reports *Little India* magazine.

Indian actors have played many prominent roles on TV, including Parminder Nagra, who starred in the medical drama *ER* for six years; Mindy Kaling who plays an OB-GYN in *The Mindy Project*; Kunal Nayyar as Raj Koothrapali in *The Big Bang Theory*; Archie Panjabi as Kalinda Sharma in *The Good Wife*; and Naveen Andrews who played Sayid Jarrah in *Lost*, among others.

The trend received a big boost in September 2010, when NBC debuted *Outsourced*, a show about India's most high-profile industry, which featured four Indian actors. There are now far more Indians employed on U.S. television than Asian characters. Margaret Cho took a sarcastic swipe at that phenomenon, "There are like two more Asian people on television now then there was 10 years ago, and that's pretty impressive." [75]

India Style will also help spark the global adoption of a more diverse cuisine. While only the U.K. now considers Indian food a non-native, national cuisine, two confluent factors will help propel this trend. One is complexity, and there's nothing more complicated than the spice blend in curry. The other is society's growing fondness of spicier food.

IMAGE COURTESY: CBS BROADCASTING INC./JUSTIN STEPHENS.

Archie Panjabi as Kalinda Sharma in CBS' *The Good Wife*

Archana "Archie" Panjabi is a British actress best known for her role as Kalinda Sharma on *The Good Wife*. She also played Pinky Bhamra in the 2002 film *Bend It Like Beckham*.

69. Sara Nathan, "Inside Nick Jonas and Priyanka Chopra's extravagant 3-day wedding," *Page Six*, 04-Dec-18.
70. "Priyanka Chopra," *Wikipedia*, ret. 26-Dec-18.
71. "Hispanic/Latino Actors," *IMDB*, 05 Nov-17
72. "Indian Actors & Actresses in Hollywood," *IMDB*, 04-Sep-16.
73. "Indian Immigrants in the United States," *Migration Policy Institute*, 31-Aug-17.
74. Antonio Flores, "How the U.S. Hispanic population is changing," *Pew Research*, 18-Sep-17.
75. Lisa Respers France, "Margaret Cho geared up for 'Dead'," *CNN*, 04-May-09.

Legalizing Former Taboos

Generation X-tasy

The trend began inauspiciously enough in an old Amsterdam brownstone located at Weesperzijde 53. It's there that in a former bakery, Wernard Bruining and his friends opened the world's first "coffeeshop," dubbed Mellow Yellow, in 1972. [76]

The original Mellow Yellow burned down in 1978 and was moved to a new location near the Heineken museum. After Dutch authorities created a new zoning law prohibiting coffeeshops within 250 meters of a school, Mellow Yellow was forced to close its doors for good on December 31, 2016. [77] That still leaves 167 coffeeshops in Europe's most adult playground.

As Bob Dylan famously intones, "The Times They Are A-Changin." In 1973, Oregon became the first U.S. state to decriminalize cannabis. [78] But it wasn't until 1996, some 23 years later, that the legalization of marijuana received its an early boost when California legalized the use of cannabis for medical purposes. [79] The most telling development came in November 2012 when both Colorado and Washington legalized marijuana for personal use, signaling a major societal shift. [80] Today, medical marijuana is legal in 33 states and Washington, D.C., while the recreational use of marijuana by adults is legal in 10 states plus D.C. and the Northern Mariana Islands.

U.S. attitudes towards marijuana have changed markedly over time. In 1969, when Gallup first asked the question, just 12% favored legalizing marijuana use. In 2017, 61% of Americans said the drug should be made legal, the highest percentage of support recorded in 48 years. [81]

IMAGE COURTESY: WERNARD E. BRUINING.

Mellow Yellow, Amsterdam's First Coffeeshop, in 1972

Wernard Bruining and a few friends decided that this former bakery was an ideal place to open a "coffeeshop" to sell marijuana and hashish. It was a very early precursor to what was to become a global Generation X-tasy trend.

76. Karin Lakeman, "De eerste coffeeshop ter wereld," *Ons Amsterdam*, ret. 25-Mar-16.
77. Gavin Haines, "Why Amsterdam's oldest cannabis 'coffeeshop' has been forced to close," *The Telegraph*, 03-Jan-17.
78. "Decriminalization of non-medical cannabis in the United States," *Wikipedia*, ret. 26-Dec-18.
79. "History of Marijuana as Medicine - 2900 BC to Present," *ProCon.org*, ret. 19-May-18.
80. Aaron Smith, "Marijuana legalization passes in Colorado, Washington," *CNN Money*, 08-Nov-12.
81. Abigail Geiger, "About six-in-ten Americans support marijuana legalization," *Pew Research*, 05-Jan-18.

The U.S. Marijuana Culture Has Out-Smoked the Law

Since at least the middle 1990s, television shows have treated marijuana smoking as a routine practice. It must have helped with popular opinion, which reached a 61% favorability rating in 2017.

IMAGE COURTESY: WENDYGAIL91/FLICKR.

And the trend is spreading globally. In December 2013, Uruguay, surprisingly, became the first country in the world to legalize cannabis in 2013 for all its citizens. [82] Marijuana can now be grown privately, bought from licensed pharmacies or through club membership. The Uruguay government controls production, pricing and sets consumption quotas. Canada legalized recreational cannabis system on October 17, 2018, while Mexico will legalize medical marijuana sales in 2018. [83] [84]

On February 24, 2015, Jamaica became the first Caribbean nation to decriminalize small amounts of marijuana. [85] Argentina and Colombia followed. Guatemala has proposed legalizing the drug, and both Chile and Costa Rica are considering allowing medical marijuana use. Meanwhile, a conservative Peruvian Congress passed a bill legalizing medical marijuana in October 2018. [86]

In Europe, Germany's political parties are considering the sale of marijuana

82. Rafael Romo, "New rules in Uruguay create a legal marijuana market," *CNN*, 06-May-14.
83. Darran Simon, Nicole Chavez, "Canada just legalized recreational pot. Here's what you need to know," *CNN*, 17-Oct-18.
84. "Mexico to legalize marijuana-based product sales next year," *Reuters*, 20-Dec-17.
85. Philip Ross, "Jamaica Marijuana Legalization: First Caribbean Country To Decriminalize Weed," *International Business Times*, 25-Feb-15.
86. "Peru Congress passes bill to legalize medical marijuana," *Reuters*, 20-Oct-17.

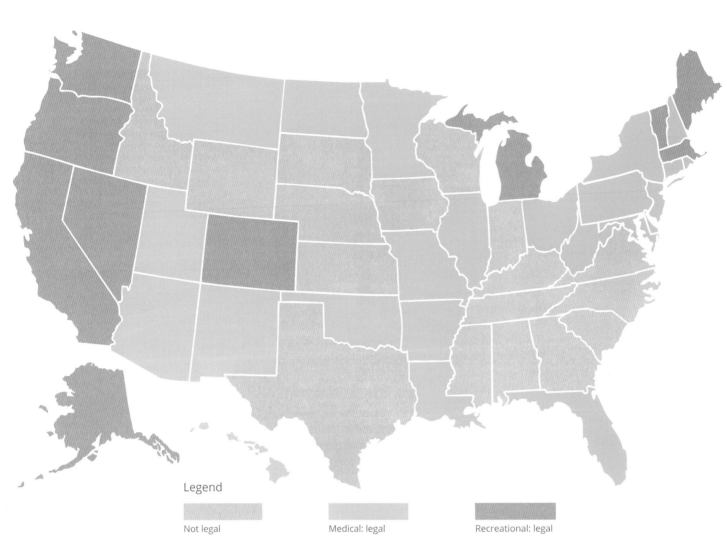

Legend

Not legal   Medical: legal   Recreational: legal

Spread of Legal Cannabis in U.S.

Thirty-three states plus the District of Columbia have legalized the medical use of marijuana, while 10 states plus D.C. and the Northern Mariana Islands now permit the recreational use of cannabis.

in pharmacies or dispensaries. [87] Spain has more than 800 "private cannabis clubs," with membership requiring minimal paperwork. [88]

CNN's Dr. Sanjay Gupta admitted on air that he had been wrong about marijuana. After examining mounting evidence that medical marijuana was benefiting users, Gupta stated, "Well, I am here to apologize." [89]

Bob Dylan was right, the times they indeed are a-changin.

Porno Chic

While Las Vegas was setting trends in one ancient vice, the city of Hamburg, Germany was becoming famous for another. In 1926, Arthur Wittkowski opened the Alkazar, a variety theater, on the Reeperbahn. [90] In low German, "reep" means rope, referring to a street lined with rope makers who were essential to Hamburg's

87. Mona Zhang, "German Parties Consider Sale Of Marijuana In Pharmacies Or Dispensaries," *Forbes*, 30-Oct-17.
88. Russ Hudson, "El futuro de los clubes de cannabis en España," *Vice*, 19-Apr-17.
89. Sanjay Gupta, "Why I changed my mind on weed," *CNN*, 08-Aug-13.
90. "Varieté Alkazar," *reeperbahn.de*, ret. 26-Dec-18.

World's Largest Brothel: Eros Center

The Eros Center housed as many as 140 prostitutes on its six floors, who plied their trade seven days a week, 24 hours a day. Real-estate magnate Willi Bartels established the brothel in 1967. It closed its doors in 1988.

Origin of "Sex Appeal"

Burlesque shows injected our vocabulary with a term still popular today, "sex appeal." It was first used in 1904 to describe the lasciviousness of these shows: "For the raw sex appeal of the burlesque 'shows' there is no defense, either. These 'shows' should be under official supervision, at the least, and boys beneath the age of eighteen forbidden, perhaps, to attend their performance, just as we forbid the sale of liquors to minors."[1]

1. Walter Prichard Eaton, "At the New theatre and others. The American stage: its problems and performances, 1908-1910," p. 335, *Boston Small Maynard and Company*, 1910.

thriving harbor. It was the Alkazar that would usher in the Reeperbahn's reputation as a hub of "exotic dancer" clubs.

In this former beer hall, Wittkowski installed the latest entertainment technology, including a stage that could be lowered and changed from a skating rink to a dance floor or a water fountain. Around this fountain, dancers would perform "dances of ecstasy," wearing revealing exotic "hula" or harem outfits.

As the Reeperbahn began to acquire its reputation as the world's first "pink zone," prostitutes, who were already aplenty in this sailor town, began flocking to Hamburg's St. Pauli area, where the Reeperbahn is located. Prostitution was never illegal in Germany, and by one estimate 50,000 women were working as prostitutes in Berlin in 1900. [91] Hamburg's oldest brothel, the Hotel Luxor opened in 1948. Luxor was followed in 1955 by Tabu, a club designed by Erwin Ross, then known as the "Rubens of the Reeperbahn." [92] Tabu was a classic "cabaret" bar featuring scantily clad hostesses who actively encouraged tourists and sailors to spend their money on expensive liquor.

Despite Hamburg's early lead, the term "Red Light District" actually originated in Dodge City, Kan., where a well-known prostitution district during the 19th century boasted a popular establishment, the Red Light House Saloon. [93]

In 1967, Hamburg institutionalized prostitution when it opened Europe's largest brothel, the six-story Eros Center on the Reeperbahn. [94] But the Reeperbahn was also in the spotlight in the early 1960s for an entirely different reason. It was here that on August 18, 1960, at a club called INDRA, just a few steps from the Reeperbahn, at Große Freiheit 64, that The Beatles first made their public debut, forever engraving Hamburg's

91. Friedrich Lenger, "European Cities in the Modern Era 1850-1914," *BRILL*, 2012.
92. bigbrotiki, "Tabu Bar, Hamburg, Germany," *Tiki Central*, 25-Mar-02.
93. "Red Light District," *Wikipedia*, ret. 26-Dec-18.
94. "Prostitution in Germany," *Wikipedia*, ret. 26-Dec-18.

Carl's Jr. Burger Ad Spokes Model Charlotte McKinney

The burger chain reported that its 2015 Super Bowl ad starring McKinney surpassed results from previous ad campaigns starring Kate Upton, Paris Hilton and Nina Agdal. Carl's Jr. has apparently given up on its "sex sells" advertising strategy.

role in the annals of music. [95]

As with any phenomenon ruled by the Generation X-tasy Ubertrend, time would bring significant changes. The Eros Center closed in 1988 due to the fear of AIDS. [96] Hotel Luxor closed in April 2008. [97] Waltraud Mehrer, the owner of Hotel Luxor, cited a number of factors, all driven by Ubertrends. She felt that the dance clubs, another Generation X-tasy trend, had become a distraction. Many clubs had begun using surveillance cameras, part of the Voyeurgasm Ubertrend (page 258), which scared off customers. The Time Compression Ubertrend (page 147), meanwhile, introduced advances in technology that reduced crew sizes and allowed ships to leave port much more quickly, thereby largely eliminating sailor leave time. Finally, The Digital Lifestyle Ubertrend popularized internet pornography, which further impacted business.

Internet sites featuring adult entertainment trace their ancestry to the 1969 legalization of pornography by Denmark, the first country in the world to do so. [98] In the U.S. there was a parallel development that year. After a lengthy legal battle, the Swedish movie *I'm Curious (Yellow)* opened in theaters across the U.S. where it was met by picket lines. Banned for its "pornographic" content, the film featured simulated sex scenes, plus displays of pubic hair and a penis. [99]

I'm Curious (Yellow) would set the stage for movies that further pushed the boundaries of morality, including *Last Tango in Paris* featuring Marlon Brando having simulated anal sex, and *Deep Throat*, which featured no such simulation, both released in 1972. *Deep Throat* made Linda Lovelace one of the first porn superstars — a trend that was recognized in February 1984 with the debut of the AVN (Adult Video News) Awards, dubbed the "Oscars of Porn." [100]

The internet and mass media have led to entirely evolved sexual sensibilities. A television show, called *Coupling*, featured a line that epitomizes the current state of affairs on television, "One swallow does not make her my girlfriend." [101] *Coupling* debuted on NBC in September 2003, some 16 years ago.

The adult entertainment trend has also infused advertising. In a world where consumers are inundated by nearly 400 ad messages each day, you can't blame marketers for wanting to raise your, ahem, awareness. [102]

If there's one marketing philosophy that's guaranteed to raise hackles, it's "sex sells." And no country has pushed the sex sells limits farther than France, where the ad technique even has its own expression, "porno chic."

While the use of sexual imagery in advertising is decried in most countries, the French have no such qualms. That France would favor this kind of

95. "Die Geschichte des Indra," *Indra Club 64*, ret. 04-May-17.
96. Tony Paterson, "Death of the Reeperbahn: Hamburg's streets of shame," *Independent*, 21-Mar-08.
97. "Hamburg's Oldest Bordello Set to Shut," *Der Spiegel*, 14-Mar-08.
98. "Pornography in Denmark," *Wikipedia*, ret. 04-May-17.
99. "The History of Sex in Cinema," *Filmsite.org*, ret. 19-May-18.
100. "AVN Award," *Wikipedia*, ret. 19-May-18.
101. iamnotfrodo, "Coupling, Ep1: "Flushed," *french fries & a soda drink*, 25-Apr-08.
102. Sheree Johnson, "New Research Sheds Light on Daily Ad Exposures," *SJ Insights*, 29-Sep-14.

Metal Band GWAR in Full Generation X-tasy Regalia

Dubbed a "shock-metal band," GWAR is well known for spewing fake blood and bodily fluids, and hurling insults at their audiences. It's an act that exemplifies the experiential trend in music performances.

IMAGE COURTESY: GWAR.

marketing should come as no surprise. The French, after all, that gave the world the saying *laissez-faire*.

As Generation X-tasy and, as you'll see later, the Casual Living Ubertrend suggest, our global culture is becoming a less buttoned-up society where just about anything goes. Today, the decency envelope is being pushed by a coterie of dauntless brands. Carl's Jr.'s ads featuring model Kate Upton and socialite Paris Hilton come to mind. It's no longer necessary to be an upstanding citizen, as model Kate Moss has famously proven.

Party Like It's 1999

What comes after drugs and sex? Rock-and-roll, of course. The famous saying speaks volumes about the role music plays in the evolution of Generation X-tasy. It's an established truth that rock concerts are one of the most lively exhibits of the exuberance and decadence that can accompany this Ubertrend.

Whether it's a steel band doing the rounds at Madison Square Garden

IMAGE COURTESY: DREAMWORKS PICTURES.

Groupie Excess: Almost Famous

The 2000 movie *Almost Famous*, starring Kate Hudson, received four Oscar nominations for telling a fictional story about the experiences, and excesses, of being a devoted rock-and-roll groupie.

> " As an anything-goes generation waits in the wings to put its tramp stamp on the future, expect vice habits to morph in all directions, as gambling, sex, drugs and rock 'n' roll explode in a firework of new and uncharted experiences."
>
> Michael Tchong
> Ubertrends

during a Rolling Stones concert; The Who's Roger Daltrey smashing his guitar to pieces; KISS lighting up the stage with fireworks; Michael Jackson doing the moonwalk; Pink dangling from a rope at the Grammy's — music acts produce experiences few are likely ever to forget. [103]

And if you do have trouble remembering these immersive experiences, despite some lasting for many hours, like those legendary Grateful Dead concerts, where clouds of marijuana would waft up to the concert hall's ceiling, CDs are still an option. Rhino Records recently released the Grateful Dead's May 8, 1977 Cornell University's Barton Hall concert as an 11-disc box set — *May 1977: Get Shown The Light* ($300). [104] Some 40 years later, that concert experience undoubtedly still resonates with Deadheads, even if all those marijuana clouds may have made them mostly forget.

Perhaps no musical act is more symbolic of the experiential nature of Generation Xtasy than Gwar, a heavy metal band that plays songs with titles like, "Let Us Slay," while wearing scarily monstrous costumes that exude their blood-and-gore *gestalt* (photo, previous page). [105]

But even such relatively straight-laced music icons as Britney Spears and Miley Cyrus are known for putting on shows that resemble circus acts. And the post-show antics of Spears, Paris Hilton and Lindsay Lohan have been well publicized. These ladies' indulgences could well make them the modern-age equivalent of the 1960s Ratpack ("Las Vegas: The Capital of Generation X-tasy," page 119).

The irrational exuberance of their stable of artists and creatives has even

103. "Smashed Guitars," *Whotabs*, 19-May-16.
104. Randy Fairman, "Not Fade Away: Grateful Dead's Legendary 1977 Cornell Concert To Get Official Release On Its Own and As Part of 11-Disc May 1977 Concert Box," *The Second Disc*, 21-Feb-17.
105. Liz Ramanand, "Gwar Bring Blood and Gore to New York City," *Loudwire*, 25-Oct-11.

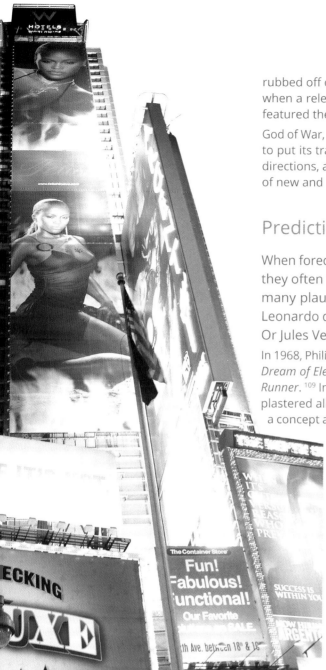

rubbed off on corporate executives. In 2007, Sony received a lot of flack when a release party for the *God of War II* videogame in Athens, Greece featured the carcass of a decapitated goat as part of the festivities. [106]

God of War, meet Gwar. As an anything-goes generation waits in the wings to put its tramp stamp on the future, expect vice habits to morph in all directions, as gambling, sex, drugs and rock 'n' roll explode in a firework of new and uncharted experiences.

Predicting the Future, Blade Runner Style

When forecasters want to peer into the future to divine what's next, they often turn to science fiction, which consistently has supplied many plausible scenarios. After all, few possess the talents of a Leonardo da Vinci, who famously predicted that man would fly. [107] Or Jules Verne who accurately foresaw the submarine. [108]

In 1968, Philip Dick wrote a powerful science fiction novel called *Do Androids Dream of Electric Sheep?* Which became the basis for the 1982 film *Blade Runner*. [109] In Ridley Scott's production, we see giant electronic billboards plastered all over skyscrapers in Los Angeles that tower far into the sky, a concept also used in 2018's *Fahrenheit 451*, a movie produced by HBO.

Scott's *Blade Runner* ignores other visionary technologies described in Philip Dick's novel, including those electronic sheep, "empathy boxes" and the Penfield mood organ. [110]

As the photo, left, shows, Scott's 1980s vision has already been realized in New York City's Times Square, where billboards soar 57 floors high against the facade of a W Hotel, albeit not yet fully digitized.

Another science fiction prediction appears in 1999's *The Matrix*, written by Lilly and Lana Wachowski (pages 16, 56), which featured futuristic displays of Asian characters continuously streaming down. Today, social media monitoring services can produce similar endless streams of characters.

And the gesture-driven, haptic interfaces on prominent display in the 2002 movie *Minority Report* were famously mainstreamed by the Nintendo Wii in November 2006. [111] The Time Compression Ubertrend has compressed the time for a prediction to become a reality in 36, 10 and four years, respectively.

Our science fiction future, it seems, is right around the corner. Unfortunately, what these seers could not have predicted is that a greedy group of Wall Street investors would actively seek to discourage companies from realizing their visions. This fiscal conservatism comes despite a world crawling with Tyrell Corporation-like behemoths.

Times Square Outdoor Advertising Billboards

New York's Times Square advertising billboards already tower 57 stories high, confirming Ridley Scott's 1982 science-fiction thriller, *Blade Runner*, which predicted that advertising would one day compete with towering skyscrapers.

IMAGE COURTESY: MICHAEL TCHONG.

106. Susan Arendt, "Sony Apologizes for Goat Carcass at God of War II Party," *Wired*, 30-Apr-07.
107. James Donahue, "The Stormberger Prophecies," *Psiomni Magazine*, ret. 27-Dec-18.
108. "8 Jules Verne Inventions That Came True," *National Geographic*, 08-Feb-11.
109. "Do Androids Dream of Electric Sheep?," *Wikipedia*, ret. 27-Dec-18.
110. James Andrews, "By The Book – Blade Runner (Do Androids Dream Of Electric Sheep?)," *One Room With A View*, 06-Oct-17.
111. "Technologies in Minority Report," *Wikipedia*, ret. 27-Dec-18.

Time Compression has bred a multitasking population that's in love with instant gratification. It's a world that treasures speedy, efficient services that are simple to understand, and that better manage their increasingly valuable disposable time.

4

Time Compression
The Acceleration of Life

Everything is going faster these days. Life has become a blur, a trend magnified by an influx of technology that helps people do things quickly. The world now moves at internet speed due to arcane time compression technologies called codecs. In the eye of the storm lie even faster algorithms that will further accelerate life. Smartphones are helping fulfill an endless thirst for instant gratification. A telltale sign that immediate satisfaction is not quick enough is a popular expression, "I want it yesterday." What was once a respectable response time is no longer acceptable. To save time, we multitask. To cope, we consume large amounts of coffee, energy drinks, and Xanax. The state of mind has become a state of time. And by the looks of things, we're even accelerating evolution.

Instant Gratification

Time Compression

A severe snowstorm was raging in New York City on Friday, February 21, 1947. Despite the inclement weather, some 650 members of the Optical Society of America had gathered at Hotel Pennsylvania on Seventh Avenue for a highly anticipated demonstration by inventor Edwin Land. [1] The audience gasped as Land took a self-portrait with his Polaroid Land camera and then produced an 8-by-10-inch photograph some 60 seconds later.

It didn't take long for this group of optical aficionados to realize that what they were witnessing nothing short of history in the making. In those days, developing photographs required mixing a batch of messy chemicals. But the Polaroid Land Camera, which went on sale in Boston on November 26, 1948, for $89.95, used a unique film that sandwiched chemicals between exposed negatives and receiving positives, and that, when peeled apart, showed images almost instantly. [2]

Little did Land know that his invention would help usher in a whole new era, one in which instant gratification would rule the day. And it was all due to the impatience of little Jennifer, Land's three-year-old daughter, who had complained that it took too long to develop photographic film.

Land's revolution would reverberate throughout the world. His invention

> " Land's revolution would reverberate throughout the world. His invention was the first in a series of products that exposed consumers to the seductive qualities of instant gratification"
>
> **Michael Tchong**
> *Ubertrends*

---

1. Sam Biddle, "The First Time the Public Ever Saw a Polaroid," *Gizmodo*, 05-Oct-12.
2. "Polaroid History," *PLR Ecommerce*, ret. 23-Jun-17.

was the first in a series of products that exposed consumers to the seductive qualities of immediate satisfaction. The art of photography has changed markedly since then. People rarely get to see prints at all. In 2005, the Photo Marketing Association estimated that 35% of digital photos were printed. [3] A reasonable estimate today would be less than 2%. And film processing is a thing of the past, just 25 years after Apple introduced the world's first, easy-to-use digital camera, the QuickTake 100. [4]

LCD screens are now the display device of choice. People huddle around the phone and digital camera screens as if peering into a digital fireplace, with faces lit up while looking through this window of wonder.

Instant gratification now rules the world of imaging, which is evident from this notable trend: In 2000, Kodak proudly announced that consumers across the globe had taken 80 billion photos, setting a new record. [5] That pales in comparison to the 1.3 trillion digital images taken in 2017.

The internet and particularly social media have played a significant role in spreading the gospel of instant gratification. By simplifying picture sharing, Facebook reported that some 350 million photos were uploaded daily back in 2013 when it had "only" 1.1 billion members. [6] Between Facebook's current membership of 2.3 billion and Instagram's 1 billion, the daily upload figure is more than likely approaching 1 billion photos a day. [7] That estimate is also based on the latest Instagram image upload figure of 80 million each day in 2016 when it had 400 million users. [8]

Sharing by e-mail, which a majority of digital photo fans do routinely, is another by-product of the Time Compression age and a far faster and more convenient way than making a trip to the local drugstore to develop prints. Sharing a photo album is an age-old habit that seems almost anachronistic in this day and age of fleeting imagery.

Land wasn't the only one working to compress time. Not far away, in Waltham, Massachusetts, self-taught engineer Percy Spencer observed something peculiar. While testing a new vacuum tube called a magnetron, the fruit of wartime radar research at defense contractor Raytheon, Spencer noticed that a peanut cluster candy bar had melted in his pocket. [9]

Intrigued by this phenomenon, Spencer placed some popcorn near the tube and watched in amazement as kernels began popping all over his lab counter. Raytheon engineers quickly refined Spencer's discovery and, in late 1946, filed for a patent covering the use of microwaves to cook food.

Tappan Stove Co. took on the challenge of mainstreaming Raytheon's technology for general use by introducing the first home microwave oven, priced at $1,295, on October 25, 1955. [10] In 1965, Raytheon acquired Amana Refrigeration, and two years later, the company introduced the first countertop microwave, a 100-volt model that cost less than $500 and was smaller, safer and more reliable than previous models. By 1975 microwave oven sales exceeded those of gas ranges for the first time. Like

IMAGE COURTESY: RAYTHEON COMPANY.

First Commercial Microwave Oven: Raytheon Radarange

This early model of the Raytheon Radarange microwave oven belongs to one of two fundamental technologies, dating to 1946 and designed for the masses, that introduced the world to the concept of "instant gratification."

3. Damon Darlin, "Why Do-It-Yourself Photo Printing Doesn't Add Up," *The New York Times*, 08-Oct-05.
4. Stewart Wolpin, "20 Years Ago, Apple and Kodak Launched the Digital Camera Revolution," *Mashable*, 21-Jun-14.
5. Stephen Heyman, "Photos, Photos Everywhere," *The New York Times*, 29-Jul-15.
6. Cooper Smith, "Facebook Users Are Uploading 350 Million New Photos Each Day," *Business Insider*, 18-Sep-13.
7. "Facebook Stats," *Facebook Newsroom*, ret. 05-Jan-19.
8. Christopher Ratcliff, "23 up-to-date stats and facts about Instagram you need to know," *Search Engine Watch*, 20-Apr-16.
9. Matt Blitz, "The Amazing True Story of How the Microwave Was Invented by Accident," *Popular Mechanics*, 23-Feb-16.
10. Suzanne Deffree, "1st domestic microwave is sold, October 25, 1955," *EDN*, 25-Oct-16.

First McDonald's Restaurant in San Bernardino, California

Located at 14th and E Street in San Bernardino, the first McDonald's featured an embryonic emblem of modern times: Speedee, a Bob's Big Boy-like character that encouraged customers to "buy 'em by the bag."

IMAGE COURTESY: MCDONALDS CORPORATION.

Polaroid's Land Camera, Raytheon's microwave technology compressed a tedious chore into a matter of mere minutes, representing a quantum leap in consumer convenience.

The most significant development in this quickly accelerating Ubertrend was yet to come. While operating their first restaurant, the Airdome, in San Bernardino, California, brothers Dick and Maurice ("Mac") McDonald realized that the future of consumer restaurants lay in mass production and speed of service.

On December 12, 1948, they opened their first McDonald's restaurant, at 14th and E Street, which sold 15¢ burgers and 10¢ fries, using their new "Speedee Service System."[11]

White Castle had beaten the McDonalds to the punch, launching the fast-food chain in Wichita, Kansas in 1921.[12] In 1961, White Castle became the first fast-food restaurant to sell 1 billion burgers, a feat repeated just two years later by McDonald's.

It was McDonald's, under the aegis of Ray Kroc, who bought out the McDonald brothers for $2.7 million in 1961 and moved the company to Des Plaines, Ill., that would come to symbolize the fast-food industry. When McDonald's reached the 1 billion mark in 1963, the milestone hamburger was served by Ray Kroc himself on national television.[13] McDonald's played a vital role in helping U.S. fast-food sales reach $210 billion in 2017.[14]

The company's ability to sell large volumes of food was promoted by signs at each outlet that advertised the chain's success in almost jackpot-like fashion with "billions sold" figures. The last year McDonald's was able to publicize its milestones without running out of display capacity was 1994, when its popular barometer of time-compressed gluttony reached

11. "History of McDonald's," *Wikipedia*, ret. 28-Dec-18.
12. Ashlee Kieler, "The White Castle Story: The Birth Of Fast Food & The Burger Revolution," *Consumerist*, 14-Jul-15.
13. "Over How Many Billions Served?," *Blogspot*, 30-Apr-10.
14. "Revenue of the quick service restaurant (QSR) industry in the U.S. from 2003 to 2020," *Statista*, ret. 23-Jun-17.

Cream of Wheat Cooking Time

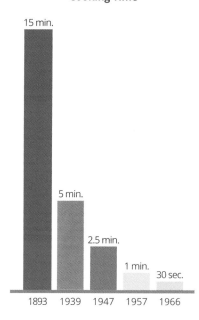

15 min.

5 min.

2.5 min.

1 min.

30 sec.

| 1893 | 1939 | 1947 | 1957 | 1966 |

June 2003 James Beard Foundation

99 billion. Relying on the math of the "Over How Many Billions Served?" blog, McDonald's is estimated to sell about 1.4 billion hamburgers each month, which suggests the company has sold approximately 440 billion burgers, as of December 2018. These staggering figures underscore just how important fast food and its value of time-saving have become in the global landscape.

Just how important is saving time? The average service time at a McDonald's drive-through in 2016 was 208 seconds, according to a *QSR* magazine study. McDonald's is testing a "Signature Crafted" line of Quarter Pounders that are made with fresh beef and are cooked to order. A Reuters report suggests that some customers are not willing to wait the extra minute it takes to get a reportedly better tasting burger. [15]

Land, Spencer, the McDonald brothers and Kroc contributed to this lifestyle undercurrent, one that was about to pull society into a fast-moving riptide and turn the definition of speed on its head.

And what better epitome for the acceleration of life than meal cooking time reduction? The James Beard Foundation observed in 2003 that it took 15 minutes to prepare Cream of Wheat back in 1893 when the sticky porridge was invented. By 1939 savvy cooks had whittled that time down to five minutes. Today it takes a mere 30 seconds to cook Cream of Wheat, which may still be too long for many (chart).

Jet Age

What Time Compression pioneers readily understood was that time was becoming of the essence. And the enemy of time was

de Havilland DH-106 Comet Jet Aircraft

The first flight of the de Havilland DH-106 Comet on May 2, 1952 ushered in the Jet Age, which allowed travelers to not only "gain time" but also become a "jet-setter."

inefficiency. To be successful, innovative products or services had to accelerate a previously time-consuming task dramatically.

That was the approach that management took at British Overseas Airways Corporation, or BOAC as it was more popularly known, as it firmly pushed the world into the Jet Age. On May 2, 1952, a BOAC de Havilland DH-106 Comet

15. Lisa Baertlein, Liz Hampton, "Will McDonald's customers wait for the new Quarter Pounder?" *Reuters*, 20-Jun-17.

IMAGE COURTESY: AIRBUS GROUP INC.

FedEx: Poster Child of Time Compression Ubertrend

Founder Fred Smith's Yale college professor gave his overnight air delivery service paper a "C" grade. In fiscal 2018, FedEx booked $66 billion in revenues because it "absolutely, positively has to get there overnight."

jet took off from London's Heathrow Airport, headed for Johannesburg, South Africa, a trip that would take 23 hours and 40 minutes, with five stops in Rome, Beirut, Khartoum, Entebbe and Livingstone. [16] In a BOAC piston-engine aircraft, the same trip took 27 hours and 55 minutes on a route 1,000 miles shorter than the Comet's, the BBC reported.

The acceleration of humanity had just taken a giant leap forward with this 503-mile-per-hour jet. Society was about to be transformed by jet propulsion, and mirroring this accelerated lifestyle was the emergence of a new term: "jet-setter," an all-too-meaningful homage to a glamorous and significantly faster lifestyle.

The jet era also introduced another time-based anomaly. Suddenly it was possible to "gain time" by arriving just a few hours later than the original departure time. This phenomenon is demonstrated most strikingly when crossing the international date line. Sure, air travel in the opposite direction negates the benefit, but jet travel added a whole new dimension to Time Compression.

De Havilland did not rule the Jet Age for long. By 1958 most airlines had begun opting for the new Boeing 707 or Douglas DC-8, which could each seat almost twice as many passengers as the Comet. Still, BOAC's bold leap set the tone for the fabulous 1950s, which, like the previous decade, would prove to be a breeding ground for Time Compression related developments — not surprising, given this period's post-World War II penchant for re-purposing trendsetting wartime technologies.

As life was accelerating and people were getting more things done in a shorter period of time, another important concept, destined to become a fixture of faster living, emerged. The word "realtime" was mentioned for

16. Richard Hollingham, "The British airliner that changed the world," *BBC*, 05-Apr-17

IMAGE COURTESY: SEIKO WATCH CORPORATION.

Seiko Quartz 35 SQ Astron Watch

Launched in 1969, Seiko's Quartz 35 SQ Astron was the first watch capable of slicing time into 8,192 beats per second, delivering a one-minute-a-year accuracy, perfect for the Time Compression Age.

the very first time in the April 1953 quarterly journal *Mathematical Tables & Other Aids to Computation*, a fact corroborated by Merriam Webster. [17] [18] If you think about it, what could be more instantly gratifying than getting realtime results?

The advent of the internet and the mobile phone would ultimately introduce the world to the era of realtime communication, but today there is also realtime weather forecasting, realtime flight tracking, realtime stock tracking, realtime traffic, realtime site tracking, realtime transit, etc., etc.

To do split-second tracking, one needs to be able to slice time into ever smaller increments, which demands time instruments of high precision. On Christmas Day 1969, Seiko launched the Quartz 35 SQ Astron, the world's first commercially available quartz watch. With a limited production run of only 100 pieces, the Seiko Quartz 35 SQ Astron featured an analog dial and sold for 450,000 yen ($1,250) in Tokyo, roughly the same price as a Toyota Corolla at the time. [19]

The Astron's use of a quartz oscillator with a frequency of 8,192 cycles per second, which was accurate to about five seconds a month, or a minute a year, was truly groundbreaking. The Seiko Quartz Astron was the first timekeeping device able to keep pace with a society that was moving toward a split-second economy.

No one appreciated split-second performance more than Fred Smith, who had submitted a term paper at Yale University describing a service that relied on jet aircraft to deliver letters and small packages overnight. Smith, a former Marine, based the idea on his belief that a highly automated society would require a completely different logistics system.

His college professor, clearly less attuned to the need for speed, gave the paper a C. His thinking must have been, "Who would pay a lot of money to send a package overnight?" But to Smith speed was more important than cost and like any self-respecting entrepreneur, Smith pushed on and used his father's inheritance of $4 million to raise an additional $91 million in venture capital, which was quite a feat in the early 1970s. [20]

In 1973, on the company's first night of operation, 389 Federal Express employees and 14 Dassault Falcon jets delivered 186 packages overnight to 25 U.S. cities. [21] Federal Express, the company changed its name to FedEx in 2000, would not catch on until the early 1980s, after it introduced the Overnight Letter, which could contain up to two ounces and was delivered overnight for $9.50.

That year, 1981, also coincided with FedEx' hiring of advertising agency Ally & Gargano, which played a key role in dramatically raising the company's profile ("Fast Talking," page 168).

The agency was responsible for creating the legendary "fast-talking" television ad campaign), which helped instill a new operational doctrine in American business, one that would resonate with the ad's mantra, "when it absolutely, positively has to get there overnight."

17. H. Gray et al., "A Technique for Real Time Simulation of a Rigid Body Problem," *Mathematical Tables and Other Aids to Computation Vol. 7, No. 42*, Apr-53.
18. "Real Time," *Merriam-Webster*, ret. 28-Dec-18.
19. "Seiko Quartz Wristwatch," *Smithsonian*, ret. 28-Dec-18.
20. "FedEx Corporation," *Encyclopedia.com*, ret. 28-Dec-18.
21. "About FedEx – Our History," *FedEx*, ret. 28-Dec-18.

Institutionalizing Energy

Time Compression

In a modest house on Atlanta's Marietta Street, John Styth Pemberton toiled all hours of the night on a replacement for an alcoholic beverage he had introduced a few years earlier, called "Pemberton's French Wine Coca." The drink was a great success, due to its unique properties as an "intellectual beverage" and an "invigorator of the brain." [22]

Not to mention that it was also an aphrodisiac due to an ingredient called damiana, derived from a shrub native to Central and South America. Pemberton's recipe also included the Kola nut, indigenous to Africa, but its primary "invigorator" was the coca leaf, the basis of cocaine. The rise of the temperance movement, however, forced Pemberton to search for a new temperance drink formula.

On May 8, 1886, Pemberton succeeded in his efforts to create a non-alcoholic successor. To the caramel-colored syrup, Pemberton added a shot of cold, carbonated water and sold the concoction for five cents a glass at the soda fountain of Atlanta's largest drugstore, Jacob's Pharmacy. [23] With the help of the pharmacy's bookkeeper, Frank Robinson, Pemberton christened his creation Coca-Cola. Robinson also designed the unique, cursive logo that has been Coca-Cola's trademark ever since.

Robinson convinced Pemberton of the great importance of advertising and on May 29, 1886 the first Coca-Cola ad appeared in *The Atlanta Journal*:

IMAGE COURTESY: THE COCA-COLA COMPANY.

Early Coca-Cola Bottle Design Dating to 1899

Dubbed "Hutchinson," this Coca-Cola bottle featured a classic rubber-seal stopper that was opened by pushing down on a metal loop. The resulting popping sound gave birth to the "soda pop" name.

22. "John Stith Pemberton (1831 - 1888), Coca Cola and Cocaine," *Business Heroes*, Jul-98.
23. Eleanor Jones and Florian Ritzmann, "Coca-Cola Goes to War," *American Studies as the University of Virginia*, ret. 25-Jun-17.

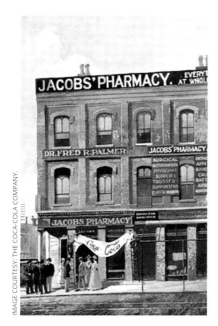

Coca-Cola's First Retail Location: Jacob's Pharmacy in Atlanta

The soda fountain at Jacob's Pharmacy, located at Marietta and Peachtree, first offered Coca-Cola on May 8, 1886 for five cents a glass. The pharmacy's bookkeeper, Frank Robinson, helped Coca-Cola creator John Pemberton name his drink and also designed the unique logo. They don't make bookkeepers like that anymore.

> " It is odd to watch with what feverish ardor the Americans pursue prosperity, and how they are ever tormented by the shadowy suspicion that they may not have chosen the shortest route to get it."
>
> Alexis de Tocqueville
> *Democracy in America*

"Coca-Cola. Delicious! Refreshing! Exhilarating! Invigorating! The new and popular soda fountain drink, containing the properties of the wonderful Coca plant and the famous Cola nuts. For sale by Willis Venable and Nunnally & Rawson."

Cocaine was first isolated from coca leaves in the 1860s, but it wasn't until the 1880s that its use began to spread in America, due to a substantial boost in the production of its purest form. [24] In plentiful supply, the coca leaf thus became the basis for the world's first "energy drink."

Pemberton was obsessed with inventing, what today would be called a multi-functional beverage: the ultimate medicine and perfect drink all rolled into one, which explains his dalliance with the coca leaf. Coca-Cola contained about nine milligrams of cocaine in each seven-ounce glass, in addition to a relatively large dose of the caffeine from the kola bean. [25]

In 1893, 10 years before cocaine was quietly removed from its secret recipe in 1903, Coca-Cola was described in advertising as an "ideal brain tonic." A 1929 slogan claiming that it produced a "pause that refreshes" clearly alluded to this history.

As cocaine use declined in the 1930s, interest grew in amphetamine — a new stimulant that had been synthesized long before but was introduced in the U.S. in 1932 as Benzedrine. By the end of the 1930s, Benzedrine was promoted as a "treatment for hay fever and melancholy and as a general pepper-upper," notes Dr. David Musto, professor of history of medicine at Yale University.

Amphetamines got off to a slow start and did not become fairly common until World War II when war pilots taking part in night-time bombing raids over Germany were the first to use the drug to not only keep them awake but also to intensify their zeal. Former war pilots helped spread the use of amphetamines to America's roadways. In the 1940s and 1950s, amphetamines were implicated in numerous trucking accidents resulting from its use by long-haul drivers, reports Musto.

While jet-setters plied the skies in fast aircraft, American truck drivers increasingly realized that delivery speed was of the essence, an awareness that would blossom in the 1960s, when "speed," as it was by then colloquially known, caught on among certain youths, a trend that can be traced to San Francisco's Haight-Ashbury district. Not that America's need for speed was a brand-new phenomenon.

The driven nature of Americans had been codified more than a hundred years earlier, when noted French author Alexis de Tocqueville pointedly observed in his 1835 tome *Democracy in America*, "It is odd to watch with what feverish ardor the Americans pursue prosperity, and how they are ever tormented by the shadowy suspicion that they may not have chosen the shortest route to get it." [26]

Like de Tocqueville, early participants in the Time Compression race realized that the goal *du jour* was instant gratification and that the shortest route to get to it would be to rewrite the rules of the order of nature.

24. David Musto, "History: The American Experience With Stimulants," *Office of National Drug Control Policy*, ret. 25-Jun-17.
25. Judd Hambrick, "Coca-cola removes cocaine from its secret formula," *Southern Memories*, 01-Sep-11.
26. Alexis de Tocqueville, ed. Harvey Mansfield, Delba Winthrop, "Democracy in America," *University of Chicago Press*, 2000.

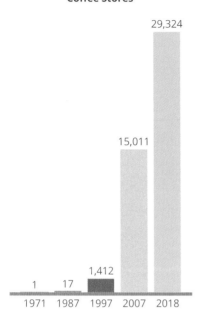

Global Expansion of Starbucks Coffee Stores

29,324

15,011

1,412

1   17

1971 1987 1997 2007 2018

29-Dec-18 Statista Starbucks - Statistics & Facts

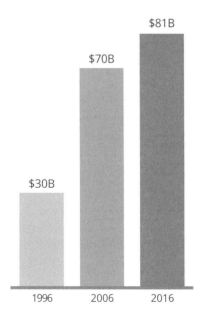

Global Coffee Market Growth 1996-2016

$81B

$70B

$30B

1996   2006   2016

2006 U.N. Food and Agriculture Organization, Mar-16 Global Coffee Report

I Want to Pump You Up!

A hilarious 1987 *Saturday Night* skit featuring two Austrian bodybuilders, Hanz and Franz, always featured their now famous gag line, "I want to pump you up!" Ironically, that very same year a local Seattle company called Il Giornale, headed up by Howard Schultz, would buy the assets of a local coffee chain, Starbucks, and change its name to Starbucks Corporation.

While Coca-Cola was proselytizing the benefits of a caffeine-laced American lifestyle, agent of change Starbucks was ready to embark on an equally auspicious journey with another energy propellant, coffee.

This auspicious history begins in April 1971, when a tiny shop called Starbucks Coffee, opened its doors for business in Seattle's Pike Place Market, where it sold high-quality coffee, dark-roasted the European way in small batches. At the time, the store did not sell coffee by the cup but sometimes offered brewed samples.

In 1982, Howard Schultz, a New York-based vice president for a Swedish housewares firm, signed on as director of marketing and convinced the company founders to test a coffee bar concept akin to Milan's espresso bars.

After leaving Starbucks in 1985, Schultz established Il Giornale, which offered brewed coffee and espresso beverages made from Starbucks coffee beans. With backing from local investors, Schultz acquired Starbucks' assets and changed Il Giornale's name to Starbucks Corporation.

Like those 1940s and 1950s truck drivers who found that amphetamines had decided advantages, coffee lovers would quickly discover that Starbucks concoctions delivered not only a significantly better taste but a stronger punch as well, at least when compared to most American coffee, which had become a weak, watery mess.

For truckers, there just was no comparison between NoDoz and amphetamines. The latter not only kept you awake but also gave you that uncanny "in control" feeling that you were moving faster than anyone else. The same can be said for Starbucks coffee, but it also offers free Wi-Fi and other amenities, including a gamified loyalty app.

The Starbucks story is startling in all its dimensions. In 1987, when Hanz and Franz were chattering about "girlie men" on NBC, Starbucks had just 17 stores. Today, Starbucks has 29,324 stores and counting (top chart). [27] Fiscal year 2018 was Starbucks' best with revenues rising 10% to a record $24.7 billion. [28] There are also now 15.3 million Starbucks Rewards members.

Starbucks has set the standard for coffee consistency and availability in a time-compressed world, helping push global coffee sales to $81 billion, up from $30 billion 20 years ago (bottom chart). [29] The graphs show the role Starbucks played in boosting global coffee sales, with the industry's growth spurt closely paralleling Starbucks' expansion between 1997 and 2007. The coffee market's slowing growth in the past decade has led to Starbucks' new focus on selling food, explaining the thinking behind

27. "Starbucks - Statistics & Facts," *Statista*, ret. 29-Dec-18.
28. "Starbucks Reports Q4 and Full Year Fiscal 2018 Results," *Starbucks Corp.*, 01-Nov-18.
29. "Jacobs Douwe Egberts aims for global domination," *Global Coffee Report*, Mar-16.

Starbucks' First Store in Seattle's Pike Place Market

Starbucks, which opened its first store in Seattle's Pike Place Market in 1971, helped reinvent the global business of coffee by introducing uniform quality and global convenience, turning coffee into the world's best-selling energy drink.

removing the word "Coffee" from Starbucks' logo. [30]

A longer timeline reveals the coffee market's wind in Starbucks' sails. From 1964, seven years before the Pike Place Market Starbucks store opened, world coffee consumption grew from 58 million 60-kilogram bags to 148 million bags in the period between October 2015 and September 2016. [31]

Business Insider reports that coffee is now the most sought-after commodity after crude oil. [32] The International Coffee Organization projects that demand will rise 25% between 2015 and 2020, which suggests a market north of $100 billion by 2020. [33] *The Wall Street Journal* reported on February 17, 2004 that domestic coffee consumption in 2002 was down 14%, compared to the 1980s, while coffeehouse sales had jumped at least 1,200%, citing industry research firm Mintel.

A little over two decades ago, there we no Starbucks drive-throughs. The out-of-home coffee consumption trend is the driving force behind the establishment of more than 35,000 specialty coffee shops in the U.S., projecting 2015 data provided by the Specialty Coffee Association of America. [34] Based on that figure, Starbucks controls about 84% of the U.S. specialty coffee shop market, based on store units alone.

The value of the U.S. retail market was $48 billion in 2015, according to SCAA, with specialty coffee shops accounting for 55% of that market. Revenues are driven by an insatiable urge to "pump up" — to have enough energy to make it through a typical overwhelming, multiple-task-laden day.

How ironic that Coca-Cola, the standard-bearer of Time Compression for a greater part of the past century would, in effect, be replaced by a new energy wave. Even its name implies that you'll make big "bucks" and become a "star," if only you drink enough of the stuff, a surreptitious message not lost on its yuppified clientele. Products with the word "star" in their name have a greater propensity to succeed, as a study reported in the 1980s — around the same time that WordStar ruled the PC world.

And so a Time Compression star was born. If you think that's unadulterated adulation, consider the residents of Murcia, Spain. In March 2010, the town launched a Facebook campaign to attract a local Starbucks. [35] As *The Guardian* tells it, "Although Spaniards have long had a variety of good quality coffee on hand at almost every street corner café, Starbucks has already established 76 outlets in Spain and continues to expand there."

Murcia coffee aficionados felt their town lacked one thing that would prove they had made it as a global city: the green, white and black sign of a local Starbucks. Observed resident Enrique Marhuenda: "The day we have a Starbucks, Murcia will be an important city." In other words, we have not arrived until we receive the Starbucks badge of honor.

And if anyone needs Starbucks, it's the Spaniards. Globalization has killed Spain's traditional siesta. [36] Since Spaniards still insist on dining late, they

30. Julie Jargon, "Starbucks Aims to Double U.S. Food Sales," *The Wall Street Journal*, 04-Dec-14.
31. Joe Tenebruso, "11 Coffee Stats that Will Blow You Away," *The Motley* Fool, 23-Jan-17.
32. Eric Goldschein, "11 Incredible Facts About The Global Coffee Industry," *Business Insider*, 14-Nov-11.
33. Nicholas Bariyo, "Coffee Consumption Expected to Jump," *The Wall Street Journal*, 16-Feb-15.
34. "U.S. Specialty Coffee Facts & Figures," *Specialty Coffee Association of America*, Dec-15.
35. Giles Tremlett, "Cafe con cookie? Spanish city in a frap over lack of Starbucks," *The Guardian*, 12-Mar-10.
36. Elizabeth Nash, "Spanish suffer lack of sleep as globalisation ends siesta," *The Independent*, 20-Dec-04.

sleep 53 minutes less than the European average, despite working 11-hour days. [37]

How much buoyancy has the Time Compression Ubertrend lent Starbucks? It has never advertised. [38]

Warning: Heaps of Energy Ahead Thanks to Energy Drinks

As many as 500 energy drinks were launched in peak years during the past decade, but innovator Red Bull commands 43% of the U.S. market, followed by 39% for Monster, according to Euromonitor. Pictured from left to right: Mother (Australia), Monster (Corona, Calif.), Red Bull (Austria) and V (New Zealand).

Coffee Startups Percolate

BLUE BOTTLE COFFEE

Venture capitalists are all in on the Time Compression Ubertrend. The first beneficiary was Oakland, Calif.-based Blue Bottle, which raised $20 million in October 2012. [1] Another Bay Area phenomenon, Philz Coffee, boosted its total to $75 million in September 2016. [2] In September 2017, Nestlé acquired a majority stake in Blue Bottle for $425 million. [3]

Wake up and smell the coffee.

1. Drew Olanoff, "Hipster Coffee Lovers Rejoice, Blue Bottle Coffee Raises $20M," *TechCrunch*, 15-Oct-12.
2. Salvador Rodriguez, "Philz CEO explains why a coffee chain needs venture capital," *Business Insider*, 14-Sep-16.
3. Matthew Lynley, "Nestlé acquires a majority stake in Blue Bottle Coffee at a valuation north of $700M," *TechCrunch*, 14-Sep-17.

Getting Your Wings

To help tackle jet lag during his travels to Thailand, Dietrich Mateschitz had come to rely on a Thai beverage, called Krating Daeng. After a long flight from Europe to Bangkok, Mateschitz would down the tonic over ice, which made his fatigue all but disappear. [39]

In 1982, Mateschitz, an Austrian, was working for German company Blendax. The boost he received from Krating Daeng, which means "red water buffalo" in Thai, made Mateschitz' curious about the Asian beverage market. Krating Daeng was a popular non-carbonated Thai drink, based on the Japanese energy drink Lipovitan, and South Korea's Bacchus-F, which were both introduced in Thailand earlier. Its ingredients included water, cane sugar, caffeine, taurine, inositol and vitamin B.

As luck would have it, a Blendax licensee in Thailand, Chaleo Yoovidhya, also owned a tonic drink company. Mateschitz proposed introducing Krating Daeng to the west and Yoovidhya agreed. In 1984, Mateschitz quit his job, and each partner invested $500,000 in the promising startup.

After tinkering with the original formula, including adding carbonation to the tonic, the new venture launched Red Bull in Austria in 1987. One of Mateschitz' friends came up with the slogan "Red Bull gives you wings." The

37. Paul Kelley, "Spaniards' lack of sleep isn't a cultural thing – they're in the wrong time zone," *The Guardian*, 22-Feb-17.
38. Paul Williams, "Why Starbucks Chose to Forego Traditional Advertising for So Long," *Observer*, 15-Oct-16.
39. Kerry Dolan, "The Soda With Buzz," *Forbes*, 28-Mar-05.

Four Loko: How a "Quick Buzz" Lead to a Ban on Alcoholic Energy Drinks

Getting a quick buzz was central to the marketing of Four Loko, a 23.5-ounce (695 ml) drink combining 12% alcohol by volume with 156 mg of caffeine, plus such energy-boosting amino acids as Taurine.[1] Created by Chicago-based Phusion Projects and popularly known as "blackout in a can," Four Loko ill-advisedly fell into the hands of teens and should-have-known-better adults, some of whom caused very serious or deadly accidents.

One high-profile case involved the 2010 death of 18-year-old Nicole Celestino, who drank one can of Four Loko and suffered cardiac arrhythmia and arrest, though her blood alcohol level was 0.05%, below the 0.08% legal limit.[2] At a press conference calling for a ban on Four Loko, Senator Charles Schumer noted that Celestino had also taken a diet pill that day, which often contain caffeine. Since the caffeine content of Four Loko is less than the 235 mg contained in a tall Starbucks coffee, Celestino may have had the equivalent of two cups of coffee, or less.[3]

Caffeine can mask the effects of alcohol, rendering drinkers unaware of how intoxicated they are. Minors, who are attracted by Four Loko's colorful packaging, are particularly susceptible to this effect due to their inexperience. As Celestino's grandmother put it, "They're calling it 'liquid cocaine,' that's how quick the effect is on the drinker."[4]

1. Gregory Conko, "Four Loko: Just How Potent is the Caffeinated Alcoholic Drink?," *Competitive Enterprise Institute*, 19-Nov-10.
2. Anthony Destefano, "State officials call for ban on Four Loko," *Newsday*, 10-Nov-10."
3. "Caffeine Chart," *Center for Science in the Public Interest*, ret. 29-Dec-18.
4. Marla Diamond, "Schumer Wants To Ban Four Loko," *WCBS 880*, 10-Nov-10.

slender silver and blue cans were another smart branding move.

Entrepreneurs are often armed with strong intuition. Mateschitz knew instinctively that a jet lag cure was just the tip of the iceberg in a society moving at warp speed. The ascent of Red Bull paralleled the growing popularity of electronic dance music (page 30), a Digital Lifestyle trend, an activity that requires a lot of energy.

Red Bull entered the U.S. market in 1997 and most likely played a role in helping fuel the "dotcom" boom. Vodka and Red Bull quickly became a bar and nightclub staple. Sometimes called a "speedball," the combination offered a depressant, vodka, to bring you down and a stimulant, Red Bull, to take you back up, much like its drug namesake, which combines heroin and cocaine.[40] It's popular among the 18-30 set, particularly the thirsty clubbing crowd, which pushes its energy boundaries nightly, seeking to pack in just one more frenetic experience.

The news media put a spotlight on deaths related to energy drinks, particularly when they are combined with alcohol (sidebar). That combination has been implicated in four deaths, three in Sweden and one in the U.S.[41] Yet adults have been mixing alcohol and coffee since at least 1930 when Kahlua was invented by a certain "Señor Blanco" in Mexico.[42] A further examination of unfortunate alcohol and caffeine incidents, however, shows a marked influence of preexisting heart or other health conditions.[43]

In a world that moves at warp speed, energy is of the utmost importance. The energy drink value proposition is compelling, especially for time-compressed millennials indulging in Generation X-tasy pursuits (page 115). People who consume caffeinated cocktails report feeling a "quick buzz." As one imbiber describes it, "It's the perfect drink because you get drunk, but you have a lot of energy."

It's that same kind of self-indulgent thinking that caused energy global drink sales to rocket 1,058% in the two decades since Red Bull arrived on the North American scene. Translated into dollars, the energy drink market grew from $3.8 billion in 1999 to $44 billion in 2015, according to Euromonitor International.[44][45] The market research firm forecasts that global energy drink sales will reach $61 billion by 2020, led by rapid growth in China.

As of 2014, the most recent year market share data is available, Red Bull owns an estimated 43% of the market worth $7.2 billion in 2017 annual sales to the Austrian trendsetter.[46]

That a company based in Fuschl am See, Austria should pioneer the field of energy drinks, borrowing techniques transferred from Japan to Thailand, demonstrates that the lessons of Time Compression are being absorbed quickly everywhere.

40. "What is a mix of Red Bull and vodka called?" *Quora*, 10-Jul-15.
41. "Red Bull and Alcohol Cocktails," *Mortal Journey*, 30-Aug-12.
42. Anita George, "A Brief History of Coffee and Booze," *Paste*, 17-Oct-13.
43. "Death By Red Bull," *Caffeine Informer*, 05-Feb-18.
44. Roberto Ferdman, "The American energy drink craze in two highly caffeinated charts," *Quartz*, 26-Mar-14.
45. Shane Starling, "The world's unquenchable thirst for energy drinks," *Beverage Daily*, 14-Jun-16.
46. "Monster Brings Plenty Of Energy To Red Bull Battle," *Investor's Business Daily*, 04-Dec-15.

Acceleration Of Dance

Time Compression

The acceleration of life began long before 1946. An excellent proxy for the speed of life is that most popular of social conventions, dancing. For it's through the speed of dance that one can see how life has accelerated over these past four centuries.

According to dance and music historian Curt Sachs, the period between 1650 and 1750 was known as "the age of minuet." [47] The minuet, the most popular dance among Europe's aristocracy during those years, is pointedly described as a "measured circling around." That measured approach was probably appropriate for people who enjoyed an average 17th-century lifespan of just 40 years. [48]

Life was languid because everything moved at a glacial pace. Around this period, the average person living in 17th century England read the equivalent of one daily issue of a *The New York Times* newspaper during their entire lifetime, reports noted author and designer Richard Saul Wurman in his book *Information Anxiety*. [49]

By the middle of the 18th century, the waltz had come into vogue, first in Germany, where it originated, then spreading to Austria and France. The German writer and statesman, Johann Wolfgang Goethe, gave the waltz a glowing review in his 1774 novel *Die Leiden des Jungen Werthers*: "Never have I moved so lightly. I was no longer a human being. To hold the most adorable creature in one's arms and fly around with her like the wind, so that everything around us fades away." As a smitten Goethe poetically

47. "Western Dance During The 17th, 18th, And 19th Centuries," *Encyclopedia Brittanica*, 09-Apr-14.
48. "Raising Children in the Early 17th Century: Demographics," *Plymouth Ancestors*, ret. 23-Jul-17.
49. Richard Saul Wurman, "Information Anxiety," *Bantam*, 01-Aug-90.

confirms with his description of "fly around," the waltz was indeed notably faster than the minuet.

The 20th century bought us modern western dance, like the Charleston, which featured a dramatic acceleration in pace. The Charleston was an expression of the unflappable "Roaring Twenties," an era in which people danced until they dropped at dance marathons and the automobile began its transformative ascent of the cultural landscape. [50] It was a time of contradictions and diversity, with Americans voting for Prohibition while imbibing copiously.

The Great Depression (1929-1932) brought that frivolity to an abrupt halt, at least temporarily. By the mid-1930s, however, prospects began to brighten again and, thanks to Cab Calloway, a new dance craze was born, the Jitterbug. [51] This fast dance features freewheeling acrobatic swings and lifts, which are performed to music with a time signature of 4/4, meaning it has four quarter-note beats.

Today most dance clubs move to the Digital Lifestyle beat of electronic dance music, a descendant of Kraftwerk's pioneering music of the early 1970s, which not only mirrors our rapidly morphing lifestyle but also echoes the influence of digital electronics in our daily lives.

Electronic Dance Music's antecedent was "Electronica," which evolved to include a broad range of electronic-based music styles but is usually misidentified with "techno" — a driving genre of electronic dance music featuring mechanical-sounding synthesizer melodies and a repetitive drum kick beat. Techno was born in Detroit during the early 1980s, which may explain its assembly line musical style.

Because electronica and techno were both hijacked by mainstream media, the U.S. dance music industry sought to undo this "negative" connotation and adopted a term that dates back to the 1980s, EDM, short for electronic dance music (page 30). EDM describes an "electro-house" hybrid that is played by such famous DJs as Calvin Harris and Skrillex. [52]

Never heard of electro house? Welcome to the club. EDM includes more music sub-categories than most people can name, including breakbeat, drum and bass, dub, electro, hardcore, house, industrial, jungle, trance, U.K. garage, plus the more laid-back ambient and chill. Add to this a bewildering array of genres, all created in about 40 years, and you can readily see Time Compression at work. The Wikipedia "list of electronic music genres" features no less than 23 major sub-categories and 214 genres (sidebar). [53] Granted, this tally includes electronic rock and hip-hop, but the vast array and subtle nuances of the burgeoning electronic music scene are simply startling.

As a society, we crave speed, and our music is starting to mirror that lust for velocity. At least now you know why dance music is so prevalent in health clubs and stores, it encourages you to exercise and shop faster.

A Roaring Twenties "Jitterbug"

The 1920s popularized a dance that was significantly faster than anything experienced before, the jitterbug.

IMAGE COURTESY: CORBIS CORP.

Speedcore

One dance music sub-category, hardcore, includes a genre dubbed "speedcore" — which is pushing the speed of dance to limits that defy human understanding. While some dance music can approach 180 beats per minute (BPM), speedcore pushes the boundaries of human dance endurance to 300 BPM. DJ en-Wout has a YouTube video that reaches 1,000 BPM. The rapid, machine-gunfire of beats that emanate from your speakers is something to be experienced. [1]

1. DJ en-Wout, "The Harmony of the Spheres [SPEEDCORE]," *YouTube*, 29-Feb-12.

50. Paula Becker, "Dance Marathons of the 1920s and 1930s," *HistoryLink.org*, 25-Aug-03.
51. "Jitterbug," *Wikipedia*, ret. 26-Jul-17.
52. Jimmy Blake, "Has EDM opened doors or slammed them shut in dance music?" *BBC*, 20-Jul-16.
53. "List of electronic music genres," *Wikipedia*, ret. 29-Dec-18.

Compression Formula

In April 1973, about five hundred miles from Federal Express' Memphis hub, two Motorola vice presidents, Marty Cooper and John Mitchell, were getting ready to leave for New York to show off a new type of phone, unlike anything ever seen before — the first "cellular phone."

In the 1970s, on-the-go people had to use pay phones to keep in touch. A few well-heeled individuals had car phones, which were 45-pound (20 kg), hardwired units that required a lot of space. Furthermore, each city could handle only about 800 subscribers on the available 32 channels, which were usually busy. During peak calling times, the chances of getting a connection were exceedingly slim. And when calls did get through, the limited amount of channels produced a lot of "crosstalk" interference, resulting in inferior call quality. Despite these service challenges, eager communicators faced mobile phone waiting lists of up to three years. [54]

Cooper and Mitchell were in the right place to demonstrate this new wireless "cellphone" technology because around that time there were just 600 mobile phone subscribers in New York with 3,500 on waiting lists. [55]

What Motorola had created was the first portable radiotelephone, later called the DynaTAC, which relied on an innovative technique of relaying messages between sender and base stations, using areas dubbed "cells," that handed each call off as mobile users traversed the boundaries.

As Cooper and Mitchell walked around Manhattan, even the usually blasé and sophisticated New Yorkers were amazed at the sight of people actually moving around while talking on a phone. The first cellphone call in history

54. "Improved Mobile Telephone Service," *Wikipedia*, ret. 05-Jan-19.
55. Brad Haines et. al., "Kismet Hacking," *Syngress Publishing*, 2008.

A Motorola Cellular Phone Prototype

Dr. Martin Cooper, pictured here, holds a replica of the Motorola cellular phone he used to make the first cellular call in 1973. The prototype weighed 2.4 pounds (1.1 kg) and took a full 10 hours to recharge while delivering "only" 30 minutes of talk time.

was placed on April 3, 1973 from the corner of Sixth Avenue, now Avenue of the Americas, between 53rd and 54th, with Cooper calling his rival, Bell Systems' Joel Engel, to tell him that the race to perfect cellular tech was over and that Motorola had won. [56]

It would be another decade before cellular service would be available to the general public. On October 13, 1983, Ameritech debuted the first U.S. cellular network in Chicago. [57] But the U.S. was not first. In 1979, Nippon Telegraph and Telephone (NTT) launched the first commercial automated cellular network in Japan. [58]

A parallel communication trend was the discovery of the fax machine. In 1966, America's largest copy machine manufacturer at the time, Xerox Corporation, launched the desktop-size, 46-pound (21 kg) Magnafax Telecopier 1, which took about six minutes to transmit a letter-size document, using an old-fashioned suction-cup modem. [59] The Magnafax was a revolution in a day and age when Western Union's Desk Fax service charged $4 to send a standard, letter-size page in the U.S. That's equal to about $30 in today's dollars.

Although fax had been invented much earlier, in 1843 to be exact, by Scottish clock and instrument maker Alexander Bain, it was Xerox that set the compression of business communication into motion. [60]

While it would take nearly two decades for fax machines to catch on, the Magnafax Telecopier helped popularize the technology, even making a cameo appearance in the 1968 movie *Bullitt*.

The fax machine would eventually give way to an even more disruptive communication technology, which would launch a scant three years later, the internet.

56. Curtis McCoy, "World's First Mobile Phone Call/World's First Cellphone," *Best Cellular*, 08-Jan-17.
57. "Ameritech Cellular," *Wikipedia*, ret. 29-Dec-18.
58. "History of mobile phones," *Wikipedia*, ret. 29-Dec-18.
59. Richard Baguley, "The Gadget We Miss: The Fax Machine," *Medium*, 04-Dec-13.
60. "Fax," *Wikipedia*, ret. 29-Dec-18.

The Internet

September 2, 1969, was a perfect summer day in Los Angeles, with temperatures hovering around 68 degrees. A military contractor, Bolt Beranek and Newman (BBN), now BBN Technology, a division of Raytheon, was putting the finishing touches on an Interface Message Processor at the University of California in L.A. [61]

The IMP, as it was known, was a key component for translating a brand-new communication protocol, called "packet switching," which was a key underpinning of a new computer network called ARPANET by the Advanced Research Projects Agency. Connecting UCLA to Stanford Research Institute on that September day launched the internet era, the greatest communication revolution in history. ARPANET later expanded to include the University of California at Santa Barbara and the University of Utah.

The defense industry's considerable contributions, including those of contributors to follow, would help make the acceleration of life arguably one of the world's most dominant Ubertrends. It was the internet that allowed Amazon.com to open its virtual doors in 1996 and take the idea of a virtual bookstore to lengths never imagined before.

It was the internet that gave Google *carte blanche* to establish its search engine technology as the dominant means of finding information. It was the internet that provided a ready platform for the "sharing economy," allowing Airbnb to revolutionize travel with its real estate optimization feats and Uber and Lyft to do the same for ride sharing. It was the internet that provided the ability for Facebook to connect 2.3 billion members into a social network that has upended the way we communicate today.

It's the internet that offers Amazon.com a realtime communication channel so its Echo speaker can show off its connected home tricks. It's the internet that will revolutionize financial transactions, if Bitcoin and, more importantly, blockchain, are any indication.

And on the horizon loom augmented and virtual reality, which are sure to completely reinvent the cyberworld's ability to entertain, inform and educate society, adding a whole new dimension to the Digital Lifestyle.

But more importantly, it's the internet that allows users to check the weather in realtime, check flight arrival times in realtime, check stocks in realtime, check our Facebook feeds in realtime. It's the ability to compress time that is the internet's most formidable asset. Flattening the time it takes to get a startup off the ground, helping homeowners sell their home instantly, allowing people to latch on to trends faster than ever before are just a few of the advances that lend Time Compression the powerful ability to reinvent and reshape in the blink of an eye.

Nothing will ever be the same again. Everything will move faster. At the heart of each quantum leap in the acceleration of communication — fax, Federal Express, cellphone and the internet — lies a decidedly opaque technology that is the actual driving force behind the acceleration of time: the codec.

> " Connecting UCLA to Stanford Research Institute on that September day, DARPA launched the internet era, the greatest communication revolution in history."
>
> **Michael Tchong**
> *Ubertrends*

---

61. Barry Leiner, Vincent Cerf et. al,, "Brief History of the Internet," *Internet Society*, 1997.

Eye of the Storm

Edwin Herbert Land died on March 1, 1991 in Cambridge, Mass. at the ripe old age of 82. During his lifetime, he was awarded the Medal of Freedom, the highest award given to a United States citizen, in recognition of his prolific output, which included 535 patents, a figure that places him third behind only Thomas Edison and one of Edison's associates. [62]

It's sad that Land was not able to witness the world-wide-web revolution and the emergence of realtime photography, both mainstreaming almost concurrently with the launch of the Mosaic browser in January 1993 and Apple's February 1994 debut of QuickTake — the second consumer digital camera. [63] [64] Later digital camera models would let users further compress the time it took to see photographic results, from Polaroid's approximately 1 minute to instantaneously. The internet did the same for communication by popularizing e-mail and chat groups.

Apple QuickTake 100

Launched on February 16, 1994, *Time* magazine included the QuickTake 100 in its list of "100 greatest and most influential gadgets." Manufactured by Kodak, the QuickTake 100 would ignite the digital camera revolution that would further compress time by allowing users to see images in realtime.

IMAGE COURTESY: APPLE INC.

But Land was most undoubtedly privy to the massive shift in consumer attitudes that emerged in the 1980s. It was during this decade that the inventions of the 1960s and 1970s would converge to uproot what was then a relatively relaxed lifestyle. The triumvirate of fax, Federal Express and cellphone was speeding up the process of business, while the growing use of voice mail was also transforming office culture.

As secretaries began to be replaced by "area associates," business executives suddenly realized that to get things done they could only flog themselves. That was a sea-change shift in the *modus operandi* of business. These evolutionary changes would provide fertile grounds for ushering in a whole new state of mind.

62. Ronald Fierstein, "How the Inventor of the Polaroid Championed the Patent," *The Atlantic*, 19-Feb-15.
63. "Mosaic (web browser)," *Wikipedia*, ret. 29-Dec-18.
64. "Apple QuickTake," *Wikipedia*, ret. 29-Dec-18.

Although Xerox was the first out of the gate with the Magnafax Telecopier, smaller, faster and more nimble fax machines entered the market in the 1980s, thanks to such Japanese stalwarts as Sharp. Between 1980 and 1990, the number of fax machines in the U.S. surged from 250,000 to 5 million, mainly due to the 1980 approval of the ITU Group 3 standard, which changed the fax standard from analog to digital and reduced transmission speed to one minute a page. [65]

A mathematical compression formula, or algorithm, was used to speed up fax transmissions. These algorithms were dubbed "codec," which was an abbreviation of COmpression/DECompression.

This arcane science would increasingly play a more significant role in society. We can thank compression algorithms for making such disruptive technologies as DVD, HDTV, satellite TV, internet telephony and DSL possible. The Digital Versatile Disc (DVD) used MPEG-2 compression, allowing a single-layer DVD to play movies over two hours long. [66] HDTV also uses MPEG-2. [67] The two major U.S. satellite TV providers, DirecTV and DISH Network, also used MPEG-2 but upgraded to MPEG-4 due to its improved compression algorithm, which was originally designed for streaming video. [68]

In February 1995, VocalTec released the first-ever Internet voice over IP (VoIP) application, Internet Phone, popularly known as "IPhone," according to *Wired*. [69] VocalTec offered Internet Phone users one of three compression algorithms: TrueSpeech, VSC (VocalTec's own algorithm) and GSM. [70]

DSL lines and dial-up modems also compressed data, using a variety of alphabet soup protocols, such as V.42bis and V.44.

This deep dive into the history of codecs is vitally important because codecs are in the eye of the Time Compression storm. By squeezing ever more data into ever smaller packages, codecs have enabled faster data transmission speeds, which, in turn, have accelerated the human experience.

The history of data compression dates back to the 1960s when work began on video conferencing systems at AT&T's Bell Laboratories. In the early 1980s, Karlheinz Brandenburg began working on digital music compression as a doctoral student at Germany's Erlangen-Nuremberg University.[71] In April 1989, the Fraunhofer Institute for Integrated Circuits of Fürth, Germany, which Brandenburg had joined, received a German patent for MP3 — an abbreviation of MPEG audio layer 3. [72] MP3 was the outcome of a collaboration between Brandenburg, working as a postdoctoral researcher at AT&T-Bell Labs with James Johnston, and Fraunhofer. On July 14, 1995, the Fraunhofer team chose ".mp3" as the official file name extension. [73]

IMAGE: FRAUNHOFER-GESELLSCHAFT ZUR FÖRDERUNG DER ANGEWANDTEN FORSCHUNG E.V.

Co-Inventor of the MP3 Codec: Karlheinz Brandenburg

Karlheinz Brandenburg began work on digital music compression in the early 1980s at Germany's Erlangen-Nuremberg University. Brandenburg later joined Fraunhofer Institute, which received a patent in 1989 for the later-renamed MP3 compression. He's generally regarded as the "father of MP3."

65. Jonathan Coopersmith, "Fax Machines," *Engineering and Technology History Wiki*, 09-Jan-15.
66. Nigel Chapman and Jenny Chapman, "Digital Multimedia, Chapter 2 – The Compact Disc," *Wiley*, ret. 29-Dec-18.
67. "HDTV (high definition television)," *TechTarget*, Apr-08.
68. Karim Nice and Tom Harris, "How Satellite TV Works," *HowStuffWorks*, 30-May-02.
69. Fred Hapgood, "IPhone," *Wired*, 01-Oct-95.
70. Kelly Ann Smith and Daniel Brushteyn, "Internet Telephony and Voice Compression," *Department of Computer and Information Science, University of Pennsylvania*, ret. 29-Dec-18.
71. "MP3," *Wikipedia*, ret. 29-Dec-18.
72. Mary Bellis, "The History of MP3," *ThoughtCo.*, 19-Apr-17.
73. "Fraunhofer IIS: Happy Birthday MP3!," *BusinessWire/ Fraunhofer Institute for Integrated Circuits IIS*, 12-Jul-05.

Brandenburg reportedly used a CD recording of Suzanne Vega's song *Tom's Diner* to refine the MP3 compression algorithm, which is why some call Vega "The Mother of MP3". [74] What makes the MP3 codec so outstanding is its pervasive cultural footprint. Propelled by such über-hot music swapping sites as Napster, MP3 became so popular that the search term outranked "sex" for a brief period in 1999, according to Nielsen/NetRatings. An unreal phenomenon, considering the codec's somewhat nerdy history. [75]

And if lifestyle changes take their cue directly from the ascent of codecs, one can only surmise from the ongoing reports of the development of ever-more-efficient compression algorithms that life will only speed up further in the future.

Advances in codecs help accelerate data transfer speeds, allowing for more rapid consumption of entertainment, a faster distillation of data, and more rapid processing of elaborate communication protocols.

Google has developed an open and royalty-free video encoding format, VP9, which is considered an equal to its competition — MPEG's High Efficiency Video Coding (HEVC or H.265). [76] H.265, which is used primarily for 4K content, is nearly twice as efficient as H.264, the Blu-ray standard. [77]

While this descent into technical minutiae may appear to be going overboard, the key point here is that compression/decompression algorithms play a crucial role in accelerating data delivery. As codecs become progressively more powerful, the H.265 codec is nearly 50% more efficient than the previous H.264 generation; one can quickly sense that as codecs become more powerful, so will the ability of humans to accomplish things much faster increase.

> ❝MP3 became so popular that the search term outranked 'sex' for a brief period in 1999."
>
> Michael Tchong
> *Ubertrends*

74. "Suzanne Vega: The Mother of the MP3?," *Music Facts - SuzanneVega.com*, 22-Jan-10.
75. Jennifer Sullivan, "More Popular Than Sex," *Wired*, 14-Oct-99.
76. Jan Ozer, "HEVC: Rating The Contenders," *StreamingLearningCenter.com*, ret. 29-Dec-18.
77. Joel Hruska, "H.265 benchmarked: Does the next-generation video codec live up to expectations?," *ExtremeTech*, 23-Jul-13.

Breedlove: A Time Compression Story

A real-life example of Time Compression was vividly recounted by film critic Hollis Frampton who wrote about the 1965 land speed record attempt by race car driver Craig Breedlove in his book *Circles of Confusion*. [1]

While traveling at 620 miles per hour, Breedlove's Spirit of America went out of control, sheared off a few telephone poles, sailed airborne upside down and landed in a salt pond. Miraculously, Breedlove was not hurt by the high-speed crash.

As Frampton recalls it: "He was interviewed immediately after

the wreck. I've heard the tape. It lasts an hour and 35 minutes, during which time Breedlove delivers a connected account of what he thought and did during a period of some 8.7 seconds.

His narrative amounts to about 9,500 words. Compared to the historic interval he refers to, his ecstatic utterance represents, according to my calculation, a temporal expansion in the ratio of some 655 to 1."

In other words, Breedlove provided a coherent account that lasted an hour and a half, while the entire crash sequence took just nine seconds.

That's an astonishing decompression ratio of 655 to 1, all made possible by traveling at an incredibly high speed. The Time Compression codec jumps to life.

1. Dean Kuipers, "The Need for Speed," *Wired*, 01-Oct-97.

And as the quality of data delivery improves due the use of AI and robotics, the quantitative leaps forward in all matters influenced by technology, i.e., social media, information analytics, entertainment consumption, health monitoring, will similarly allow for a greatly sped-up life.

An excellent example of how cross-disciplinary competition fosters speed is the case study of the fax vs. FedEx. Sensing that its core business might be swept away by a fax tidal wave, which made huge leaps forward in the early 1980s due to a much faster Group 3 codec, FedEx tried to hedge its bets in 1984 by introducing ZapMail, a centralized facsimile service. [78]

Telecommunications giant MCI banked its fortunes on e-mail, introducing MCI Mail in September 1983, which rode the internet wave well into the early 1990s while e-mail became the standard of business communication. [79] Like voicemail and fax, e-mail was a "store-and-forward" platform that made communicating with anyone particularly fast and efficient.

FedEx shut down ZapMail in 1986, after losing $340 million on its ill-fated experiment, which was plagued by technology issues. [80] MCI, meanwhile, lost its battle against the wide-open internet, officially decommissioning MCI Mail in June 2003. While fax machines continue to sell, more than 35 million were shipped worldwide in 2011 and 2012, according to Gartner, that's primarily due to fax being included in "all-in-one" devices. [81] Today, you rarely hear anyone asking for your fax number, unless they're a healthcare professional or lawyer.

78. "Zapmail," *Wikipedia*, ret. 29-Dec-18.
79. "MCI Mail, *Wikipedia*, ret. 29-Dec-18.
80. "FedEx Corporation," *Encyclopedia.com*, ret. 29-Dec-18.
81. Kat Ascharya, "Facing the Fax," *Time*, 21-Jun-13.

Fast Talking

In 1974, New York ad agency Ally & Gargano took on Federal Express when the company could only afford $150,000 on media advertising.

One evening in 1982, Patrick Kelly and Mike Tesch, Ally & Gargano's creative team for the Federal Express account, caught a per-  formance of "the world's fast-est-talking man" on an episode of ABC's *That's Incredible*. After an audition, which he passed with flying colors, John Moschitta was hired to star in Federal Express' TV commercials. The TV spots were directed by Joe Sedelmayer, a legendary TV producer who had gained a reputation for making funny commercials featuring quirky personalities and mini-malist settings, such as Clara Pel-ler's unforgettable "Where's the Beef?" campaign for Wendy's. Moschitta could rattle off 586 words per minute, fast enough for an entry in the Guinness Book of World Records. Although Moschitta no longer holds the record — that distinction now belongs to a host of other fast talkers — his machine-gun patter remains forever etched in the memories of many a viewer.

"Peter, you did a bang-up job. I'm putting you in charge of Pittsburgh, Peter. I know it's perfect, Peter; that's why I picked Pittsburgh. Pittsburgh's perfect, Peter. May I call you Pete? Dick, what's the deal with the deal? Are we dealing? We're dealing. Dave, it's a deal with Don, Dork and Dick. Dork, it's a deal with Don, Dave and Dick...gotta go, disconnecting..."

At the end of this fast-talking ex-change, according to *The Life and Career of Carl Ally*, a slow talker announces, "In this fast-moving, high-pressure, get-it-done-yes-terday world, aren't you glad there's a company that can keep up with it all?"

That voiceover was followed by the tagline: "When it absolute-ly, positively, has to be there overnight." Is it any wonder that FedEx, a $66 billion giant has become synonymous with the speed of business?

Speed Thrills

At 2:32 pm on Thursday, May 6, 2010, an automated algorithm trading system at the mutual fund investment firm of Waddell & Reed, based in Overland Park, Kan., issued a $4.1 billion sell order for Chicago Mercantile Exchange contracts known as "e-minis." [82] The bearish trade lasted 19 minutes and amounted to 9% of Standard & Poor's e-mini futures contract volume; the largest futures account tracking U.S. stock prices. [83]

After Waddell & Reed's trading stopped at 2:51 pm, the Dow Jones industrial average plunged a record-breaking 998.5 points, in what became known as the "Flash Crash." In under 20 minutes, some 2 billion shares worth $56 billion changed hands.

The Flash Crash erased $1 trillion in market value at a velocity never witnessed before and was caused, in part, by high-frequency traders. [84] Since the world's first stock exchange opened in 1602 in Amsterdam, investors have been on a never-ending quest to find more innovative ways of trading assets to generate profits. [85]

Computerized trading traces its roots to the 1980s when Merrill Lynch invested $30 million in the first computer system capable of using realtime market data to relay information and quote stock prices, a system designed and built by Bloomberg.

Bloomberg terminals and a late 1990s SEC ruling in favor of electronic stock exchanges formed the basis for high-frequency trading or HFT. These high-speed platforms rely on algorithms to analyze data ranging from news headlines to stock-price moves to interest rates and other market factors and can issue computer-assisted buy and sell orders at unprecedented speeds. Remember that 1969 micro-second-capable Seiko Quartz watch touched upon earlier? High-frequency trading is the continuation of that time-slicing trend.

As more high-frequency traders joined the party, high-frequency trading trades grew from 10% of all trades in the late 1990s to 49% by 2014. Assuming that 49% of all shares traded worldwide continue to be transacted via HFTs, the global dollar volume of high-frequency trading leaped from $3 trillion in 1999 to $38 trillion in 2017. [86]

That is a safe assumption given that Waddell & Reed used an algorithm provided by Barclays Capital, which *The New York Times* reports, is "one of many off-the-shelf programs available to investors these days." [87] And reports from Australia to Zambia have red-flagged the spiraling rise in high-frequency trading.

Increased competition has forced industry suppliers and their HFT speed junkies to hone their edge. Most celebrated was Spread Networks, which spent $300 million on a fiber-optic cable between Chicago and New Jersey

Southwest: A Case Study

Southwest Airlines has become an airline giant by operating on the wings of Time Compression. The Dallas-based carrier has an enviable record of 45 consecutive years of profit in a low-margin business. [1] That's due to its ability to turn planes around faster than most legacy carriers. It also helps that Southwest never charges bag fees and is known for its customer-centric "no change fee" philosophy. Until August 2018, they also served peanuts to live up to their "flying for peanuts" marketing tagline.

1. "Southwest Airlines Reports Record Fourth Quarter And Annual Profit; 45th Consecutive Year Of Profitability," *Southwest*, 25-Jan-18.

82. Jill Treanor, "The 2010 'flash crash': how it unfolded," *The Guardian*, 22-Apr-15.
83. Andrew Clark, "Single trader may have sparked Dow Jones 'flash crash'," *The Guardian*, 12-May-10.
84. Ben Rooney, "Waddell & Reed responds to 'flash crash' reports," *CNN Money*, 14-May-10.
85. Daniel Cross, "The Rise of High-Frequency Trading: A Brief History," *TraderHQ.com*, 01-Jul-15.
86. "Stocks traded, total value (current US$)," *The World Bank*, ret. 29-Dec-18.
87. Graham Bowley, "The New Speed of Money, Reshaping Markets," *The New York Times*, 01-Jan-11.

Zara: Moving Even Faster in the Fast-Fashion Lane

Harvard Business Review reports that Zara's designers create approximately 40,000 new designs each year, of which 10,000 are actually produced. Its "fast fashion" inventory system handles around 300,000 new stock-keeping units (SKUs or inventory items) annually, on average.

> **The U.S. stock market, the most iconic market in global capitalism, is rigged."**
>
> **Michael Lewis**
> *Flash Boys*

to connect Chicago futures traders with New York exchanges a whole three milliseconds faster. [88]

Latency, meaning the length of delay, has become a big market buzzword. Nasdaq once boasted of an average order "round-trip" latency of 98 microseconds, or 98 millionths of a second. [89] Keep in mind that there are 1,000 microseconds in one millisecond, and an eye blinks lasts a mere 300-400 milliseconds. Some trading platforms already claim round-trip latencies of just 16 microseconds, making Nasdaq sound positively slow. [90]

The odds of "high latency trading" are stacked against you, which was the subject of *Flash Boys* — a 2014 book by Michael Lewis. The author summarized his take on *60 Minutes* in no uncertain terms, "The United States stock market, the most iconic market in global capitalism, is rigged."

Stock trading is not the only market to benefit from Time Compression. Retailers H&M, Mango and Zara, have scored notable successes with "fast fashion," a retail supply chain system that, in Zara's case, turns inventory six times faster than the typical U.S. clothing chain. In 2006, *Bloomberg Businessweek* reported that Zara's successful implementation of fast fashion had already vaulted it ahead of fast-fashion pioneer H&M before most apparel shoppers were even aware of what Zara was.

By compressing time, Zara Founder Amancio Ortega has become the sixth richest person in the world with a net worth of more than $70 billion. [91] You may well be asking: "Amancio who?"

Another vivid example of the competitive advantage Time Compression offers is Southwest Airlines, which has been able to generate a profit in a marginal business for 45 consecutive years. Its success formula: The ability to turn planes around faster than anyone else ("Southwest," page 169). [92]

88. Christopher Steiner, "Wall Street's Speed War," *Forbes*, 09-Sep-10.
89. Graham Bowley, "The New Speed of Money, Reshaping Markets," *The New York Times*, 01-Jan-11.
90. "ALGO Technologies Unveils Fastest-Ever Exchange/MTF Matching Engine," *Presswire*, 19-Apr-10.
91. "The World's Billionnaires," *Wikipedia*, ret. 12-Dec-18.
92. "Southwest Airlines Reports Record Fourth Quarter And Annual Profit," *Southwest Airlines*, 25-Jan-18.

SST Slow Lane

In 1971, U.S. Congress halted federal funding for a next-generation supersonic transport, called the SST. [1] It was one the most short-sighted acts ever perpetrated in the name of the American public.

The move would hold the entire aviation industry back for nearly half a century. Since then, commercial airlines have been stuck cruising at 460-575 mph, despite Chuck Yeager breaking the sound barrier way back in 1947.

The privileged few did get to briefly fly the Concorde, which used 1960s Rolls-Royce turbojet technology. The resulting earth-shattering take-off noise, loud sonic booms and high fuel consumption doomed it as a commercially viable solution. Now, 48 years later, a glimmer of hope for faster air transportation is due to arrive thanks to Reno, Nev.-based Aerion Supersonic. Texas billionaire Robert Bass is an early supporter and chairman of the company. The eight-passenger Aerion AS2 promises to deliver a top speed of Mach 1.4 (924 mph; 1,487 kph) and was promoted with the trademarked tagline, "Boomless Cruise." [2]

In 2014, Aerion announced a strategic partnership with Airbus. That relationship was usurped by Lockheed Martin, which announced in December 2017 that it was partnering with Aerion to assist in the development of its Supersonic Business Jet (SSBJ), a project that had been in the works for 15 years. [3]

As envisioned, the $120 million AS2 will allow a crew and 12 passengers to fly faster than the speed of sound. Overland, the Aerion will lower its speed to Mach 1.2 (792 mph; 1,275 kph) to prevent sonic booms from reaching the ground, thus enabling the AS2 to venture over fly-over states free from traditional noise restrictions that would otherwise prevent supersonic jets from passing overhead.

It's good to see that we can finally compress time despite past congressional blunders.

1. "Why the SST Took A Nosedive," *The Washington Post*, 21-Jul-82.
2. Larry Bean, "Aerion Is Bringing Supersonic Flight Back . . . And This Time It's Private," *Robb Report*, 31-Jul-18.
3. Jay Bennet, "Lockheed Martin Joins Aerion to Build Supersonic Business Jet," *Popular Mechanics*, 18-Dec-17.

A New State Of Mind

The communication revolutions of the 1980s, fax, FedEx, personal computers, e-mail and voicemail, brought our global village closer together but also lead the way to a whole new work ethic, one that produced one particularly striking change in attitude.

> "Sometime around the end of the 1980s decade, a new response emerged: "Busy." The state of mind had become a state of time."
>
> Michael Tchong
> *Ubertrends*

Around the beginning of the 1980s, most people would answer "good" or "fine" when asked, "how are you?" Then the marketing department woke up in all of us, and the popular hyperbole "great" caught on. Sometime during the 1980s decade, a new response emerged, "busy." The state of mind had become a state of time.

By 1996, a WSJ/NBC News study reported that 59% of Americans polled described themselves as busy, with 19% saying they were "painfully busy."

No precise year can be pinpointed as to when this mental switch was flipped but the go-go days of the 1980s, during which the personal computer became the *de facto* productivity tool, apparently contributed to it. That new workflow included happily receiving faxes and FedEx packages, while attentively listening to voicemail and raving about the wonders of e-mail.

Between the years of 1975 and 2004, middle-income couples with children increased their annual work output by 770 hours, equal to nearly five months of full-time work. [93] More women joining the labor force partly propelled this trend. Another factor that led to longer hours was more work following people home. At least 10 million Americans with college degrees now spend an average of three hours each week on work brought home from the office.

---

93. Alex Williams, "Pencil It In Under 'Not Happening'," *The New York Times*, 18-Jun-06.

Since 1973, the median number of hours U.S. adults say they work, including housekeeping and studying, has risen from 41 hours per week to 46, according to Harris Interactive. [94] Leisure time, meanwhile, dropped from 26 to 16 hours per week over the same period.

And now that car-sharing services such as Lyft and Uber have made getting a second job relatively easy, 44 million Americans report having a second job, according to personal finance site Bankrate.com. [95]

Modern-day pressures have lengthened the workday worldwide. *The Telegraph* reports that nearly half of all U.K. workers are too busy to leave their desks for lunch. [96] Like the U.S., U.K. business lunches have been disappearing since the 1980s. The high pressure of Time Compression is evident from the 34% of those who do manage to get out for a client lunch and readily admit they "race through the meal," spending an hour or less.

This attitude shift has ushered in another fascinating change. We used to look forward to lunch; now we're happy when someone cancels lunch. No sweeter words are heard in the office today than, "Can we reschedule?" Thank you, thank you, for giving me back a time slice of my day! That is a significant value change — all due to Time Compression.

And lunch is not the only victim. Vacations have also taken a backseat in this new work ethic. On average, U.S. employees only took half, or 54%, of their paid vacation days in the past 12 months, reports Glassdoor. [97] That was up from 42% in 2013, according to a similar study, the U.S. Travel Association's Project Time Off. The biggest reason for not taking all their vacation days? The fear of falling behind on their job, mentioned by 34%.

And when they do go on vacation, 42% of employees say they feel obligated to check their e-mail. [98] Worse, 26% feel guilty using all of their vacation time.

And why should vacations be exempt from checking e-mail? After all, 68% of employed American adults with work e-mail accounts check their messages during such traditional family holidays as Thanksgiving and Christmas. And among those who check their e-mail, 27% do so multiple times each day. [99]

Vacation guilt has lead to another trend, hybrid travel, the practice of "multitasking" vacations — combining a business trip with a vacation, sometimes jokingly referred to as "bleisure." As many as 60% of travelers report having extended a business trip for personal reasons. [100] The blending of business and leisure trips is the result of the blurring of work and life due to our always connected world.

Karōshi, the Japanese phenomenon of working yourself to death was thought to be uniquely part of the culture of the Rising Sun. Not anymore, it looks like the rest of the world is catching up, quick.[101]

TBD: Too Busy Disorder

In a classic skit from Ellen Desgeneres' HBO special, *Here and Now*, which aired on Saturday, June 28, 2003, the comedian delivers a humorous take on a new societal disease: TBD — Too Busy Disorder. In the skit, Ellen remarks that "I believe that someday sitcoms will be 30 seconds long. Because that's all we'll need, that's all our attention span can take, because our attention span is shot. We all got attention deficit disorder, ADD or OCD or one of those disorders with three letters because we don't have the time and patience to pronounce the entire disorder. That should be a disorder right there, TBD, Too Busy Disorder!" That was just one of many sharp takes on modern life Ellen delivered during her comedy show.

94. "Americans today have less free time, study says," *Public Relations Society of America*, 08-Dec-08.
95. Selena Maranjian, "44 Million Americans Are Doing a Side Hustle – and Maybe You Should, Too," *The Motley Fool*, 22-Jul-17.
96. Sam Dean, "The death of the boozy business lunch: British workers are too busy to leave their desks," *The Telegraph*, 02-Jun-16.
97. Quentin Fottrell, "The sad reason half of Americans don't take all their paid vacation," *MarketWatch*, 28-May-17.
98. Kathryn Dill, "You're Probably Checking Your Work Email On Vacation--But You Shouldn't Be, Study Shows," *Forbes*, 17-Jun-14.
99. Zoe Fox, "Shocker: Most Americans Check Work Email During Holidays," *Mashable*, 28-Nov-11.
100. Ronald Hobson, Catalin Ciobanu, "How Many People Really Combine Work Trips with Vacation?," *Harvard Business Review*, 16-Sep-16.
101. Karōshi, *Wikipedia*, ret. 29-Dec-18.

No Time for Leisure

Longer work hours and less leisure time have had a big impact on all types of activities. In 2007, *Newsweek* writer Steve Tuttle launched into an article with this punch line, "If you're a squirrel or a trout, we've got some good news for you: Americans are hunting and fishing less." The story covered an outdoor recreation study conducted every five years by the U.S. Fish and Wildlife Service. According to Tuttle, the 2006 survey revealed ominous trends: the number of anglers had dropped 12% since 2001, while the number hunters had fallen by 4% during the same five-year period.[102]

Compared to the first U.S. Fish and Wildlife Service study conducted in 1991, the latest available 2011 survey shows an even more pronounced trend. [103] Over those two decades, the number of anglers dropped by 7%, and the number of hunters fell by 3%. Why is that more significant when the percentage declines are actually lower? That's due to the U.S. population surging from 253 million in 1991 to 312 million by 2011. [104] So, while there was a 23% increase in the talent pool, both hunting and fishing showed a notable decline during that time period.

The same is true for that leisurely game of golf. In its peak year of 2005, some 30 million people played golf. That number was down to 24.7 million in 2014, or 17%, while the U.S. population rose 8% over the same period. [105] The vanishing golfer is part of a broader decline in all outdoor activities — including tennis, swimming, hiking, biking and downhill skiing — all staggering after the 1-2 punch thrown by the Digital Lifestyle, primarily due to the use of social media, and Time Compression.

The lack of time for work or leisure has also affected cooking. In 2014, 60% of dinners eaten at home were home cooked, down from 75% in 1984. [106] With time so precious, prepared foods have cooked up a $26 billion market. [107]

One of the most successful new product introductions in Campbell Soup history was the launch of Soup At Hand, which featured Starbucks-like packaging and "sippable soup" positioning — optimized for a grab-and-go culture. [108] It was a timely launch. According to the 2002 NPD Group National Eating Trends study, 59% of all U.S. meals are rushed, and 34% of lunches are eaten on the run, a trend that drives the $210 billion U.S. fast-food business. In the U.K., an average adult spends just 23 minutes daily eating breakfast, lunch *and* dinner. [109] The Brits, like everyone else, are living an "eat and run" lifestyle.

Last-Minute Culture

Even America's favorite attitude adjustment, retail therapy, has fallen under the yoke of Time Compression. As early as 2002, the International

Campbell's Soup on the Go

Campbell's Soup At Hand, now rebranded to more closely align itself with the Time Compression phenomenon, was the most successful product launch in company history, proving that innovations that leverage Ubertrends can significantly contribute to the bottom line.

IMAGE COURTESY: CAMPBELL'S SOUP COMPANY.

102. Steve Tuttle, "Fewer Americans Are Hunting and Fishing," *Newsweek*, 15-Jun-07.
103. "Wildlife & Sport Fish Restoration Program," *U.S. Fish and Wildlife Service*, 01-May-15.
104. "Population, Total for United States," *FRED Federal Reserve Bank of St. Louis*, ret. 15-Aug-17.
105. Mike Stachura, "Number of golfers steady, more beginners coming from millennials," *Golf Digest*, 30-Apr-15.
106. Roberto Ferdman, "The slow death of the home-cooked meal," *The Washington Post*, 05-Mar-15.
107. Phil Lempert, "Prepared trends will outpace foodservice, packaged foods growth," *SupermarketGuru.com*, 13-May-14.
108. "Campbell Launches Major New Convenience Platform For Soup," *Campbell Soup Company*, 18-Feb-03.
109. Sara Malm, "Britain's minute meals: The average adult only spends 23 minutes a day eating breakfast, lunch and dinner," *Daily Mail*, 09-Jun-13.

Council of Shopping Centers reported that browsing by mall shoppers was down to 23%, compared to 37% in 2000. That was an early distant warning for future retail turbulence to come.

Bloomberg Businessweek provided another perspective on the future of retailing in a May 9, 2005 article: "What's hurting many malls is the new economic calculus of shopping. Suppose it takes a total of an hour to drive to an old-style mall, park, find your way to your intended store, and drive home. The value of that hour, as economists reckon it, is about equal to your average hourly pay — about $30 per hour for managers and professionals. Since that $30 would probably cover shipping charges for a large online order, it becomes harder to justify the shopping trip." [110] In other words, your time is too valuable to waste on shopping.

Yankelovich took that notion one step further with its December 2006 assessment that time is more valuable than money: "More than half (56%) of all consumers, at all income levels, say that a lack of time is a bigger problem for them than a lack of money," reported *USA Today*. [111]

Time-strapped shoppers have unsurprisingly become reliant on time-saving shortcuts. According to CEB TowerGroup, consumers are spending big on retail gift cards and certificates, which are expected to reach $160 billion in 2018, up from just $19 billion in 1999. [112]

The convenience of ordering from home and the benefits of two-day shipping have made saving time a recurring theme among online shoppers. Ditto for shopping in physical stores, "I need something to wear now."

What consumers want to wear is increasingly influenced by the Digital Lifestyle Ubertrend. Blogs, Instagram and other social media allows people to instantly gauge the coolest runway fashions, making shoppers harder to please. That obsession with the latest and greatest has fueled the success of such fast-fashion retailers as Forever 21, H&M and Zara. But it has also become the death knell for traditional retailers, such as Bebe and The Limited, which couldn't produce the newest must-haves fast enough.

That "must have the latest" mindset, combined with booming, instant gratification services like FedEx and a more recent, and faster, phenomenon, same-day delivery, has contributed to a last-minute mentality.

Everyone now waits until the very last possible moment, whether it's shopping, booking travel or buying a conference ticket. The International Council of Shopping Centers reports that 76% of adult shoppers say they plan on making holiday purchases right up until Christmas. [113] On December 22, 2004, a holiday shopper proclaimed to KNTV, NBC's San Jose, Calif. television station, that "Shopping three days before Christmas is not late, it's early!"

That same year, then Toys R Us CEO, John Eyler, observed, "Christmas shopping has come later every year for the past 20 years. Pretty soon we'll have a two-day shopping window." With more people waiting until the last possible minute to shop, stores opening on Christmas Day could one day be a reality, judging by Black Friday sales on Thanksgiving. The

---

110. Joseph Weber, Ann Therese Palmer, "How The Net Is Remaking The Mall," *Bloomberg Businessweek*, 08-May-05.
111. Laura Petrecca, "Stores, banks go speedy to win harried customers," *USA Today*, 01-Dec-06.
112. Alina Comoreanu, Gift Card Market Size, *WalletHub*, ret. 12-Dec-18..
113. Kit Yarrow, "The Simple Reason You Wait Until the Last Minute to Do Your Christmas Shopping," *Money*, 19-Dec-16.

now-defunct Tower Records chain debuted in San Francisco with "Open Nine to Midnight 365 Days A Year" as a key selling point in April 1968. [114]

Some may consider shopping during a family holiday offensive, but on Christmas Day 2016, Amazon.com's total share of online sales shot up from an average of 38% to 46%, pointing to the success of its Prime Now two-hour delivery service. That service promise is influencing the buying habits of procrastinating shoppers. [115]

Last-minute plans have impacted leisure travel. People used to take months to plan a vacation. Now it's often a snap decision: 64% of U.S. leisure travelers plan at least one of their vacation trips within two weeks before taking that trip, according to the Travel Industry Association of America.

The stock market is headed in the same direction. More than 18% of S&P 500 stock trades in 2014 took place between 3:30 and the 4 pm closing bell, according to Credit Suisse Trading Strategist Ana Avramovic, up from 13% in 2007. [116] For shares of smaller companies, 19% of trades were in the final 30 minutes, up from 14% in 2007. The U.S. stock market is now relatively quiet during the middle of the day due to the growing use of index funds, which generally prefer to trade at the close, and computer algorithms, which are programmatically searching for the best possible trading times. The final five minutes have turned into a stampede, accounting for 6% of all volume in 2014, a figure that has risen each year since 2010, according to Trade Informatics.

Much like shoppers, who have been trained by their digital tools to wait until the last moment to buy, so too have Wall Street traders become reliant on the last-minute syndrome to sniff out the best deals.

Blips of Imagery

That's so 70s...so 1995...so last year...so last week...so yesterday. It's abundantly clear that the meaning of time is rapidly morphing, left behind in a cloud of time-tunnel dust. A timely example of the Time Compression experience is that well-worn business cliché, "I want it yesterday!"

The 1980s saw the rapid rise of personal computing and computer chips; both markets whipped into a froth by "Moore's Law" — the observation by Intel Co-Founder Gordon Moore that the number of transistors per square inch of integrated circuit chips was doubling every 18 months. [117] Technology is Time Compression's central force, so the impact of this Ubertrend on its own industry is nothing short of breathtaking. By creating ever shorter design and manufacturing cycles, the technology industry ushered in fleeting product half-lives for anything deserving notice in an attention deficit society.

Predictably, "18 months" has become a business forecasting cliché, often warping marketplaces in the process, as exemplified by the heady

114. Joel Selvin, "For S.F. rockers, Tower Records was where it was all happening – now the party's over," *S.F. Gate*, 19-Oct-06.
115. Elizabeth Weise, "Amazon grabbed half of last-minute, online Christmas shoppers," *USA Today*, 06-Jan-17.
116. Dan Strumpf, "Stock-Market Traders Pile In at the Close," *The Wall Street Journal*, 27-May-15.
117. "Moore's Law," *Wikipedia*, ret. 30-Dec-18.

Life Has Become a Blur

This cartoon by Donald Reilly appeared in the November 25, 1996 issue of *The New Yorker*. Its message remains presciently clear: Phenomena appear and disappear faster than ever before, as society is being consumed by the Time Compression "cycle."

"And step on it. This restaurant may be over any minute."

IMAGE COURTESY: THE NEW YORKER COLLECTION DONALD REILLY, VIA CARTOONBANK.

> " Bowing to the demands of the American people, U.S. officials sped up instant gratification yesterday, making wish fulfillment more immediate than ever before."
>
> *The Onion*
> 11-Sep-96

dotcom boom days, when every product development forecast or life cycle was predicted to take or last 18 months. Rapid development cycles are now standard procedure, with "sprints" a key element of that process. Technology businesses start up, and disappear, faster than ever before.

CB Insights reports that startups typically close their doors about 20 months after their last financing round and after having raised an average of $1.3 million. [118] Notice how close that answer is to 18 months in this self-reported study. The social media frenzy, not surprisingly, produced the largest of number of startup failures.

Gradually, the Time Compression cycle began to extend its tentacles beyond technology, by first speeding up business and then society (cartoon). Not that people hadn't already experimented with compressing their time schedules before. The emergence of amphetamines, presciently labeled "speed," and the spectacular growth of Starbucks and the energy drink category are testaments to this trend.

Polaroid may have revolutionized the photography market, but quality- and cost-wise, it ended up lagging behind film-based cameras. As noted before, Kodak once reported that 80 billion photos were taken in 2000. [119] Film processing, however, was slow. This August 3, 2003 quote from Albany, N.Y.'s *The Times Union* is revealing: "One-Hour Photo? Takes too long. Digital is instant. Minute Rice? Who has the time? You can buy a pre-made pilaf at the grocery store on the way home from work. Instant tea? Why, when you can buy it in a bottle?"

The rat race's insatiable demand to speed up life is the subject of much humor, as this "news item" from *The Onion* humorously illustrates, "Bowing to the demands of the American people, U.S. officials sped up instant gratification yesterday, making wish fulfillment more immediate than ever before." Continues *The Onion*'s right-on report, "...from now on,

---

118. "The R.I.P. Report – Startup Death Trends," *CB Insights*, 18-Jan-14.
119. Stephen Heyman, "Photos, Photos Everywhere," *The New York Times*, 29-Jul-15.

gratification will actually be faster than instantaneous, occurring some .002 milliseconds before desire is even felt." [120]

Today's television viewer has little time to devote to news, which has made caption writing an art. Fox News anchor Shepard Smith does not like verbs. Whenever he finds one, he deletes the offending word or adds "ing," turning the verb into a participle and his script into a strange shorthand that passes for English on cable news, writes Warren Saint John in a story called *News Reports for Ultra-Short Attentions*. [121] The results end up sounding like little blurbs of bad grammar, such as "Amazon.com celebrating a birthday! The Internet company 10 years old."

Explains Smith, "We don't communicate in full sentences anyway. We don't need all those words. And it allows us to go faster."

Movie and television dialogue has accelerated too. Older movies and TV shows seem downright plodding compared to, say, an episode of Aaron Sorkin's, *The West Wing*, which was widely regarded as one fastest talking shows on television. Many thought its whip-fast chatter was almost impossible to follow. [122]

Attention Deficit Disorder

In a hyper-change world where a multitude of media, websites, social media posts, plus an avalanche of ads for tens of thousands of new products each year all beg for a sliver of your time, the most besieged part of our mind is the attention span.

The best evidence of how impatient we have become was provided by the former CEO of Akamai Technologies, Paul Sagan, who at a November 2006 Adtech industry confab noted that 75% of 1,058 people surveyed by Jupiter Research would not return to a site that took longer than four seconds to load. [123] That figure was down significantly from the seven or eight seconds mentioned just five years earlier in 2001, according to Sagan.

While many officially link this affliction to the attention deficit disorder disease (ADD), it should be noted that ADD, a neurodevelopmental type of mental disorder, was redefined as ADHD, or Attention Deficit Hyperactivity Disorder, in 1987. [124] So, perhaps society's incorrect application of "ADD" has come full circle and we can now safely label our short attention spans as suffering from ADD.

Another fascinating insight into our ADD culture was uncovered by Google while testing how many search results to optimally display on a page. The findings, presented by then Google Vice President, Marissa Mayer, at Web 2.0 in November 2006, revealed that in Google's study pages with 10 results took 0.4 seconds to load, while one with 20 results took 0.9 seconds to load. That half-a-second delay in page loading caused search traffic to drop 20% — half a second. [125]

That half-a-second attention span aligns with a study by researchers at

120. "Instant Gratification Sped Up," *The Onion*, 11-Sep-96.
121. Warren Saint John, "News Reports for Ultra-Short Attentions," *The New York Times*, 28-Mar-04.
122. D.L. Stewart, "'West Wing' dialogue is too racy," *Dayton Daily News*, 18-Oct-02.
123. "Websites face four-second cut-off," *BBC News*, 09-Nov-06.
124. "Attention deficit hyperactivity disorder," *Wikipedia*, ret. 19-Aug-17.
125. Greg Linden, "Marissa Mayer at Web 2.0," *Geeking with Greg*, 09-Nov-06.

Carleton University in Ottawa, which reported that people are registering likes and dislikes of websites in as little as one-twentieth of a second. [126] Psychologist Gitte Lindgaard, who led the study, tells *The Wall Street Journal*, "We are hard-wired to make up our minds very quickly."

A growing lack of patience is to blame for the decline in the use of voicemail. That 1980s revolution, which began an upheaval in the office, displacing secretaries, is fading away quickly. The number of voicemail messages left on Vonage user accounts was down 8% in July 2012 from a year earlier. [127] And checking voicemail is now an even a bigger chore than leaving one, with voicemail retrieval falling an even steeper 14% over the same period.

The trend is accelerating. In its latest study, Vonage voicemails left and checked declined an even steeper 8% in *six months*. [128] In June 2015, JPMorgan Chase & Co. announced that it was cutting off voicemail for 136,000 consumer banking employees, saving the company $16 million a

126. Jeffrey Zaslow, "First Impressions Get Faster," *The Wall Street Journal*, 16-Feb-06.
127. Roger Yu, "Voice mail in decline with rise of text, loss of patience," *USA Today*, 03-Sep-12.
128. Shane Dingman, "'Press 7 to delete': The decline of voice mail," *The Globe and Mail*, 07-Jun-15.

Speeding Up Media

Evidence that we don't have the patience for slow-moving words has surfaced in audiobooks and media. The need for speed has spawned a new generation of audiobook and podcast "speed-listeners."

Wired reports that nearly 10% of Audible audiobook listeners listen at speeds greater than 1x, equal to hundreds of thousands of book fans. [1] More than half of Overcast podcast app users use its Smart Speed setting, which eliminates moments of silence. For some, that's not enough. Max Deutsch tells *The Wall Street Journal* that he couldn't find any apps with speeds of more than 3x, so he created his own $2.99 app, Rightspeed, which accelerates podcasts in barely noticeable 0.1x increments every two minutes, using a feature called "Automatic Speed Ramping." [2] A typical one-hour podcast that starts at 2x ends at 5x and takes just 17 minutes.

Scientists say that people can

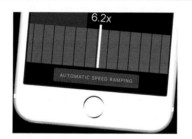

understand speech at speeds of up to 400 words per minute and, sometimes, beyond. That's about three times the pace of ordinary speech, which falls somewhere between 140 and 180 words per minute. [3] People who listen at 3x have gotten used to it — their brain adjusted to higher speeds over time, much like human beings adapted to a faster movie and television dialogue over a period of many decades.

The process of listening more intently to fast-spoken words makes you more likely to retain content, which is a benefit we have already gleaned from all those Evelyn Wood Reading Dynamics ads. It's a Digital Lifestyle approach to book consumption: downloading information as quickly as possible.

Joggers say that faster listening speeds make them feel like they're running faster. Does that sound familiar?

It's the same subconscious tactic mentioned in "Acceleration of Dance" (page 160). Stores and health clubs tend to use background dance music to speed up shopping and gym exercises, or at least make people feel like they're accomplishing more.

The get things done faster trend has spread beyond audiobooks and podcasts.

In 2015, TiVo introduced a "Quick Mode" feature that speeds up television recordings by 30% without sounding funny.

In case you missed it, YouTube offers a similar feature when playing back any video. Just click "Settings" and choose either 1.25x or a faster 1.5x speed. Going faster is what we like.

1. Clive Thompson, "If You Want to Learn Faster, Overclock Your Audio and Video," *Wired*, 17-Feb-17.
2. Ben Cohen, "How Do Podcast Nuts Find the Time? They Listen at Chipmunk Speed," *The Wall Street Journal*, 13-Jul-17.
3. Douglas Heingartner, "Now Hear This Quickly," *The New York Times*, 02-Oct-03.

year. [129] "We realize that hardly anyone uses voicemail anymore," banking arm CEO Gordon Smith was quoted as saying. E-mail, text messaging and social media have made voicemail a redundant tool. New voicemail transcription services that convert voice messages for delivery as e-mail or text are stanching the loss, for now.

But the most modern manifestation of this trend is the use of the symbol TL;DR, which stands for "Too Long, Didn't Read." While it's often used on Reddit and other online communities to indicate a summary of the text, it's increasingly being used to let people know that something is just too long to read. Notice the use of a smiley in the middle of TL;DR. It could serve to appease the recipient because the message is somewhat offensive.

Then again, in 2015 college-bound seniors scored a record low of 495 in the "critical reading" portion of the SAT. Ditto for SAT writing test scores, which hit a low point in 2015, declining 13 points since first being administered in 2006. Could TL;DR article compression help a reading deficient generation improve their comprehension? [130] Only time will tell, but any shortcut in this age and age is a big plus.

Time Compression has even rewritten the rules of our love life, judging by the growth of online dating and speed dating. According to Pew, 15% of U.S. adults report they have used online dating sites or mobile dating apps. [131] The fastest growing age groups were 18-24 and 55-64, with the former group tripling their use between 2013 and 2015, and the latter doubling in the same period.

The popularity of apps like Tinder, which lets users swipe right on profiles of people they want to sleep with, is perhaps the most extreme example of Time Compression in the modern love era. "It's instant gratification," 26-year-old Brooklyn photographer, Jason, tells Vanity Fair when asked to comment on the Tinder "dating" app. [132]

It may not exactly be progress, but we must face the music of our tech- and time-obsessed lives. Speaking about music, the first performances of *Der Ring des Nibelungen*, Wagner's Ring cycle, took an average of 14 hours and 20 minutes from 1876 to 1950. After 1960, the tempo increased, and it took about 14 hours. The last complete performance, in 1998, conducted by Hartmut Haenchen, took 13 hours and 30 minutes, nearly one hour less.

Even that most sacred of music institutions, the opera, is being tinkered with in the name of Time Compression. In a move decried by traditionalists, San Francisco Opera cut roughly half an hour from *Carmen*, to keep from turning off "time-pressed modern audiences." [133] With operas routinely lasting three or four hours, the now-retired San Francisco Opera General Director David Gockley tells *The New York Times*, "I don't think we can any longer fail to hear what our audience is saying about length."

If you do plan to attend a lengthy opera in some far-away U.S. city, don't expect to be soaking in a hotel bathtub much longer. In deference to hotel guests who are too busy for a long soak, hotels are foregoing the tub in favor of more time-efficient showers.

129. Robert Hackett, "This Massive Bank Just Killed Voicemail," *Fortune*, 02-Jun-15.
130. "Performance on SAT Verbal/Critical Reading and Writing Exams," *Humanities Indicators*, Sep-16.
131. Aaron Smith, "5 facts about online dating," *Pew Research*, 29-Feb-16.
132. Nancy Jo Sales, "Tinder and the Dawn of the 'Dating Apocalypse'," *Vanity Fair*, Sep-15.
133. Michael Cooper, "Could You Shorten That Aria? Opera Weighs Cuts in the Classics," *The New York Times*, 06-Jul-16.

Paris' Trottoir Roulant Très Rapide

In 2002, the Paris Metro put in high-speed walkways that moved at three times the speed of normal walkways. Busy Parisians loved it, but its high speed led to some unexpected landings, convincing authorities to cancel the experiment.

At Holiday Inn, 55% of new hotels have tubs compared to 95% a decade ago. Marriott will equip the majority, 75%, of its rooms with showers only. One day, the only bubbles you might see in most hotels will be in your machine-dispensed sparkling water bottle.

And if there's no time for love or music, why should we get any sleep? In the 1920s, the average U.S. adult slept 8.8 hours every 24 hours. That figure has declined to 7.1 hours, nearly two hours less, according to a 2015 Sleep in America poll conducted by the National Sleep Foundation. [134] According to an earlier foundation study, even children are getting less sleep than recommended, with infants now averaging almost 90 minutes less sleep per 24-hour period than the 14-hour minimum recommended by doctors. [135] Could that be due to a time-compressed evolution?

Our digital devices are a fundamental reason for the decline of sleep. Just about everyone, 95% of people, uses some kind of electronic device, be it a TV, computer, phone or tablet, within an hour of bedtime, reports the National Sleep Foundation. A study by RAND Corporation researchers found that 20-30% of workers complain of lack sleep on a daily basis, costing the U.S. economy $400 billion in annual losses. [136]

Of course, it's entirely possible that future technologies may help offset our lack of sleep, or at least provide us with more insight into our deficient sleeping habits. In December 2018, Finland-based Oura Health, a sleep-improvement wearable platform, landed a $20 million round for its sleep-tracking Oura ring. [137] Investors include Dell Founder Michael Dell, YouTube Co-Founder Steve Chen and Twitch Co-Founder Kevin Lin, the people who brought us laptops, video streaming and videogaming, respectively. Could they all be feeling guilty for what they have wrought? 😌

Sleep Training: Oura Ring

Finland-based startup Oura Health has an innovative solution for bad sleeping habits. The Oura Ring tracks your sleep while a smartphone app coaches you and, hopefully, induces a positive attitude adjustment regarding the importance of sleep.

134. "Sleep in America Poll Finds Pain a Significant Challenge When It Comes to Americans' Sleep," *National Sleep Foundation*, 02-Mar-15.
135. "2004 Children and Sleep," *National Sleep Foundation*, 01-Mar-04.
136. Bilal Choudhry, "You're Getting Very Sleepy. (So Is Everyone Else.)," *The New York Times*, 21-Aug-18.
137. Megan Rose Dickey, "Sleep-tracking ring Oura raises $20 million from Michael Dell, Lance Armstrong and others," *TechCrunch*, 03-Dec-18.

Stress

The acceleration of life had one major consequence, growing societal angst. Hans Selye, a Hungarian professor, then living in Montreal, Canada, was the first to popularize the concept of "stress" in his groundbreaking 1956 book *The Stress of Life*.

In a July 4, 1936 letter to the editor of *Nature*, entitled *A syndrome produced by diverse nocuous agents*, Selye described stereotypical manifestations of the "general alarm reaction" of the human body, including "thymicolymphatic involution, gastric ulcers, lipid discharge from the adrenal and loss of chromaffinity in the medulla," which Selye believed was a "non-specific, adaptive response to various kinds of agents." [138] In layman's terms — the physical mechanisms of stress. He first coined the word in a 1950 monograph, simply entitled *Stress*.

It was not happenstance that Selye's book would appear in a whirlwind, post-war boom period during which the first series of Time Compression artifacts would make their societal debut. The Polaroid camera, the Raytheon microwave oven, jet aircraft, the use of "speed" by long-distance truckers, the concept of "realtime," all joined existing means of accelerating time, including radio, television and the rapidly proliferating automobile.

Stress in all its expressions was about to reverberate through society, and many would attempt to mitigate this by-product of faster living with a host of increasingly popular therapies, ranging from massage to yoga and, most singularly, the 1981 launch of the anti-anxiety drug Xanax.

When The Upjohn Company, now part of Pfizer, introduced Xanax, it was considered an aspiring me-too competitor of Valium, America's most popular 1970s anxiety drug. [139] In 1980, "panic disorder" — the medical term for panic attack — was first officially recognized with the publication of the American Psychiatric Association's *Diagnostic and Statistical Manual of Mental Disorders*. [140] Within two years of its availability, Xanax was a blockbuster drug. [141] Xanax sales rose 85% in 1985 from $82 million to $152 million. [142]

During the 1980s, Upjohn produced a number of studies to show that Xanax also ameliorated the effects of panic attacks. The FDA's 1990 approval of Xanax to treat panic disorders lead to another surge in the drug's popularity. [143] Today, Xanax remains America's most popular psychiatric prescription (table, page 183), and ranks number nine overall among all U.S. prescriptions. [144]

It has become a staple of popular culture, with the slogan "I need a Xanax" landing on memes, mugs and t-shirts. Xanax even became the rap artist's

> **"** It's not stress that kills us. It's our reaction to it."
>
> **Hans Selye**
> *The Stress of Life*

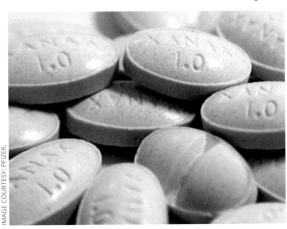

IMAGE COURTESY: PFIZER.

Upjohn's Anti-Anxiety Drug Xanax

When Upjohn launched Xanax in 1981, it became the first drug approved to treat panic attacks. Today, Xanax is a generic drug, yet earns its maker, Pfizer, some $385 million annually.

138. Sandor Szabo, Yvette Tache et al., "The legacy of Hans Selye and the origins of stress research," *Informa Healthcare USA*, Sep-12.
139. Matthew Herper, "America's Most Popular Mind Medicines," *Forbes*, 17-Sep-10.
140. Layton McCurdy et. al., "Treatment of Panic Disorder," *National Institutes of Health*, 25-Sep-91.
141. Aprazolam, *Wikipedia*, ret. 30-Dec-18.
142. April Dougal, "The Upjohn Company," *Encyclopedia.com*, ret. 30-Dec-18."
143. "F.D.A. Approves Medication For Treating Panic Disorder," *The New York Times*, 10-Nov-90.
144. Lydia Ramsey, "The 10 most popular prescription drugs in the US," *Business Insider*, 26-Oct-16.

drug of the choice when Tyler, The Creator referred to it on *Yonkers* in 2011. Since then, such artists as Young Thug, Future and 2 Chainz have mentioned it in music, according to Genius' *Drugs in Hip-Hop: A 30-Year Analysis*. [145]

The "Top 2013 U.S. Psychiatric Prescriptions" table points to a society that either suffers from more anxiety, is obtaining better care, or abuses it, as the case may be for Xanax or its benzodiazepine cousin Ativan.

Top 2013 U.S. Psychiatric Prescriptions			
Rank	Brand	Used For...	Number
1.	Xanax	Anxiety	48.5M
2.	Zoloft	Depression, Anxiety, OCD	41.4M
3.	Celexa	Depression, Anxiety	39.4M
4.	Prozac	Depression, Anxiety	28.2M
5.	Ativan	Anxiety, panic disorder	27.9M
6.	Desyrel	Depression, Anxiety	26.2M
7.	Lexapro	Depression, Anxiety	24.9M
8.	Cymbalta	Depression, Anxiety	18.6M
9.	Wellbutrin XL	Depression	16.0M
10.	Effexor ER	Depression, Anxiety, Panic disorder	15.8M
Total for Top 25 U.S. Psychiatric Prescriptions:			428.9M
2014 IMS Health			

In 1954, Dr. Leo Sternbach, a pharmacist and chemist working for Hoffmann-La Roche, was tasked with developing a safer alternative to barbiturates and meprobamate ("Miltown"). Over the next few years, Sternbach tested 40 new compounds, finally developing a new "anxiolytic" drug under the trade name Librium. [146] As the name suggests, anxiolytic describes a class of drugs that are used to reduce anxiety.

Librium was the world's first clinically useful benzodiazepine (BZD or "benzos"). The second successful BZD was diazepam, which was introduced in 1963 under the trade name Valium. Between 1969 and 1982, Valium was the most prescribed drug in the U.S., with sales peaking in 1978 at more than 2.3 billion pills.

This exploration of pharmaceutics history is critical to understanding the invisible dynamics of Time Compression. The dimensions and scope of the anxiolytic drug category are astonishing, especially considering how quickly it evolved. And it will continue to develop, for percolating in our midst is perhaps the greatest inducer of stress ever, the information revolution. That trend is reflected in the number of adults filling a benzodiazepine prescription, which increased 67%, from 8.1 million in 1996 to 13.5 million in 2013. [147]

A preview of the information juggernaut was provided by the October 1996 *Dying for Information?* survey of 1,300 global managers by Benchmark Research on behalf of Reuters Holdings PLC, which discovered that two out of three (68%) managers surveyed associate "information overload" with tension with colleagues and loss of job satisfaction — in other words, stress. [148] The study found that 38% of management consider their working environment extremely stressful and 94% don't believe the situation will improve, contributing to "Information Fatigue Syndrome."

You might label it poetic justice that a poet would envision this anxious state of affairs first. In 1947, W.H. Auden published *The Age of Anxiety* — 138 pages of allegorical poetry that attempted to describe this hectic scenario. While few may have read the entire poem, influenced by a condition characterized later in this chapter, its title has become the mantra of modern humankind, appearing in the titles of subtitles of no less than two dozen books since 1990. [149]

145. Ben Carter, "Drugs in Hip-Hop: A 30-Year Analysis," *Genius*, 01-Apr-16.
146. Erik MacLaren, "Valium History and Statistics," *DrugAbuse.com*, ret. 12-Dec-18.
147. "Increasing Benzodiazepine Prescriptions in the U.S., 1996–2013," *American Journal of Public Health*, 09-Mar-16.
148. Paul Waddington, "Dying For Information?," *Coalition for Networked Information*, 19-Jan-98.
149. Daniel Smith, "It's Still the 'Age of Anxiety.' Or Is It?," *The New York Times*, 14-Jan-12.

Screensucking

December 25, 2015 was an absolutely gorgeous Christmas Day in San Diego, Calif. Deep blue skies provided a perfect backdrop for the sun setting in the Pacific Ocean. That's what Joshua Burwell, 33, visiting from Indiana, set out to do that day. He never returned.

> "Forget DWI. The big new traffic-safety issue is DWT: Driving While Texting."
>
> *The Wall Street Journal*
> 14-Mar-07

Burwell was last seen looking down at his phone shortly before falling off a ledge to his death. [150] It was another sad example of our digitally distracted culture, which loves to multitask while either driving, bicycling or walking. Still, can you blame smartphone users? That lovely screen literally sucks you in and won't let go. It's a phenomenon called, appropriately enough, "screensucking," and it's creating a new world order all around us.

Burwell is one in a long line of people who have made headlines because of their screensucking addiction. The most famous case was that of Cathy Cruz Marrero, who mindlessly tumbled into a mall fountain in January 2011, while busily texting a friend from church. After surveillance footage of the incident was posted on YouTube, she became a viral sensation. [151]

Cruz Marrero and her lawyer, James Polyak, declared they intended to hold the responsible parties accountable. But the story had a big twist. As it turns out, Cruz Marrero had other legal problems, including allegedly using a co-worker's credit card to make more than $5,000 in unauthorized store purchases. [152]

As if to bring the point home, a 2016 State Farm study discovered that

150. Samantha Tatro and Omari Fleming, "Man, Distracted by Electronic Device, Identified After Falling to Death at Sunset Cliffs," *NBCSanDiego.com*, 25-Dec-15.
151. Jeanne Moos, "CNN: 'The Fountain Lady', Cathy Cruz Marrero who fell in a fountain while texting gets lawyer," *CNN*, 20-Jan-11.
152. Juju Chang et al.," Fountain-Falling Texter in Court for Alleged Theft," *ABC News*, 20-Jan-11.

Chongqing, China: Separate Lanes for Phone Users

Le trottoir de Chongqing avec une file réservée aux utilisateurs de smartphone. Hope you understand French. Just making sure you're not screensucking! 😂

IMAGE COURTESY: CHINA DAILY VIA REUTERS.

> 66 That lovely screen literally sucks you in and won't let go. It's a phenomenon called, appropriately enough, 'Screensucking."
>
> **Michael Tchong**
> *Ubertrends*

people who participate in distracting cellphone activities are more likely to exhibit other "dangerous behavior." The U.S. driver survey found that 35% used text messaging while driving, even though 69% found them distracting.[153] The use of text messaging was significantly higher among drivers 18-29, with 61% reporting text messaging while driving. A 2015 Distracted Driver Study published in *Preventive Medicine Reports* found that nearly 60% of respondents reported multitasking activity within the pasts 30 days involving a mobile phone, with reading texts (48%), writing texts (33%) and viewing maps (43%) most frequently mentioned. [154]

That six out of 10 people would readily admit to multitasking while driving prompted *The Wall Street Journal* to declare eight years earlier, "Forget DWI. The big new traffic-safety issue is DWT: Driving While Texting." [155]

That story was written a few months before the iPhone was introduced with its beautiful, high-resolution screen that would take screensucking to an entirely new level, transfixing pedestrians as well. In another article, *The Wall Street Journal* reporter Geoffrey Fowler analyzed Consumer Product Safety Commission data and discovered that emergency room visits involving distracted pedestrians using cellphones rose 124% between 2010 and 2014, contributing to a 10-fold increase since 2006. [156]

Why do people do it? The top answer in the State Farm study: 49% of respondents agreed with the statement, "It is an efficient use of my time." Besides suffering from Time Compression, another reason is that hypnotic screen, which sucks you in, and much like a ferocious pit bull, once it sinks its fangs into your feeble attention span, it just won't let go.

Authorities are beginning to catch on. The city of Chongqing, China has created separate lanes for smartphone users, which includes this dire

153. "Smartphones While Driving: We Know It's Risky. So Why Do We Do It?," *State Farm*, 30-Mar-17.
154. Emily Gliklich et al., "Texting while driving: A study of 1211 U.S. adults with the Distracted Driving Survey," *Preventive Medicine Reports*, 07-Sep-16.
155. Christopher Cooper, "Legislators Aim At a New Misdeed On the Road: DWT," *The Wall Street Journal*, 14-Mar-07.
156. Geoffrey Fowler, "Texting While Walking Isn't Funny Anymore," *The Wall Street Journal*, 17-Feb-16.

warning, "Walk in this lane at your own risk." South Korea has installed signs to warn smartphone users about too much screensucking. [157] And, like Chongqing, Antwerp, Belgium has also introduced its text-walking lanes.

In October 2017, Honolulu became the first the U.S. city to ban pedestrians from using digital devices while crossing the road. [158] The Distracted Walking Law bill, which was signed into law by Honolulu Mayor Kirk Caldwell, will fine first offenders caught screensucking using any digital device, including laptops(!) and digital cameras, between $15 and $35.

Honolulu's city council cannot be faulted for trying to slow down an exploding trend. In the past two years, the U.S. experienced the two highest numbers of pedestrian deaths in the previous 27 years with 5,977 pedestrians killed in 2017, down 1.7% from the year before, and 6,080 pedestrian fatalities in 2016, according to NHTSA.[159]

The popularity of mobile apps such as Facebook, Google Maps, Snapchat and others have created temptations that drivers and passengers find difficult to resist. Snapchat, in particular, has been implicated in many high-speed accidents due to its "Speed Filter," which tracks a car's speed in realtime and superimposes that number on the smartphone's screen, incidents discussed more extensively in the Voyeurgasm Ubertrend (page 241).

Even Silicon Valley, the creators of all these distractions, is concerned that its powerful magnets of 24/7 stimulation — the relentless demand of app alerts, e-mail pings and social media updates — is creating a profound physical craving that can hurt productivity and personal interactions. [160] *Et tu, Brute?*

Multitasking Abilities Perspective

Randy Glasbergen expresses a popular sentiment about our multitasking abilities: that we are not good at it. At least for now.

IMAGE COURTESY: RANDY GLASBERGEN

Multitasking

Multitasking is, of course, not a new phenomenon. Juggling multiple tasks is a human gift that dates back ages. The word first appeared in a 1966 computer business magazine, *Datamation*: "Multitasking is defined as the use of a single CPU for the simultaneous processing of two or more jobs." [161]

Aha! Remember the Digital Lifestyle convergence path of computers and human beings? The human race is on a trajectory to assimilate computer traits, while computers and robots are evolving to mimic us. It's only logical to conclude that our multitasking abilities will improve over time.

Most observers believe that human beings are not really multitasking but simply handling a single task at a time and that we're not good at it, as the cartoon, above, illustrates. But if Charles Darwin's theory of natural selection is any indication, evolutionary forces will eventually favor those who can adapt more readily to multitasking, for it is survival of fittest that

157. "South Korea brings in road signs in a bid to reduce smartphone-related accidents," *Alphr*, 27-Jun-16.
158. "Honolulu bans texting while crossing streets in bid to curb injuries," *BBC News*, 29-Jul-17.
159. Nathan Bomney, "More than 37,000 people were killed in car crashes in 2017," *USA Today*, 03-Oct-18.
160. Matt Richtel, "Silicon Valley Says Step Away From the Device," *The New York Times*, 23-Jul-12.
161. Derek Thompson, "If Multitasking Is Impossible, Why Are Some People So Good at It?," *The Atlantic*, 17-Nov-11.

will determine who best succeeds at life.

There is emerging evidence that suggests that the secret to success in an age of universal distraction is to multitask smartly. The National University of Singapore found that workers who spend 20% or less of their time browsing the ultimate source of distraction, the internet, were 9% more productive than those who never went online at all. In other words, short bursts of focused attention broken up by equally intense breaks allow us to be most productive.

And whether one likes it or not, multitasking is becoming a requisite job skill. Evidence of this trend emerged in a story by P.J. Bernardski, who wrote, "Everything is fast, very fast, in these days of time poverty. I hate to multitask when I don't have to, but when don't I? I've actually seen 'good at multitasking' mentioned on resumes. It's a bona fide good thing." [162] That was written in 2004, so it's safe to assume that multitasking as a required skill set showed up in job descriptions earlier.

Highly fragmented and multi-threaded television programming, such as *Sesame Street* and MTV, planted the seeds for a nation of multitaskers. The advent of computers with their multiple windows, browser tabs and applications helped users become adept at what usability expert Jakob Nielsen refers to as "interlaced browsing" — tabbing around from topic to topic like a jack of all information trades and a master of no memory. [163]

Multitasking is now part of our fast-moving culture, and, being an offshoot of the Time Compression Ubertrend, has begun to surface as a consumer benefit. First came S.C. Johnson's Windex Multi-Task, which was launched in 2004. Its TV commercial connected the product to the growing multitasking trend and its ability to "multitask" while cleaning. [164]

But Windex Multi-Task only had a superficial connection to multitasking. Expect to see more products and services that actually multitask, saving consumers time, like Pantene Pro-V Daily Moisture Renewal, which is a "2 in 1" convergence innovation — both a shampoo and conditioner (photo).

Multitasking in Haircare Products

Pantene's 2 in 1 Shampoo & Conditioner saves users time by combining two activities into one. This innovative product is one of the most highly rated hair cleaning products on Amazon.com.

Multi-media Tasking

The history of multitasking products that actually seek to divide our attention span got its start in 1983, when the consumer electronics giant Philips introduced a television set that offered a feature called "Picture In Picture, or PIP, which allowed one TV channel to be displayed full screen, while at same time showing another program in a small inset window. [165]

It was the first manifestation of a trend that has rocked the world of media and advertising. Only these days, it's our laptops and mobile devices that are enveloping us in a multi-screen world and that have led to a pervasive consumer trend: Multi-media Tasking.

In 1999, a digital marketing media company, ICONOCAST, founded by

162. P.J. Bernardski, "Let's Speed Up TV," *The Business of Television*, 11-Jan-04.
163. Daniel Kao, "Intro to HCI Lecture 4 – Cognition and Design," *Diplateevo*, Mar-15.
164. "Windex - Multi-Task (2004) 0:30 (USA)," *Adland.tv*, 22-Jan-05.
165. "Picture-in-picture," *Wikipedia*, ret. 30-Dec-18.

yours truly, commissioned NPD Research to study a new trend: Watching TV while surfing the internet — a phenomenon we dubbed "Multi-media Tasking." That year, 57% of U.S. internet users said they could use their computer while watching TV.

That was a time when, unlike today, most users were relegated to desktop computers and few owned laptops. Many had resorted to installing desktops in areas near a television. Scarborough Research reported in 2001 that 50% of internet users had a TV in the same room as a computer. The researcher discovered that 91% of those with a TV in the same place where the internet was used most often said they watched TV and surfed simultaneously, up from 86% who did so in 1999.

> "Interlaced browsing — tabbing around from topic to topic like a jack of all information trades and a master of no memory."
>
> **Michael Tchong**
> *Ubertrends*

The runaway popularity of Multi-media Tasking was evident from those sky-high, early adoption figures. Today, virtually everyone multitasks while watching TV. According to TiVo, 99% of consumers admit to multitasking while watching TV. [166]

If anything, Multi-media Tasking is even more deliberate today. That's due to the media now actually inviting viewers to interact with their broadcast programming on social media. This phenomenon, called "Second Screen," relies on the internet to provide enhanced program information. It involves using a companion device, such as a laptop, tablet or smartphone, to enhance the show-watching experience, with interactive audience voting, quizzes, games and contests.

An Ericsson ConsumerLab survey of 30,000 internet users worldwide in 2016 found that 31% of respondents browse content on the internet related to the program they're currently watching, up from 23% in 2014. [167]

With almost universal access to a computer or mobile device in the living room, television is no longer the focal point of entertainment it once was. What started as a small number of TV watchers tweeting their thoughts and opinions about a particular show or sharing a favorite quote on their Facebook account has exploded into a mass, multi-screen market, with 87% of consumers now reporting using a TV and second device together, according to a global Accenture study.[168]

This means that, for many, television has been reduced to "background noise" or, worse, turned off altogether. Data from the Adobe Digital Index supports that assessment. One in three U.S. consumers now watches live sports on a device other than traditional television. [169]

Multitasking and internet streaming services, such as Hulu and Netflix, have altered the media landscape. Accenture reports that TV viewership declined 10% globally in 2015 and 9% in the U.S. In 2017, Nielsen saw a 3% drop in cable TV watching, compared to the year before. [170] In a major feat, Netflix surpassed the total number of cable TV subscribers in 2017, with 52 million to 49 million. [171] Netflix is so popular that during peak hours its bandwidth usage accounts for nearly 37% of all internet traffic. [172]

166. "Distracted, but Still Watching: Survey Finds 99% of Viewers Are Multitasking While Watching TV," *TiVo*, 05-Nov-15.
167. "TV and Media 2016," *Ericsson ConsumerLab*, 03-Nov-16.
168. "Digital Video and the Connected Consumer," *Accenture*, 17-Apr-15.
169. Daniel Burrus, "Super Bowl Notebook: Has TV Become The Second Screen?," *LinkedIn*, 08-Feb-16.
170. Mathew Ingram, "TV Watching Is in Decline, But News Consumption Is Booming," *Fortune*, 03-Apr-17.
171. Ian Morris, "Netflix Is Now Bigger Than Cable TV," *Forbes*, 13-Jun-17.
172. Todd Spangler, "Netflix Bandwidth Usage Climbs to Nearly 37% of Internet Traffic at Peak Hours," *Variety*, 28-May-15.

Second Screen Trend Is "Picture In Picture" on Steroids

Why not interact with your laptop or tablet while watching television? It's the ultimate expression of multi-media tasking — the simultaneous use of multiple media devices. Why stop at two? Add your smartphone to send tweets!

IMAGE COURTESY: UMAMI.

In the past, television has been the dominant advertising medium, with as much as a 37% share of all ad dollars spent globally in 2015. [173] In 2017, digital ad spending overtook television reaching $209 billion worldwide, 41% of the market, while TV brought in $178 billion. [174]

Many factors influence influence advertising, but it mirrors the diminishing stature of television, which, comparatively speaking, is losing momentum to digital media. The explosive growth of streaming has led to a doubling of streaming TV content consumption in the past year, while the number of people who are joining the cord-cutting trend increased by 33%. [175]

But TV watching is not the only activity being forced into a subsidiary role by Multi-media Tasking. The trend is also responsible for surfer's voice, that "absent-minded voice you hear on the phone, accompanied by a clicking keyboard, which suggests that your party is perhaps answering e-mail or, worse, involved in an online chat," as *The Wall Street Journal* observed in a November 10, 2003 article.

Business meetings have similarly been impacted. A RoperASW/Tandberg study of workers in the U.S., U.K., Germany, Norway and Hong Kong, found that less than half pay full attention during audio conferences in all countries except Norway and the U.S., with 29% of U.K. workers saying they doodle, 22% of Germans surfing the web and 20% of Americans having a conversation with someone else during conference calls. [176]

Even sex is taking a backseat to multitasking. After German magazine *Focus* reported in February 2005 that 56% of Germans left their mobile phone on during sex, a BBDO study a few months later noted that 22% of Germans had actually answered their mobile during lovemaking, compared to only 15% of Americans, proving that multitasking is a rampant, global addiction.

173. Jemma Brackebush, "How TV ad spending stacks up against digital ad spending in 4 charts," *Digiday*, 20-Jul-16.
174. Peter Kafka and Rani Molli, "2017 was the year digital ad spending finally beat TV," *Recode*, 04-Dec-17.
175. Sarah Perez, "Streaming TV consumption more than doubled since last year," *TechCrunch*, 02-Aug-18.
176. "Survey Reveals What Workers Are Really Doing During Conference Calls," *NetCent Communications*, 21-Nov-03.

Darwin On Steroids

Time Compression

> "We're compressing human evolution. Call it 'Darwin on Steroids.'"
>
> **Michael Tchong**
> *Ubertrends*

There's no question that the human body has changed markedly over the past century. One glance at photographs from the 1920s and 1930s shows how much human physiology has evolved in a relatively brief period. We're compressing human evolution. Call it "Darwin on Steroids."

Although one could argue that the physical attributes of people merely mirror changing cultural attitudes, a casual stroll by your nearest high school confirms that major body transformations are well underway.

The first thing you might notice is that today's high school kids are taller than ever before. That observation is backed by two studies conducted for the Centers for Disease Control and Prevention.

Men and women alike have added an inch since 1960, with the average American woman now standing 5-foot-4 (1.62 m) and the average male reaching 5-foot-9 (1.76 m). [177] [178]

Another aspect of today's adolescent is their tendency to "grow up too fast," which is a recurring complaint of parents these days. A survey conducted by U.K. firm Bullguard found that 80% of parents believed their children were growing up too quickly. [179] The chief cause of the precociousness of youths? Technology, including access to digital gadgets, social media such as Facebook and Snapchat, and the Google search engine.

One data set identified with this trend is the disproportionate growth of arrests of children under 15. While these juveniles still represent a minority of total court cases, according to a report by the Office of Juvenile Justice

177. "Four-Decade Study: Americans Taller, Fatter," *Live Science*, 27-Oct-04.
178. "FastStats – Body Measurements," *National Center for Health Statistics (CDC)*, Aug-16.
179. Victoria Woollaston, "Kids ARE growing up faster today - and it's all down to technology," *Daily Mail*, 14-Nov-14.

and Delinquency Prevention, "offenders under age 15 represent the leading edge of the juvenile crime problem, and their numbers are growing." [180]

That trend lasted until 1996 when the juvenile arrest rate for all offenses reached a peak level. It has subsequently declined 68% as of 2015. [181]

However, it should be noted that fewer than half of serious violent crimes by juveniles are ever reported to law enforcement. [182]

Dutch Teen Sails Around the World Solo

On January 20, 2011, 15-year-old Laura Dekker left the port of St. Maarten for a solo voyage around the world, which she completed on January 21, 2012, making her another exceptional example of the "KAGOY" trend— Kids Are Growing Older Younger.

IMAGE COURTESY: JUDY FITZPATRICK/ASSOCIATED PRESS PHOTO.

KAGOY

Criminal cases that do surface tend to underscore this accelerating trend, which lives under the acronym "KAGOY — Kids Are Growing Older Younger." One such case involved an 11-year-old girl who was charged with drunken driving after she led police on a car chase at speeds of up to 100 mph that ended when she flipped her car in the town of Orange Beach, Alabama.[183] Eleven years old!

In marketing circles, children between the ages of eight and 12, a transitioning period between childhood and adolescence, are known as "tweens." In an article by the Manhattan Institute think tank, then Nickelodeon Vice President Bruce Friend proclaimed that "The 12-14-year-olds of yesterday are the 10-12s of today." [184] A Yankelovich Youth Monitor, study, sponsored by Nickelodeon, found that by the time they reach 12, children already describe themselves as "flirtatious, sexy, trendy, athletic and cool." That was in 1998, some two decades ago.

Child development experts say that physical and behavioral changes that would have been typical of teenagers decades ago are now common

180. Kay Hymowitz, "Kids Today Are Growing Up Way Too Fast," *Manhattan Institute*, 28-Oct-98.
181. "Juvenile Arrest Rate Trends," *Office of Juvenile Justice and Delinquency Prevention*, 27-Mar-17.
182. "Juvenile Justice," *Frontline/ WGBH*, ret. 30-Dec-18.
183. "11-year-old charged with driving drunk," *Reuters*, 06-Jul-07.
184. Kay Hymowitz, "Kids Today Are Growing Up Way Too Fast," *Manhattan Institute*, 28-Oct-98.

among tweens. The most extreme example of the KAGOY phenomenon is the earlier arrival of puberty.

A landmark 1960 U.K. study reported that puberty began, on average for girls at age 11. [185] In April 1997, Marcia Herman-Giddens, along with her research associates, published a seminal study, entitled "Secondary Sexual Characteristics and Menses in Young Girls Seen in Office Practice," which reported that at age three, 3% of African-American girls and 1% of white girls showed breast and/or pubic hair development, with proportions increasing to 27% and 7%, respectively, at seven years. By age eight, 48% of African-American girls and 15% of white girls had begun puberty.

In August 2010, researchers at Cincinnati Children's Hospital, Kaiser Permanente of Northern California and Mount Sinai School of Medicine in New York published another study that found that by age seven, 23% of black girls, 15% of Hispanic girls, 10% of white girls and 2% of Asian girls had started to develop breasts.

The story for boys is the same. It was generally accepted that boys began puberty at age 11½. A 2012 study released by the American Academy of Pediatrics found that, on average, black boys showed signs of puberty, primarily identified as the growth of testicles, at a little over age nine, while white and Hispanic boys were a bit older than 10. [186]

Evolution is proceeding much more quickly in other areas too. Digital Natives are acquiring multitasking skills that will be essential to their future. A Kaiser Family Foundation study quoted in the April 16, 2007 issue of eMarketer noted that "Kids between the ages of 2 and 12 years old spend more than a quarter of their leisure time doing two or more activities at the same time."

Outstanding KAGOY Examples: Child Prodigies		
Name	Age	Talent
Elise Tan Roberts	2	Youngest member of Mensa with an IQ of 156 (Einstein was 160).
Aelita Andre	4	Called *Das Wunderkind*, Aelita is the youngest professional painter.
Ainan Celeste Cawley	7	Passed "Chemistry O" level exam. Entered Singapore Polytechnic at 8.
Akrit Jaswal	7	Read Shakespeare in English at 5. Performed his first surgery at 7.
Elaina Smith	7	Became British radio's youngest life advisor.
Marko Calasan	8	Marko was the world's youngest certified computer system admin.
Alex Prior	8	Music composer who has written more than 42 classical works.
Hamad Al Humaidhan	9	Stunned the world of art and is compared to cubist genius Picasso.
Ethan Bortnick	9	Youngest musician ever to have his own PBS concert.
Gregory Smith	12	Received his first of four Nobel Peace Prize nominations at age 12.
Source: TopTenz 27-Sep-11.		

A fascinating insight into the generational adaptation to Time Compression was provided by Facebook Director of Ad Product Marketing Graham Mudd who observed that many users, particularly younger ones, can recall a message seen for less than three seconds. [187] The social network also found that fast-scrolling teens consume ads and content 2.5 times faster than people in their 60s. The technical aptitude of Digital Natives clearly plays a role in this finding, but the fundamental fact remains that the human species is adapting to a faster moving world.

Precociousness does have many upsides. An ever-growing list of talented progeny reaches milestones that in the distant past were just unheard of.

185. Elizabeth Weil, "Puberty Before Age 10: A New 'Normal'?," *The New York Times*, 30-Mar-12.
186. Pam Belluck, "Boys Now Enter Puberty Younger, Study Suggests, but It's Unclear Why," *The New York Times*, 20-Oct-12.
187. Garret Sloan, "Facebook: Fast-scrolling millennials consume ads 2.5 times faster," *Digiday*, 30-Sep-15.

One is a 15-year-old Dutch girl, Laura Dekker, who sailed around the world solo (page 191). [188] In the dotcom days, there was Canadian Keith Peris, a 12-year-old CEO. [189] Then there is Cecilia Cassini, who, at age 10, became the youngest fashion designer complete with her own trunk show. [190]

Or how about the teen genius who developed a cancer test? That is precisely what Jack Andraka did at age 16 when he created a new tool to detect pancreatic cancer. [191] There are many, many others, of course. The table on the facing page lists some of the truly outstanding ones.

Contrast: People Then and Now

Nearly half of Americans are obese or very obese. Today, the average U.S. adult consumes an extra 505 calories each day, enough to add 50 pounds (23 kg) per year to a rapidly expanding waistline. The trend is spreading globally.

IMAGE COURTESY: CREATIVE COMMONS LICENSE.

Globesity

There is another Darwin on Steroids evolution taking place. People weigh more than ever before. Centers for Disease Control data shows that the average weight for men rose "dramatically" — from 166 pounds (75 kg) in 1960 to 196 pounds (89 kg) in 2014. Women also gained weight, going from an average of 140 pounds (64 kg) in 1960 to 169 pounds (77 kg) in 2014. [192]

As a result, there are more overweight people than ever before. In 1960, 46% of U.S. adults were considered overweight. [193] By 2013 that figure had risen to 71%. [194] And 46% of U.S. adults are considered obese or very obese now, compared with just 14% in 1960. Overweight is commonly defined as a body mass index of 25.0–29.9, while obesity is a BMI equal to or greater than 30.0, while extreme obesity is a 40.0 or higher BMI.

188. "16-year-old Dutch sailor ends globe-circling solo voyage in St. Maarten," *Toronto Star*, 22-Jan-12.
189. "12-year-old CEO to join Canada trade trip to China," *Reuters*, 27-Jan-01.
190. "Cecilia Cassini ~ The Kid with a Passion for Fashion," *Fashion & Style Guru*, 21-Nov-12.
191. Donisha Dansby, " Teen Genius Develops Cancer Test," *National Geographic*, 10-Apr-13.
192. "Four-Decade Study: Americans Taller, Fatter," *Live Science*, 27-Oct-04.
193. Cheryl Fryar et al., "Prevalence of Overweight, Obesity, and Extreme Obesity Among Adults Aged 20 and Over: United States, 1960–1962," *National Center for Health Statistics (CDC)*, Jul-16.
194. "FastStats – Obesity and Overweight," *National Center for Health Statistics (CDC)*, Jun-16.

Body mass index is expressed as weight in kilograms divided by height in meters squared (kg/m^2). Worldwide, the proportion of men with a BMI of 25.0 or higher increased from 29% in 1980 to 37% in 2013, and from 30% to 38% in women. [195]

What the world is witnessing is an acceleration of evolution. The human body is adapting rapidly to changes in diet, lifestyle and perhaps even psychological influences, think FOMO — the fear of missing out. The latter phenomenon is visible at your local health club, where sitting on exercise equipment and staring at a phone has displaced actual workout time. Americans are as active today, on average, as they were in 1970, when they consumed 2,169 calories per day, according to the U.S. Department of Agriculture. By 2008, the daily intake had ballooned to 2,674 calories, a 23% increase. [196] Those 505 extra daily calories can easily add a pound of body weight each week, or 50 pounds (23 kg) a year.

Weight gain is impacting everything, from ambulances that need to be outfitted with heavy-duty equipment to enable them to carry more obese patients, to army recruiting, which rejects 27% of enlisting recruits because they are overweight. [197]

The obesity trend has become a global epidemic, hence the term "Globesity." It is promoted by aggressive marketers who brainwash 8- to 12-year-old children with 21 commercials a day on average, just for food, equal to some 7,600 ads per year, according to a 2007 study by the Kaiser Family Foundation. It is overfed with processed food saturated with an over-abundance of cheap, high-fructose corn syrup. It is overserved by restaurant chains like The Cheesecake Factory, which launched the supersized food portion trend in 1978, imitated by many other restaurants over the past three decades. Portion sizes in all kinds of foods and beverages have exploded as a result, as the table at left vividly shows.

The Cheesecake Factory Founder and CEO David Overton claims its large portions are appreciated by its patrons "because of the perceived value." [198]

In a morbidly obese 308-item menu, Cheesecake Factory diners can find such items as Bruléed French Toast, which serves up nearly 2,800 calories and 93 grams of saturated fat, or a Breakfast Burrito with 2,730 calories and 73 grams of fat. [199] It's not entirely clear what perceived value these preposterous menu items offer.

The globesity scourge is leading to changes in many business sectors. A Las Vegas ambulance company had to adopt larger vehicles, equipped

Food Size and Calorie Comparison				
Food or Beverage Item	Size 20 Years Ago	Calories 20 Years Ago	Size Today	Calories Today
Bagel	3 inches	140	6 inches	350
Muffin	1.5 oz.	210	4 oz.	500
Coffee vs. Mocha Coffee	8 oz.	45	16 oz.	350
Burger King Whopper vs. Burger King Triple Whopper	4 oz.	630	12 oz.	1,220
French Fries	2.4 oz.	210	6.9 oz.	610
Theatre Popcorn	5 cups	270	Tub	630
Pizza	2 slices	500	2 slices	850
Soda	6.5 oz.	85	20 oz.	250
Source: 28-Apr-16 Your Weight Matters; ret. 22-May-18 Burger King				

195. Hideki Higashi et al., "Global, regional, and national prevalence of overweight and obesity in children and adults during 1980–2013," *The Lancet*, 28-May-14.
196. Diane Suchetka, "Americans are consuming more calories than ever: Fighting Fat," *The Plain Dealer*, 05-Apr-10.
197. Catherine Elsworth, "Las Vegas ambulances solve a spreading dilemma," *The Daily Telegraph*, 31-Mar-06.
198. Caroline Fairchiled, "Questions for... Cheesecake Factory's David Overton," *Fortune*, 16-Jan-14.
199. Lindsay Moyer and Bonnie Liebman, "Xtreme Eating 2018," *Center for Science in the Public Interest*, 30-Jul-18.

with heavy-duty equipment, to handle the growing girth of obese patients. That might be welcome news to overweight Sin City residents and visitors, but patients who exceed air ambulance limits are not so lucky. They're increasingly denied emergency transportation due to an inability of helicopters to lift off. [200]

The expanding girth of its citizens is one of the biggest threats facing the western world, which has welcomed the American diet with open arms and looser fitting clothes.

Even in France where the national cuisine is considered sacred and *de rigeur*, the classic jambon-beurre baguette, or ham-and-butter sandwich, is now outsold by hamburgers. A study by Gira Conseil, a restaurant consulting firm, found that around 1.2 billion ham-and-butter sandwiches were sold in 2017, while 1.4 billion of burgers were eaten over the same period. [201] *Sacre bleu!*

The invasion of *L'Americain* burgers in the French diet has caused waists to expand at alarming rates. The number of obese people in France, which has a reputation as being the land of the slim-waisted, has doubled in the past 15 years, reaching 7 million. [202]

Japan's Okinawa islands provide the starkest example of the impact of an imported western diet. Administered by the U.S. from World War II until 1972, Okinawa boasts more than two and a half times the Japanese national average of people over 100 years old plus an exceptional number of people in good health well into their eighties, reports *The Telegraph*. [203]

Unfortunately, the next Okinawa generation is Japan's fattest and subject to a range of obesity-related illnesses that could kill them by middle age. The culprit: Japan's first fast-food outlet opened on Okinawa in 1963, seven years before Tokyo got one, and it continues to count more fast-food outlets per resident than anywhere else in the land of the rising sun.

Among the generation that grew up eating American food, nearly 30% of men die before reaching 65, and almost half of all men in their 40s are obese. In the 1995 census, Okinawa claimed the highest longevity of all 47 prefectures in Japan. When the 2000 census was taken, it had tumbled to 26.

As Darwin has so convincingly and incisively taught us, life on earth is ruled by the survival of the fittest. If the rampant globesity trend is not reversed soon, the fittest may well be a tiny group indeed. It's incumbent on government and society to try and halt this ill-advised supersizing strategy

In 2004, my company created a "No Supersize" button and sticker, which we mailed out for free for anyone who asked. We also sent the sticker with a letter to the top 100 CEOs in food, healthcare and insurance industries. Only one bothered to respond.

Cut It Out: No Supersize Button

In January 2004, I sent a letter to more than 100 chief executives in the food, healthcare and insurance industries, describing our pro-active "No Supersize" campaign. Then Safeway CEO Steven Burd was the only executive to respond.

200. JoNel Aleccia, "Too fat to rescue? More heavy patients denied air ambulances," *NBC News*, 02-Nov-15.
201. "Burgers now outselling classic jambon-beurre baguette sandwiches in France," *Associated Press*, 21-Mar-18.
202. Henry Samuel, "Number of obese people in France doubles to seven million," *The Telegraph*, 16-Oct-12.
203. Colin Joyce, "Japanese get a taste for Western food and fall victim to obesity and early death," *The Telegraph*, 04-Sep-06.

Juan Martín del Potro Towers Over Not-So-Short Frenchman

At 6 foot, six inches (1.98 m), Argentine tennis player Juan Martín del Potro is a perfect exponent of the greater heights humans are reaching everywhere, except in the U.S. Shown here at Wimbledon 2018 with six-foot (1.83 m) Gilles Simon of France, who is by no means short.

Reaching New Heights

The 2009 U.S. Open final between Juan Martín del Potro and Marin Cilic featured not one but two 6-foot-6 (1.98 m) tennis players. As *The Wall Street Journal* reported, the participants in that year's men's draw were, on average, one inch (2.5 cm) taller compared to players two decades earlier at the 1989 U.S. Open. [204]

Over 150 years, the average height of people living in industrialized nations has increased about four inches (10 cm). Michael Dougherty, writing for *Scientific American*, attributes this height growth spurt to improved nutrition, supported by the discovery that skeletons from the stone age through the early 1800s showed no meaningful differences in height. [205]

As Dougherty puts it, "evolution requires two things: variation in physical and/or behavioral traits among the individuals in a population; and a way of selecting some of those traits as adaptations, or advantages to reproduction." Those adaptations to an evolving environment are already evident in widely practiced multitasking habits.

While humans may not excel at texting while walking or driving, one has to remember that the first text messages were only sent in 1992. [206] The iPhone was launched in June 2007. Both technologies lead to huge behavioral shifts.

The far-reaching and pervasive impact of new technologies, such as robots, self-driving cars and AI, is only now beginning to emerge.

204. Tom Perrotta, "Men's Tennis Reaches New Heights," *The Wall Street Journal*, 09-Sep-09.
205. Michael Dougherty, "Why are we getting taller as a species?," *Scientific American*, 29-Jun-98.
206. "Text messaging," *Wikipedia*, ret. 30-Dec-18.

If technology is at the core of the "creative destruction" cycle, one can intuitively divine that multitasking is a prerequisite for future job success. We already know that height can also affect lifetime earnings. The *Journal of Applied Psychology* reports that someone who is 6-feet (1.80 m) tall earns, on average, nearly $166,000 more during a 30-year career than someone who is 5-feet-5 (1.65 m), even accounting for gender, age and weight variances. [207]

This study of the relationship between body height and salary was authored by University of Florida psychologist Timothy Judge and University of North Carolina researcher Daniel Cable. Judge and Cable analyzed data from four U.S. and U.K. longitudinal studies that tracked nearly 8,500 participants from adolescence to adulthood and recorded their personal characteristics, salaries and occupations. The pair also performed a meta-analysis of 45 previous studies on the relationship between height and workplace success.

Judge and Cable are not alone in these observations. In a *Journal of Human Capital* article entitled *Height, Human Capital, and Earnings: The Contributions of Cognitive and Noncognitive Ability*, Andreas Schick and Richard Steckel report that a jump from the 25th percentile of height to the 75th, equivalent to about four or five inches (10-12.5 cm), results in a salary increase of between 9% and 15%. [208]

Anthropological studies about the desirability of greater height predate these findings. In the 1960s, Vanderbilt anthropologist Thomas Gregor observed a primitive tribe that lived in Brazil's tropical rainforest, the Mehinaku. He also spent time with various indigenous people in Papua New Guinea. As Gregor observes, "In no case have I found a preference for short men." [209] Research further suggests that height makes only slightly more of a difference for men than women.

Given all this evidence, it's without doubt of great concern that America is falling behind other countries in terms of population height gain. Based on an analysis of 1,472 population studies, encompassing some 19 million participants, the U.S. had the third tallest men and fourth tallest women in 1914 (table). [210] Today, Americans are in 37th and 42nd place, respectively. [211]

U.S. Men and Women Versus Dutch Men and Women				
Year	U.S. Men	U.S. Women	Dutch Men	Dutch Women
1914 (foot)	5' 7"	5' 2"	5' 7"	5' 1"
1914 (cm)	171.1	158.5	169.4	154.8
2014 (foot)	5' 10"	5' 4"	6' 0"	5' 6"
2014 (cm)	177.1	163.5	182.5	168.7

26-Jul-16 Imperial College London, eLife

The height of U.S. men and women started to plateau in the 1960s and 1970s, around the same time that McDonald's and The Cheesecake Factory began to help Americans grow faster horizontally. The study's lead author, Professor Majid Ezzati from the Imperial College of London's Faculty of Medicine and School of Public Health, said America's relatively modest increase in average height could be due to the "deteriorating quality of the diet."

Indeed, America, the land of plenty, has begun to stunt its own growth.

207. "Standing tall pays off, study finds," *Journal of Applied Psychology*, Jul/Aug-04.
208. Andreas Schick and Richard Steckel, "Height, Human Capital, and Earnings: The Contributions of Cognitive and Noncognitive Ability," *Journal of Human Capital*, Spring 2015.
209. Joe Pinsker, "The Financial Perks of Being Tall," *The Atlantic*, 18-May-15.
210. James Bentham et al., "A century of trends in adult human height," *eLife Sciences*, 26-Jul-16.
211. Henry Bodkin, "British overtake Americans after growing 11cm in 100 years," *The Telegraph*, 26-Jul-16.

Football Players Then and Now

The evolution of American football players clearly shows the "Darwin on Steroids" effect. The U.S. is breeding their favorite gladiators bigger and stronger, so they can better compete in their aptly named "sudden death" matches.

IMAGE COURTESY: CREATIVE COMMONS LICENSE.

Performance Enhancing Drugs (PEDs)

In 2007, Marion Jones publicly admitted she used a steroid called "The Clear" for two years starting in 1999 to prepare for the 2000 Sydney Summer Games. Jones plead guilty to lying to Federal agents, which sent shock waves through the world of sports. [212] But Jones was merely a pawn in the chess game of big-money sports, where the use of artificial stimulants is an unstoppable force.

The truth is that many sports fans now care less. Shortly after Marion Jones captured all the headlines, I conducted a poll of Facebook users and discovered that 13% of those participating believed steroids should be legalized, while another 12% were not so sure. In other words, a nagging "approval creep" had begun to set in.

A 2003 poll conducted by *The New York Times* already uncovered the source of this approval creep. The publication found that "younger Americans are much less troubled by drug use in sports and believe it to be more widespread than do Americans age 30 and above." [213]

And no wonder, steroids use starts young. The National Institutes of Health's ongoing "Monitoring the Future" study found in 2004 that 270,000 eighth, 10th and 12th graders nationwide (3.4%) admitted steroid use, a 62% increase in use among 12th graders since 1991. [214]

In 2002, *USA Today* reported that "teenagers, looking up to those elite athletes whose muscles ripple with steroid-enhanced power, are picking up some dangerous training tips, health experts warn." [215] At the time,

> ❝Younger Americans are much less troubled by drug use in sports and believe it to be more widespread than do Americans age 30 and above."
>
> **The New York Times**
> 16-Dec-03

212. Amy Shipley, "Marion Jones Admits to Steroid Use," *Washington Post*, 05-Oct-07.
213. Jere Longman and Marjorie Connelly, "Drug Testing; Americans Suspect Steroid Use In Sports Is Common, Poll Finds," *The New York Times*, 16-Dec-03.
214. "ATHENA Targets Steroid Abuse," *Coaching Management*, Oct-05.
215. Anita Manning, "Kids, steroids don't mix," *USA Today*, 09-Jul-02.

estimates of steroids-using kids were in the 500,000 to 600,000 range with abuse by non-athlete females said to be "twice as high." Many experts report its application is increasing among college and high school students.

The reason drugs have so thoroughly infiltrated sports is due to its long, storied history. The first documented use occurred at the 1904 Olympics in St. Louis, where American marathoner Tom Hicks was given small bits of strychnine with brandy and a little egg white by his coach Charles Lucas. [216]

Russian weightlifters began using testosterone, which was first synthesized in Germany in 1935, during the 1952 Summer Olympics in Helsinki. [217] Word quickly spread and at the 1954 World Weightlifting Championships in Vienna, a Soviet doctor confirmed to U.S. team physician, Dr. John Ziegler, that the Soviets were indeed experimenting with testosterone. Upon his return, Ziegler tested testosterone on himself and some other weightlifters, and the trend began its upward rise.

Another case study is that of Barry Bonds. Although most of America, and the rest of the baseball-loving world for that matter, did not seem to care whether Bonds took steroids or not, there's no question that in less than 20 years, he morphed from a normal 185-pound (84 kg) Pittsburgh Pirate to a hulking, 230-pound (104 kg) San Francisco Giants outfielder, who, suddenly at age 37, hit a record-setting 73 home runs.

The adulation shown this questionable feat was genuinely stunning. Fashion designer Marc Ecko, who paid an astonishing $752,467 for the ball Bonds hit for his record-setting 756th home run, announced that the ball would be branded with an asterisk before being donated to baseball's Hall of Fame. [218]

While a majority of fans disapprove of the use of steroids, there is also growing evidence that the pendulum is swinging in the opposite direction due to the volume of media coverage drug use in sports has received. From 2003 to 2005, the disapproval rating was 80%. In 2006, it sunk to a low of 60%. It's evident that we are moving toward a culture that tacitly approves of the near-robotic performance of its steroid-pumping athletes. That fast-flowing undercurrent points to a future that will produce superhuman, android-like performers who will battle each other in nightmarish scenarios, much like those portrayed in many science-fiction movies.

If you're skeptical about this outcome, witness the growing popularity of ultimate fighting spectacles, a spectacularly violent sport that amazingly enough seems to have an increasing appeal among female sports fans.

Marion Jones merely joined a club that now also includes the once-lauded 2006 Tour de France winner Floyd Landis and, most famously, Lance Armstrong, who won the Tour from 1999 to 2005, plus Alex Rodriguez.

The Darwin on Steroids trend is unstoppable because science has become an integral part of human evolution. At the going rate, society will one day join the Romans and hail its "gladiators" with a likewise famous saying, "*Ave, Caesar, morituri te salutant.*" Only, in this case, Caesar is the almighty dollar, and those who are dying are the non-steroid-using athletes.

In the Blink of an Eye

At the September 2002 British Association's science festival in Leicester, Professor Andrew Prentice, an international nutrition expert from the London School of Hygiene and Tropical Medicine, remarked that people are now undergoing changes similar to those occurring two centuries earlier, when Europeans grew 12 inches (30 cm) in height, or more. "I'm talking about the remarkable change that has occurred in man's evolution in just the twinkling of an eyelid," the BBC quoted him as saying. [1]

1. Jonathan Amos, "Obesity's huge challenge for humans," *BBC News*, 09-Sep-02.

216. Michael Kremenik et al., "A Historical Timeline of Doping in the Olympics," *Kawasaki Journal of Medical Welfare*, 17-May-06.
217. "Steroids and Other Appearance and Performance Enhancing Drugs (APEDs)," *National Institutes of Health*, Feb-18.
218. Mike Nizza, "Asterisk to Mark Bonds' Record Ball," *The New York Times*, 26-Sep-07.

Time Compression Timeline

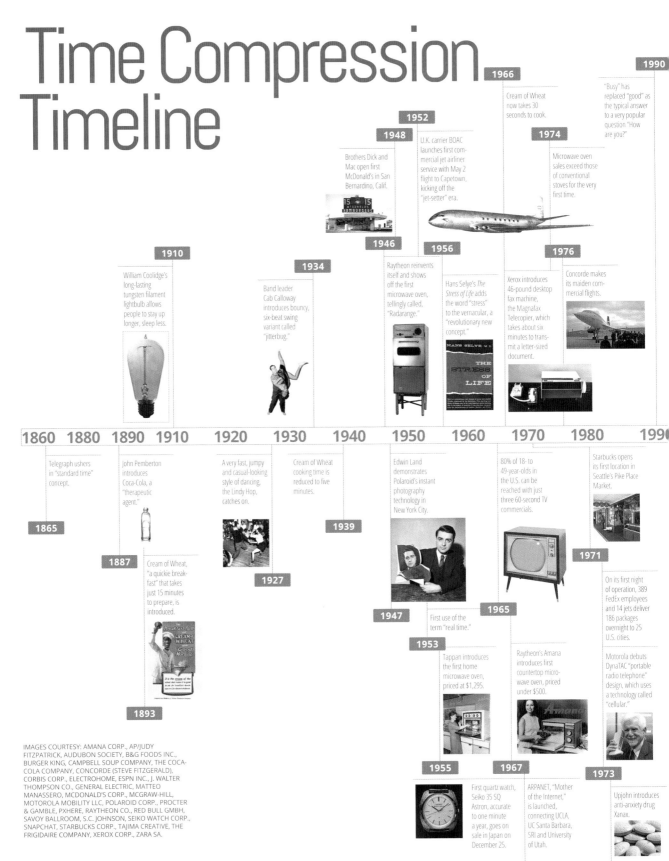

1910 — William Coolidge's long-lasting tungsten filament lightbulb allows people to stay up longer, sleep less.

1934 — Band leader Cab Calloway introduces bouncy, six-beat swing variant called "jitterbug."

1948 — Brothers Dick and Mac open first McDonald's in San Bernardino, Calif.

1952 — U.K. carrier BOAC launches first commercial jet airliner service with May 2 flight to Capetown, kicking off the "jet-setter" era.

1946 — Raytheon reinvents itself and shows off the first microwave oven, tellingly called, "Radarange."

1956 — Hans Selye's *The Stress of Life* adds the word "stress" to the vernacular, a "revolutionary new concept."

1966 — Cream of Wheat now takes 30 seconds to cook.

1974 — Microwave oven sales exceed those of conventional stoves for the very first time.

1976 — Xerox introduces 46-pound desktop fax machine, the Magnafax Telecopier, which takes about six minutes to transmit a letter-sized document.

Concorde makes its maiden commercial flights.

1990 — "Busy" has replaced "good" as the typical answer to a very popular question "How are you?"

Timeline axis: 1860 1880 1890 1910 1920 1930 1940 1950 1960 1970 1980 1990

1865 — Telegraph ushers in "standard time" concept.

1887 — John Pemberton introduces Coca-Cola, a "therapeutic agent."

1893 — Cream of Wheat, "a quickie breakfast" that takes just 15 minutes to prepare, is introduced.

1927 — A very fast, jumpy and casual-looking style of dancing, the Lindy Hop, catches on.

1939 — Cream of Wheat cooking time is reduced to five minutes.

1947 — Edwin Land demonstrates Polaroid's instant photography technology in New York City.

1953 — Tappan introduces the first home microwave oven, priced at $1,295.

1955 — First quartz watch, Seiko 35 SQ Astron, accurate to one minute a year, goes on sale in Japan on December 25.

1965 — 80% of 18- to 49-year-olds in the U.S. can be reached with just three 60-second TV commercials.

1967 — Raytheon's Amana introduces first countertop microwave oven, priced under $500.

1969 — ARPANET, "Mother of the Internet," is launched, connecting UCLA, UC Santa Barbara, SRI and University of Utah.

1971 — Starbucks opens its first location in Seattle's Pike Place Market.

On its first night of operation, 389 FedEx employees and 14 jets deliver 186 packages overnight to 25 U.S. cities.

1973 — Motorola debuts DynaTAC "portable radio telephone" design, which uses a technology called "cellular."

1981 — Upjohn introduces anti-anxiety drug Xanax.

First use of the term "real time."

IMAGES COURTESY: AMANA CORP., AP/JUDY FITZPATRICK, AUDUBON SOCIETY, B&G FOODS INC., BURGER KING, CAMPBELL SOUP COMPANY, THE COCA-COLA COMPANY, CONCORDE (STEVE FITZGERALD), CORBIS CORP., ELECTROHOME, ESPN INC., J. WALTER THOMPSON CO., GENERAL ELECTRIC, MATTEO MANASSERO, MCDONALD'S CORP., MCGRAW-HILL, MOTOROLA MOBILITY LLC, POLAROID CORP., PROCTER & GAMBLE, PXHERE, RAYTHEON CO., RED BULL GMBH, SAVOY BALLROOM, S.C. JOHNSON, SEIKO WATCH CORP., SNAPCHAT, STARBUCKS CORP., TAJIMA CREATIVE, THE FRIGIDAIRE COMPANY, XEROX CORP., ZARA SA.

1996

Reuters finds that two thirds of global managers suffer from "information anxiety" syndrome.

59% of Americans complain about being too busy, reports an NBC/WSJ poll, while 19% say life has become busy to the point of discomfort.

1994

The term "hybrid travel" is coined to describe a multitasking vacation combining both business and leisure.

HYBRID TRAVEL

2002

A very high-speed moving walkway debuts at Paris' Montparnasse metro station.

Only 23% of mall shoppers now browse, compared to 37% in 2000.

59% of all meals in the U.S. are rushed, and 34% of lunches are eaten on the run.

117 prime-time TV commercials are now required to produce the same result as three in 1965.

1998

Last complete performance of Wagner's Ring cycle lasts nearly one hour less than first performance.

First speed-dating event takes place at Peet's Café in Beverly Hills.

2004

"Good at multi-tasking" appears on resumes.

More than half of married women would rather have more time to cook than more money for takeout.

Infants sleep an average of 90 minutes less each day than the 14-hour minimum doctors recommend.

Stovetop cooking down from 58% in 1994 to 50%. Use of microwave steady at 26%.

TV has "become background noise," Susan Young tells *The Wall Street Journal*.

S.C. Johnson is first to jump on the multitasking trend with Windex Multi Task.

2006

Half of women decide within 30 seconds of meeting a man whether he is potential boyfriend material.

Carleton University study says people register likes and dislikes of sites in as little as 1/20 of a second.

Time is now more valuable than money, reports research firm Yankelovich.

75% would not return to websites that took longer than four seconds to load, compared to 7 or 8 seconds in 2001.

2008

Survey reveals that one in three drivers has dozed off while driving.

Number of golf players declines from 30 million to 26 million.

2010

Matteo Manassero, a 16-year-old from Italy, becomes youngest person ever to make cut at the Masters golf tournament.

May 2010 "Flash Crash" causes the biggest intra-day Dow Jones trading drop ever, 1,000 points, briefly erasing $1 trillion in market value.

High-frequency trading is responsible for nearly half of all trade executions.

2012

Ten-year-old Cecilia Cassini is the youngest fashion designer in the U.S.

2016

Snapchat "speed filter" feature is blamed for many high-speed car accidents.

2014

27% of teens experience "extreme stress" during the school year, compared to 21% of adults who suffer from same level of stress.

35% of all drivers continue to text while driving, up from 31% in 2009.

2018

Americans are finally getting more sleep, 18 minutes more each weeknight, than in 2003.

Multitasking shampoo and conditioner combination products are gaining popularity.

ESPN's new Apple TV 4K app lets you watch four screens of live sports at the same time — the ultimate PIP.

2000

2010

2018

World Wide Web ushers in realtime media era.

1993

MP3, a compression/decompression (CODEC) algorithm, is more popular that the word "sex" in online searches.

After launching in in Austria in 1987, Red Bull reaches the U.S. in 1999. Its energy properties quickly make it a popular drink and mixer.

1999

The first "3 Minute Dating" cruise sets sail from Port Canaveral, Fla.

Average audience drop-off between a film's opening weekend and second weekend is 51%, compared to 40% in 1998.

In the 1920s, the average U.S. adult slept 8.8 hours each day. By 2001 that figure had declined to 6.8.

2001

Campbell's Soup At Hand is designed for an eat-on-the-run food culture.

2003

54% of Germans leave their mobile on during sex...22% have answered a call.

The median number of hours people say they work has risen from 41 a week in 1973 to 49.

Fast fashion retailer Zara surpasses longtime leader H&M in sales.

2005

Wall Street Journal: "Forget DWI. The big new traffic-safety issue is DWT: Driving While Texting."

DWT

No Leisure: Americans are hunting and fishing less.

2007

Google reports that a page-load delay of 400 milliseconds can translate into a 1% drop in search query volume.

Google

Giftcard volume reaches $87 billion.

2009

68% of women would prefer to have more free time than a bigger paycheck.

Laura Dekker, a 16-year-old Dutch girl, is the youngest person to sail solo around the world.

68% of Americans check work e-mail during such major holidays as Thanksgiving and Christmas.

2011

Burger King online video promotes "hands-free Whopper Holder" to test multitasking concept.

The average duration of a web page viewed is 75 seconds, reports Nielsen.

75 SECONDS

2013

At 31 years, Sebastian Kurz became the youngest leader of a European Union state, taking on the role of chancellor of Austria.

Approximately 50% of American workers do not take vacations.

73% of Reddit posts are voted on by users who haven't actually clicked through to view content being rated.

In less than 15 years, a Florida bird, the snail kite, has evolved larger beaks and arid bodies to handle an invasive new species of snail.

With an average height of 182.5 cm (5 feet, 11 inches), Dutch men are the tallest in the world. Latvians have the tallest women at 170 cm (5 feet, 7 inches).

2017

Unwired is creating a highly independent, mobile lifestyle. The chief value impelling people to untheter is freedom. They want to decide when and where to use services, while seeking greater control over life's daily interfaces. Think "control enthusiast."

5

Unwired

Untethered and Unfettered

Whether sitting in a café on a Parisian boulevard or are lying on a Caribbean beach, the feeling one gets from being able to shop, search for information, or connect with friends and family, completely free from wires, is liberating. It almost feels like flying. That's what the Unwired Ubertrend is all about; it's about freedom. Freedom from wires, and perhaps even freedom from relationships. The tentacles of the Untethered and Unfettered Ubertrend have touched lives in unexpected ways. There is the emerging phenomenon of control enthusiasm, which projects the ability to swipe left or right with an app to life. The power we now all wield from the palm of our hand is casting a culture that is more demanding, more exacting and far more desiring of personalization.

Untethered And Free

It's the year 1955. Inside a nondescript building on Chicago's West Side, Robert Adler is hard at work on Zenith Radio's latest product, a cordless remote control. His challenge: Get four aluminum rods to emit a distinct sound.

There was a lot of urgency. A few months earlier, Zenith President and Founder Eugene "The Commander" McDonald had requested an immediate redesign of the Zenith Flash-Matic, the first wireless TV remote control. [1] The Flash-Matic, which resembled a ray gun, had just launched that year. Unfortunately, Flash-Matic used light signals to control a television's four photocells and would not work in bright sunlight.[2]

The Flash-Matic, designed by Zenith engineer Eugene Polley, had solved a major challenge with the first TV remote ever, the Zenith Lazy Bones, launched in 1950, which was *tethered* to the television with a long wire. McDonald knew that wires were a major stumbling block, literally and figuratively, for television owners. When Polley showed up at his house in Spring 1955 with the first prototype of the Flash-Matic TV, he was sold.

Now it was up to Adler to undo the Flash-Matic fiasco. He was tasked with coming up with a new wireless protocol that did not need batteries. Using batteries was out of the question because viewers might think something was wrong with the TV when the batteries were depleted. So, Adler's Space Command, named after Zenith's founder, was entirely mechanical.

Pushing a button caused a tiny hammer inside the control to hit an aluminum rod that produced an ultrasonic sound. The TV used a six-vacuum-tube circuitry to decode the clicks to turn the TV receiver on or

Midwest Innovator: Genie

Alliance, Ohio, less than 400 miles east of Chicago, was  home to another Unwired innovator, Alliance Manufacturing Company. In May 1954, the company introduced Genie, the world's first mass-produced, radio-controlled residential garage door opener. [1] That was two years before Zenith launched its third TV remote control. Genie helped propel the Unwired Ubertrend by providing drivers with a remote control for their garage.

1. "The Genie History," *The Genie Company*, ret. 14-Dec-18.

---

1. Jon Gertner, "A Clicker Is Born," *The New York Times*, 30-Dec-07.
2. "Channel Surfing Redux," *IEEE Consumer Electronics Magazine*, Oct-12.

Zenith Space Command TV

When Zenith's Space Command TV went into production in 1956, Robert Adler could never have predicted that his ultrasonic creation would one day lead to a plethora of wireless gadgetry. The Zenith Space Command ad featured no less than Jack Benny saying, "Look out, Gracie! With Zenith Space Command TV I can change programs from across the room..."

off, change the channel up or down, or turn the sound on or off. Now you know why remotes are sometimes called a "clicker."

The Zenith Space Command TV, which boasted "Zenith's revolutionary new 'Sunshine' Picture Tube" and four "High Fidelity Speakers," went on sale in Fall 1956. Showing that some things have not changed in the 63 years since, Zenith's ad featured this line, "Shut off the sound of long, annoying commercials while the picture remains on the screen." 😄

Today, Zenith's ultrasonic technology has been replaced by infrared or radio-frequency-controlled remotes that boast color touchscreens, internet connectivity, system automation and built-in TV guides. The humble clicker is now the access point of the digital entertainment hub.

Polley and Adler were not the first inventors to dream up a remote. Much earlier, in 1898 to be exact, Nikola Tesla showed off a remote device that wirelessly controlled a four-foot (122 cm) boat at the Electrical Exhibition held in New York's Madison Square Garden. [3] And on December 12, 1901, Guglielmo Marconi sent the first radio transmission across the Atlantic Ocean, jump-starting the wireless revolution. [4]

The wireless history predates the Digital Lifestyle substantially, which took off in the 1970s during the personal computer revolution. The keyword of the Unwired Ubertrend is control. Many digital devices these days can be controlled remotely. Many households have five, or more, remote controls cluttering up the living room. While the remote control has come to symbolize the Unwired Ubertrend, it's just one element of untethering.

The bomb cyclone of Unwired is the smartphone and its controlling apps.

3. Steve Brachmann , "From Tesla to Zenith, the Birth of Television Remote Controls," *IPWatchdog*, 17-Dec-14.
4. "Marconi sends first Atlantic wireless transmission," *History*, ret. 14-Dec-18.

Were You Standing in Line on Friday, June 29, 2007?

A long line is forming in San Francisco. Harry Potter movie? No, it's "iDay" — the line waiting to buy the first Apple iPhone ever sold. Some people even camped out in front of Apple Stores waiting for the popular smartphone to go on sale.

> " The only time kids go camping now is in front of a Circuit City waiting for a videogame to go on sale."
>
> **Jay Leno**
> The Tonight Show
> 20-Nov-06

The Smartphone Revolution

It's Friday, June 29, 2007, and a very long line is forming on Stockton Street in San Francisco. Is it a *Breaking Dawn* movie? A celebrity photo signing? No, it's "iDay" — the line waiting to buy the first Apple iPhone to go on sale. Some people are even camped out to wait for the much-anticipated smartphone.

Camping to buy a cellphone? How crazy is that? Are these people Looney Tunes? While I was standing in line, I thought of that joke Jay Leno had shared just a few months earlier: "The only time kids go camping now is in front of a Circuit City waiting for a videogame to go on sale." Store names may have changed, but this point of view remains true to this very day.

If the CrackBerry taught us anything, it was that cellphones could be truly addictive. But no one had ever seen anything like the iPhone before. BlackBerry Co-CEO Jim Balsillie reportedly uttered these famous last words the next day, "It's OK — we'll be fine." [5]

Balsillie was not the only one who was dumbfounded. Steve Jobs had to repeat the description of the iPhone several times: "It's an iPod, a phone and an internet communicator. An iPod, a phone...are you getting it?" Jobs used that memorable line during the iPhone launch, which took place on Tuesday, January 9, 2007 in front of thousands of Mac faithful.

Little did those Apple fans know that they were witnessing the complete reinvention of Apple and the entire mobile phone industry. They also didn't realize that backstage Apple engineers were keeping their fingers crossed that Jobs would not cause his iPhone to crash during the demo.

5. Parmy Olson, "BlackBerry's Famous Last Words At 2007 iPhone Launch: 'We'll Be Fine,'" *Forbes*, 26-May-15.

We Don't Need No Stinking Wires!

Who wants to manage this massive jumble of wires? It's a catastrophe waiting to happen. There has to be a better way, and there is. Go wireless! Be free. Be untethered and unfettered.

Reina Hardesty: Texting Wizard

In December 2008, 13-year-old Reina Hardesty, from Lake Forest, Calif., sent a mind-boggling 14,528 text messages. The paper version of her family's AT&T phone bill was only 23 pages long, but when her mother went online, she discovered that the actual bill contained 440 pages. Too bad Reina is an actress today, she would have made a spectacular social media influencer manager.

That's because the iPhone's software was largely unfinished and buggy. [6]

The iPhone launch was unusual in another way. Apple usually debuts products that are available shortly thereafter, typically less than six weeks later. The iPhone wouldn't go on sale for another six months, an eternity in Silicon Valley terms.

Despite these hurdles, Apple sold 700,000 iPhones the first weekend it went on sale, which was marked by long lines in front of Apple Stores across the U.S. [7] Long lines became an iPhone launch tradition, humorously dubbed "iDay" by a clever punster.

The combination of iPod, phone and internet communicator — all packaged behind an unusually sharp, almost three-dimensional, touch screen — was a complete departure from anything available at the time, including Nokia and BlackBerry smartphones.

Staring at the iPhone that evening, I knew instinctively that I was witnessing a revolution, one that would completely upend the entire technology industry. The first chance I got, in front of 2,000 NAR real-estate executives that August in Chicago, I sang the praises of the iPhone. Many people in the audience were skeptical.

In 2018, Apple became the first company to be valued $1 trillion dollars, and the company has sold more than 1.4 billion iPhones to date. [8] Apple may have surrendered some of that valuation, yet it remains the most striking example of the value innovation contributes to the bottom line.

In the past decade, the iPhone has redefined modern living, from swiping to selfies to emoji, a host of smartphone phenomena have changed behavior globally, becoming an instant cultural touchstone. But what would set the iPhone apart was yet to come, the App Store.

6. Fred Vogelstein, "And Then Steve Said, 'Let There Be an iPhone'," *The New York Times*, 04-Oct-13.
7. "iPhone Weekend One: 700,000 Sold, $200million+ Profit For Apple," *TechCrunch*, 04-Jul-07.
8. Jack Nicas, "Apple Is Worth $1,000,000,000,000. Two Decades Ago, It Was Almost Bankrupt.," *The New York Times*, 02-Aug-18.

There's an App for That

Apple iPhone iOS 2 App Store at Launch in July 2008

When the App Store opened for business on Thursday, July 10, 2008, just 500 apps were available. Eager aficionados downloaded some 10 million apps that first weekend, which was a spectacular success for Apple and the iPhone.

> " The intimacy and distributed power of a smartphone in the hands of a person is so different than anything we've faced in our business careers."
>
> Brian Moynihan
> CEO, Bank of America

Steve Jobs, being the control freak that he was, didn't want to provide third-party developers with unfettered access to the iPhone. His argument was, "The full Safari [browser] engine is inside of iPhone. And so, you can write amazing Web 2.0 and Ajax apps that look exactly and behave exactly like apps on the iPhone." [9]

One year later, the App Store made its formal debut. Jobs' hand had been forced by iPhone rebels who "jailbroke" the iPhone to customize it with non-approved apps, backed by a loud developer uproar.

And so, Apple was backed into a concept that has paid 20 million third-party developers $100 billion in software royalties as of June 2018. [10] At the launch of the App Store in July 2008, there were just 500 apps, but eager early adopters downloaded some 10 million apps, mostly games, during the first weekend of availability. [11]

The large variety of apps available for the iPhone lead Apple to trademark that famous phrase, "there's an app for that," which gained so much currency that it became an integral aspect of pop culture. [12]

The iPhone also had a major impact on the cellphone industry. Within a year, Google scrapped the first iteration of Android and showed off a new version running on a touchscreen phone. The Samsung Galaxy, Samsung's first touch screen phone, debuted in 2009. If imitation is the sincerest form of flattery, the Android camp was certainly very charming.

The debate between Android and iPhone became so heated for two Tulsa roommates that they ended up stabbing one another while arguing over their preferred brand. [13] The odd part is that this happened in Oklahoma, which demonstrates just how far the smartphone culture has spread.

But we all know it's not about the hardware, it's about the apps. The booming app economy represents a paradigm shift for users. Millions of apps have literally put the world under their control while offering them the ability to customize and personalize their smartphones infinitely.

Bank of America CEO Brian Moynihan described that control this way, "The intimacy and distributed power of a smartphone in the hands of a person are so different than anything we've faced in our business careers." [14]

That power encouraged VeritasGenetics to launch a service that delivers the results of your sequenced genome to a smartphone app. The company's myGenome genetic testing service sequences the entire human genome for $999. To grasp the significance of this, you must know that the first attempt at sequencing the human genome cost $2.7 billion and took 15 years. [15] Now you can carry around personalized genome results that required billions of dollars decades ago in the palm of your hands. That's intimacy *and* distributed power.

9. "Jobs' original vision for the iPhone: No third-party native apps," *9To5Mac*, 21-Oct-11.
10. Emil Protalinski, "Apple has paid $100 billion to developers," *VentureBeat*, 04-Jun-18.
11. Michael Liedtke, "There are now more than 2 million apps for the iPhone alone," *Associated Press*, 10-Jul-18.
12. Jennifer Van Grove, "Apple Trademarks 'There's an App for That,'" *Mashable*, 11-Oct-10.
13. Ana Lastra, "Tulsa Roommates Stab Each Other Over Debate Between iPhone & Android," *KTUL*, 17-Apr-15.
14. Edward Robinson, "The Never-Ending Story: Europe's Banks Face a Frightening Future," *Bloomberg*, 15-Feb-16.
15. Meg Tirrell, "Unlocking my genome: Was it worth it?," *CNBC*, 10-Dec-15.

Besides tracking your ancestry and monitoring your health, apps can now control just about everything in your home, thanks to the connected home trend to be explored later. Apps can provide feedback on your driving habits. They can monitor your finances and investments. They can even report on visits to your website and alert you if your web server is down.

They provide highly accurate mapping, making calling for directions a thing of the distant past. Even ringing the doorbell has been rendered redundant when you can text your imminent arrival. Apps have also become our umbilical cord to the world of social media, keeping us engaged while helping others overthrow governments.

Apps that leverage the mobile platform are growing in power. Of particular interest are apps that use Apple's augmented reality (AR) framework ARKit to create AR applications, such as IKEA Place and Amazon's AR View.

In 2009, Yelp launched augmented reality in an app feature called Monocle that layered its restaurant database over a 360-degree pan of your surroundings. IKEA and Amazon take augmented reality a step further by letting you actually "place" furniture in your surroundings, so you can visualize how new pieces will look in your place.

A new Apple app called Measure, included in the iOS 12 operating system, uses ARKit to measure real-world objects and spaces using the iPhone camera. Third-party apps, like MeasureKit, boast even more impressive features. Apps like these will revolutionize industries that are in constant need of measurements, like construction.

Other applications that interact with your environment include the category of object scanners. The first wave of these types of apps were document scanners like Scanbot, which automatically recognizes the contours of, say, an expense receipt and quickly scans it while eliminating the background. Then came apps that scanned wine bottle labels, cigar labels and car license plates, providing extensive information on the scanned object, such as vintage, price, cigar maker or car make and model.

Expect these types of apps to grow more powerful over time, able to scan all kinds of objects and quickly provide users with a host of related data. Google has already added such a feature, called Google Lens, to its Google search app. Google Lens scans any object and uses AI-powered analysis to identify items. Google Lens can, for example, what kind of breed that dog in the park is. [16] Does Mr. Spock come to mind?

One day, you'll use an app to scan the garden, get an inventory of all plants, each plant's health, watering requirements, plus any needed remedies.

Quantum leaps forward in AI-based analytics will deliver a new generation of apps that can readily diagnose a person's health, identify symptoms, and offer treatments and solutions, all by pointing an app at areas of interest, be it a lesion, a skin discoloration or body part. Sound implausible? An app like that already exists, it's called SkinVision.

The app future looks bright indeed. Apple has maintained a torrid pace of innovation, ushering in such breakthrough ideas as Retina screens, Apple Pay, Touch ID and Face ID, the latter two in rapid-fire succession. Third party developers are about to get access to Face ID, so get ready to rumble.

Pizzahut App to the Rescue

If ever there was a story that speaks volumes about the impact apps have had on our lives this may be it. A Florida woman, Cheryl Treadway, and her children were being held hostage by her estranged boy-friend, Ethan Nickerson. [1] She eventually convinced him to let her use her phone to order a pizza and wrote, "Please help. Get 911 to me" in the notes section of the order form:

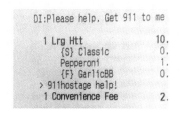

```
DI:Please help. Get 911 to me

1 Lrg Htt            10.
   {S} Classic        0.
   Pepperoni          1.
   {F} GarlicBB       0.
 > 911hostage help!
1 Convenience Fee     2.
```

Saved by the app.

1. Chris Plante, "Hostage uses Pizza Hut app to save herself and children," *The Verge*, 06-May-15.

16. Shelby Brown, "Google Lens launches on iOS to power visual searches within the Google app," *CNET*, 11-Dec-18.

Social Insurrection

Social media apps helped propel the massive upheavals of the Arab Spring revolution. Activists orchestrated Egypt's January 25, 2011 protests by reaching out to Egyptian youths on Facebook and Twitter. Their smartphone apps were instrumental in quickly spreading viral messages to get out the crowds.

Wael Ghonim, a Google marketing manager, played a crucial role in organizing the protests. Shortly after Egyptian President Hosni Mubarak stepped down from power, Ghonim credited Facebook and the internet with the success of the Egyptian people's uprising. [17] According to a popular Egyptian newspaper, *Al-Ahram*, one Egyptian man even named his first-born daughter "Facebook" to pay tribute to the role the social network played in organizing the Tahrir Square protests. [18]

The uprising had begun on Friday, December 17, 2010 in Tunisia, when a fruit vendor, Mohammed Bouazizi, set himself on fire to protest corrupt police officers who had harassed him and stolen his fruit. His bold act reverberated across the Middle East. [19]

The social media revolution of the aughts began, inauspiciously enough, with Friendster, a social network that leaped to 1 million users after just six months, a feat that had company servers straining under demand.

Friendster was not the first social network to leverage the assets of a personal contact network. That honor belongs to Six Degrees, which

17. Catharine Smith, "Egypt's Facebook Revolution: Wael Ghonim Thanks The Social Network," *HuffPost*, 11-Feb-11.
18. Alexia Tsotsis, "To Celebrate The #Jan25 Revolution, Egyptian Names His Firstborn 'Facebook'" *TechCrunch*, 19-Feb-11.
19. Marc Fisher, "In Tunisia, act of one fruit vendor sparks wave of revolution through Arab world," *The Washington Post*, 26-Mar-11.

Spelling Egypt with Mobile Apps

The Arab Spring uprisings were enabled by the widespread use of social networks and such digital tools as smartphones and apps that let participants spread viral messages about the protest movement.

A Trumpian Revolution

When Donald Trump emerged in 2015 from an early field of Republican candidates running for president, most observers discounted Trump's chances of becoming president. It was his formidable, and boisterous, army of Twitter followers, however, that quickly turned the tables in the election contest to follow. The U.S. was utterly unprepared for the upheaval social media was about to unleash. [1] The unbridled harvesting of Facebook data by Cambridge Analytica added more fuel to the social media fire. [2] Trump, Brexit and the Arab Spring are the most compelling case studies yet of how social media have profoundly shaken up world order.

1. Farhad Manjoo, "Social Media's Globe-Shaking Power," *The New York Times*, 16-Nov-16.
2. Carole Cadwalladr and Emma Graham-Harrison, "Revealed: 50 million Facebook profiles harvested for Cambridge Analytica in major data breach," *The Guardian*, 17-Mar-18.

launched in May 1997 during the dotcom boom and was named after the Stanley Milgram theory that every human is separated from others by no more than six degrees. A theory now confirmed by Facebook, which says it is either 3.57 intermediaries or 4.57 links, based on analysis of its 1.6 billion member network at the time of the study. [20]

Friendster quickly gave way to an even faster-growing phenom: music-oriented MySpace, which rose to 22 million accounts by the time of its acquisition in 2005 by News Corp. for $650 million. Those early social nets pale in comparison to Facebook today, with its 2.23 billion members. [21] Or LinkedIn, which launched around the same time as Friendster and now reports some 562 million members. [22]

The association of social media and smartphone use is quite evident. Both ignited with the launch of the iPhone in 2007. The reason is simple. Having untethered and unfettered access to one's social circle increases your social currency, as followers take delight in seeing experiences detailed in glorious smartphone images that are growing more detailed over time.

For Twitter, the mobile inflection point came in 2011. That's when then-CEO Dick Costolo reported as part of his "State of Twitter talk" that 55% of active users accessed Twitter via their mobile device. [23] By 2013, it was 60%. In 2015, it was 80%.

Posting updates with smartphones is the leading culprit of FOMO, the "fear of missing out" phenomenon (page 16). FOMO is to blame for some teens checking their social media 100 times a day. [24]

These same teens report feeling "naked" or like they're "going to die" without their phone. Naked and dying, that's how many feel when deprived of social media.

20. Jonah Engel Bromwich, "Six Degrees of Separation? Facebook Finds a Smaller Number," *The New York Times*, 04-Feb-16.
21. "Facebook Newsroom," *Facebook*, ret. 05-Aug-18.
22. "About LinkedIn," *LinkedIn*, ret. 05-Aug-18.
23. Greg Finn, "Twitter Hits 100 Million 'Active' Users," *Search Engine Land*, 08-Sep-11.
24. Chuck Hadad," Why some 13-year-olds check social media 100 times a day," *CNN*, 13-Oct-15.

Connected Home

When Amazon launched the nine-inch-tall (24 cm) Echo smart speaker on June 23, 2015, no one expected that its intelligent voice-activated assistant Alexa would one day become the connected home hit it is today.

Canalys says 56 million smart speakers were sold worldwide in 2018 — a "defining year" for smart-speaker adoption. [25] The research firm reports that smart speakers, including units made by Apple, Google and others, are today's fastest growing consumer technology. This market ferment is stirred up by the more than 4,000 devices that are powered by Alexa, offered by some 1,000 brands. [26] Alexa now boasts more than 56,750 skills or third-party apps, and Amazon has sold 100 million Alexa devices. [27] [28]

Once an Echo is connected to a Wi-Fi network, users can issue voice commands to adjust the Nest thermostat, turn Philips Hue LED lights on or off, control the TV volume, or even order pizza from Domino's. These commands can also be sent via connected home apps, allowing users to control devices remotely. Using Echo quickly becomes addicting.

The connected home trend traces its roots to the 1975 launch of X10 — the first home automation networking technology. [29] Since CES 2005, wireless entertainment has been chiefly identified with Santa-Barbara, Calif.-based Sonos and its Digital Music System. [30] Sonos speakers play music throughout the home using a proprietary, AES-encrypted peer-to-peer mesh network, known as SonosNet. Did you get that?

IMAGE COURTESY: AMAZON.COM INC.

Amazon Echo Speaker "Powered by Alexa" Debuts in June 2015

More than 100 million units of the popular voice-activated speaker have been sold. A "Prime" position on Amazon's hugely popular e-commerce site does not hurt. Pictured above is the third generation launched in September 2018.

25. Sarah Perez, "Smart speakers top AR, VR and wearables to become fastest-growing consumer tech," *TechCrunch*, 04-Jan-18.
26. Jennifer Jolly, "Do we really need an Alexa-powered toilet?," *USA Today*, 11-Jan-18.
27. Sarah Perez, "The number of Alexa skills in the U.S. more than doubled in 2018," *TechCrunch*, 02-Jan-19.
28. Lucas Matney, "More than 100 million Alexa devices have been sold," *TechCrunch*, 04-Jan-19.
29. "Home Automation," *Wikipedia*, ret. 02-Jan-19.
30. "Sonos," *Wikipedia*, ret. 02-Jan-19.

A Connected Home First: Belkin WeMo-enabled Crock-Pot

At the 2014 Consumer Electronics Show in Las Vegas, Crock-Pot, now owned by Hoboken, N.J.-based Newell Brands, together with Los Angeles-headquartered Belkin debuted the WeMo-enabled Smart Slow Cooker ($109). Now you can tell office mates that you just fired up your Crock-Pot at home using a smartphone app, how cool is that?

IMAGE COURTESY: NEWELL BRANDS INC.

Alexified

The popularity of Alexa speech recognition devices took the connected home market by surprise.

Amazon's success proves that when the user experience is greatly simplified, the market will respond. Alexa applications are proliferating so quickly I have dubbed the trend, "Alexified." Alexa-driven products include audio components, home security gear, refrigerators, toasters, shower heads, trash bins, dog collars and even toilets, such as the Kohler Numi intelligent toilet ($6,000). [1] Alexa is now a royal flush.

1.Steve Huff, "This $6,000 'Intelligent Toilet' Is The Self-Warming and Bluetooth-Enabled Throne of your Dreams," *Maxim*, 11-Jan-18.

Today, there is a panoply of wireless home platforms, including Belkin WeMo (launched in 2012), Lowe's Iris (2012), Lutron Clear Connect (2011), Samsung SmartThings (2012), Wink Labs (2014), plus Zigbee (Philips Hue; 2012), Z-Wave (Honeywell; 2014) and Wi-Fi-based systems (like TP-Link). Most offerings were initially sold as complete solutions with one vendor supplying hardware, communications protocol, a central hub and user interface. But that changed with the entry of Amazon's Echo speaker, Apple's HomeKit and Google Assistant, which are now the three most dominant voice and app-driven connected home platforms.

Consumer demand is well-established. A Lowe's study found that 70% of consumers wish they could control something in their home from their mobile device without getting out of bed, a shocking finding! [31] 😄

Not surprisingly, market researchers are bullish. A conservative forecast, provided by Statista, predicts that the U.S. smart home market, which includes home automation, security, entertainment and ambient lighting, will grow from $20 billion in 2018 to $35 billion by 2022. [32] IDC believes that the global smart home market will top $201 billion by 2022. [33]

These forecasts may sound wildly optimistic, but the connected home market is headed in many different directions. It's part of the IoT, Internet of Things, trend which is defined as a system of connected devices, objects, animals(!) or people, each with a unique identifier (UID) and the ability to transfer data over a network without requiring any interaction. IoT includes business use, covering a myriad of industrial controls, with predictions for device proliferation reaching into the billions.

In the home, new frontiers also abound. Philips announced that its Hue lighting is now available to shower your garden with a rich palette of colors.

31. "Lowe's 2014 Smart Home Survey," *Lowe's*, 25-Aug-14.
32. "Smart Home," *Statista*, ret. 14-Aug-18.
33. "New IDC Smart Home Device Tracker Forecasts Solid Growth for Connected Devices in Key Smart Home Categories," *International Data Corp.*, 29-Mar-18.

Drones

At the January 2010 Consumer Electronics Show, a French company hailing from Paris, Parrot S.A., was demonstrating a new type of gadget. The headline in Engadget, a blog for technology fans, tells all, "Parrot's AR.Drone helicopter brings military-style amusement to the iPhone." [34]

> "Parrot's AR.Drone helicopter brings military-style amusement to the iPhone."
>
> **Engadget**
> 05-Jan-10

That was the inauspicious debut of a technology that would make the world fly in just a few a years. Now stories of drone rescues surface frequently, like that of Guillermo DeVenecia, an 82-year-old ophthalmologist suffering from dementia, who went missing during the summer of 2014.

David Lesh, who uses a drone to shoot videos for his Colorado ski and snowboard business, happened to be visiting his girlfriend when he decided to pitch in with the search. His decision followed a three-day effort involving search dogs, a helicopter and hundreds of people that had proven unproductive. Lesh found DeVenecia just 20 minutes after surveying a 200-acre Wisconsin bean field from the air. "I never thought that I would be using it to find somebody," Lesh told NBC. [35]

It's stories like these that provide an inkling of a future where drones play a prominent role in many aspects of our untethered life. What is truly remarkable is that this scenario played out just four years after the introduction of the Parrot drone, which helped mainstream the category.

Parrot squandered its first-mover lead, surrendering the high-end market to Shenzhen, China-based DJI, which grew from a small office in 2006 to more than 6,000 employees worldwide. DJI, which is world-renowned for its high-end drones holds a 70%-plus market share in the $500-and-above

34. Chris Ziegler, "Parrot's AR.Drone helicopter brings military-style amusement to the iPhone," *Engadget*, 05-Jan-10.
35. Jeff Roberts, "Drone pilot locates missing 82-year-old man after three-day search," *GigaOM*, 23-Jul-14.

IMAGE COURTESY: DJI.

DJI Matrice 600 Drone Used in Venezuela Assassination Attempt

Packed with 13 pounds (6 kg) of explosives, the DJI Matrice 600 was allegedly used by terrorists aiming to assassinate Venezuelan President Nicolas Maduro. Their flying skills fell short as the drone exploded far above its intended target.

A Self-Flying Drone

Redwood City-Calif.-based Skydio Inc. has raised more than $70 million in funding to build what some might call  the ultimate selfie drone. The Skydio R-1 ($2,500) is the world's first fully autonomous drone.[1] Able to fly at up to 25 mph (40 kph), the Skydio R1 is equipped with 13 cameras (!) that use AI to detect obstacles and avoid them. To start flying, you launch the smartphone app and have your subject stand in front of the drone. The subject is now locked in and will be auto-followed by the R1. We have seen the future, and it's following us.

1. Lucas Matney, "Skydio R1 review: a mesmerizing, super-expensive self-flying drone," *TechCrunch*, 02-Apr-18.

drone market.[36] Two DJI Matrice 600 drones were used in the assassination attempt of Venezuela's President Nicolas Maduro (photo, top).

The potential of the drone market is so outsize that the FAA projected in 2012 that 30,000 drones could be plying the U.S. skies by 2020.[37] This prediction was overly optimistic, but while the forecast may be off by a few years, or more, that future drone market size is not.

Goldman Sachs estimated that the drone market could be a $100 billion opportunity between 2016 and 2020. The investment banker's projection includes $70 billion for military drones.[38] Global Market Insights says worldwide UAV, or Unmanned Aerial Vehicles as drones are officially called, spending will reach $17 billion by 2024.[39]

The market will be buoyed by growth in aerial imaging applications in advertising, archeology, cartography, disaster risk reduction and prevention, forestry management, natural resource management, search and rescue, and travel, among others. Research and Markets believes that applications in natural resource management, geospatial technologies, construction and infrastructure development will account for 52% of expenditures.

But the most transformative application may well be in farming. Drone use in agriculture includes crop field scanning with multi-spectral imaging sensors that can detect plant health; far cheaper crop dusting/spraying; GPS map creation; and livestock monitoring using thermal-imaging cameras.

In El Salvador, drones are crop dusting fields that were never sprayed before. And cost savings can be substantial too. One South African farmer claims that drones reduced pesticide use on her farm by 30%.[40]

That's just one market segment. Researchers in the U.K. and India are using machine learning and an inexpensive Parrot AR.Drone to detect violent behavior in crowds.[41] In 2010, no one could ever have imagined that a toy Parrot drone would be used for such an application.

36. "Drone Market Share Analysis & Predictions For 2018 – DJI Dominates, Parrot And Yuneec Slowly Catching Up," *DronesGlobe.com*, 24-Dec-17.
37. Shaun Waterman, "Drones over U.S. get OK by Congress," *The Washington Times*, 07-Feb-12.
38. "Drones Reporting for Work," *Goldman Sachs*, 2016.
39. "Commercial Drone Market to hit $17 billion by 2024," *Global Market Insights*, 28-Feb-18.
40. Chris Baraniuk, "The crop-spraying drones that go where tractors can't," *BBC News*, 03-Aug-18.
41. James Vincent, "Drones taught to spot violent behavior in crowds using AI," *The Verge*, 06-Jun-18.

GPS Tracking

Imagine for a moment that you are transported to the early 1990s — a time when no digital maps were available, and you had to revert to looking up addresses on paper maps. No GPS, no geolocation. Where is 77 Sunset Strip? Better call for directions. What a dark age!

> " Just as speed dialers eliminated the need to remember phone numbers, GPS will render users slavishly dependent on navigation technology, leading to a world where few can find their way around without a navigational device."
>
> **Michael Tchong**
> *Ubertrends*

That was how we navigated before 1996 when the first digital maps arrived on desktop computers thanks to MapQuest, a service that was acquired by AOL in 2000 and is now owned by Verizon. MapQuest evolved out of a division of RR Donnelley Publishing called Cartographic Services that began life in the 1960s, which goes to show how some legacy companies can be utterly clueless about emerging opportunities. [42]

Desktop mapping, while fun and productive, is no match for a smartphone. In the early days, desktop directions had to be printed out. You had to grapple with confusing printouts, and numerous "make a left turn at Main Street" and "bear right at Park Avenue" instructions while driving.

In 1999, the world got its first mobile phone with integrated GPS, the Benefon Esc!, which was sold mostly in Europe. [43] Cellphone companies didn't initially want to put GPS receivers into cellphones, but in June 2005 the Federal Communications Commission (FCC) required U.S. cellphone carriers to come up with a solution to locate customers for 911 calls. [44]

Cingular (AT&T) balked and hacked together a cell-tower triangulation method. Nextel, Sprint and Verizon, however, decided to add a GPS receiver to every cellphone. Like HDTV, this was another example of a government

42. "What is the history of online mapping?," *Quora*, 22-Jul-11.
43. Mark Sullivan, "A brief history of GPS," *PCWorld*, 09-Aug-12.
44. "First Report And Order And Notice Of Proposed Rulemaking," *Federal Communications Commission*, 03-Jun-05.

Toyota Yaris Driver Puts Too Much Faith in GPS

In March 2007, the trusting driver of a £96,000 ($125,000+) Mercedes SL500 had a lucky escape after her GPS device directed her down a winding road and straight into the River Sence in Leicestershire, U.K. Ten years later the same thing happened to a 23-year-old female who drove her Toyota Yaris into Lake Huron in Ontario, Canada. While she blamed her GPS, there was a reasonable explanation. It happened in dense fog and rain.

Waze Baiting

Waze, a mapping app owned by Alphabet (Google), lets users report the exact map location of police vehicles and label them as "visible" or "invisible" to alert other Waze users. In a digital game of cat and mouse, Miami police officers are posting false information to the traffic app in an attempt to deceive Waze users.[1] Their goal: make Waze's cop-reporting function less useful. Wonder if Wazers have any tricks left? Let me count the Waze.

1. Lizzie Plaugic, "Miami cops are falsely reporting their locations on Waze to trick drivers," *The Verge*, 12-Feb-15.

leading a trend. In 2006, NPR reported that while GPS was available to 100 million people in the U.S., few were able to use them due to a lack of applications.[45] Only one company, Nextel, allowed developers access to GPS coordinates in its phones. Then came the iPhone. By 2009, two years after its launch, 80% of owners used the iPhone's turn-by-turn directions. For all cellphone owners, the figure was half that, 40%.[46]

GPS, whether in standalone devices, built into cars or smartphones, has reshaped human behavior. Blind trust in GPS has led to several notable accidents, including a Canadian woman who drove her Toyota Yaris into a lake in Ontario, Canada in May 2016 (photo). Embarrassed, she explained that she expected her GPS unit to guide her in the right way.[47]

Today, smartphones and tablets are a cartographer's dream come true: 3D elevations, realtime traffic reports, Google Street View, and in apps like Waze, even socialization, avatars and police spotting (sidebar).

GPS ushered in another technology: geolocation — identifying the geographic location of an object. Geolocation lets companies offer advertisers location-based marketing — targeting ads based on a specific map position. That explains why Google has come under fire for tracking users even after Google Maps' Location History feature has been turned off.[48]

The impact of GPS-based navigation on our lifestyle extends far beyond mere convenience. Just as speed dialers eliminated the need to remember phone numbers, GPS will render users slavishly dependent on navigation technology, leading to a world where few can find their way around without a navigational device.

Up next: GPS chips from Broadcom that will boost accuracy to 12 inches (30 cm).[49] OK Google, where are my chocolate chip cookies?

45. Dan Charles, "GPS Is Smartening Up Your Cell Phone," *NPR*, 25-Sep-06.
46. Jenna Wortham, "Sending GPS Devices the Way of the Tape Deck?," *The New York Times*, 07-Jul-09.
47. Sebastian Toma, "Woman Drives Her Car into a Lake, Blames the GPS," *autoevolution*, 16-May-16.
48. Shannon Liao, "Google still tracks you through the web if you turn off Location History," *The Verge*, 13-Aug-18.
49. Samuel Moore, "Superaccurate GPS Chips Coming to Smartphones in 2018," *IEEE Spectrum*, 21-Sep-17.

Control Enthusiast

In February 2006, Libby Copeland, a writer for *The Washington Post*, penned this notable quote: "There's something peculiarly modern about this [pickiness] phenomenon, something aligned with our dark privilege of too much, this consumeriffic culture in which jeans and houses and breasts and ringtones are customizable." [50]

IMAGE COURTESY: BREVILLE USA INC.

Breville/PolyScience The Control Freak Lives Up to Its Billing

Sydney, Australia-based Breville acquired PolyScience Culinary product distribution rights in 2014. The resulting collaboration yielded the first product to proudly use "Control Freak" as a badge of honor. True to its label, The Control Freak ($1,800) lets you cook with uncanny precision, accurately measuring, setting and holding every cooking temperature between 86-482° Fahrenheit (30-250° Celsius).

What Copeland was alluding to but couldn't quite put her finger on was a dark new phenomenon, an unattractive by-product of a world where many are being spoiled beyond belief. Continued Copeland, "Centuries from now, scientists may point to this as the moment in time when the pickiness gene became dominant."

That pickiness was abundantly clear in this Craigslist ad that one particularly intrepid woman ran in April 2006 — a excellent example of personal ads that seek partners "spec'd" in practically impossible to satisfy terms:

"Fabulous Femme Foodie - Seeking Similar Gastronome - 34 (pacific heights). So, if you know the difference between Thai and Laotian, Basque and Tapas, Afghani and Indian, or El Salvadorian and Mexican; know or are willing to believe that the same dish cooked in a clay pot, a cast iron pan, a Le Creuset pot, and a stainless steel one will in fact taste different..."

The naked truth, pardon the dating pun, is that our indulgent culture has made everyone far more exacting. That power harbored in your smartphone is conspiring to make you a control freak. But that term is

50. Libby Copeland, "Picky, Picky," *The Washington Post*, 06-Feb-06.

IMAGE COURTESY: JUNECLOUD.

Deliveries iPad Package Tracking App: A Control Enthusiast Delight

Why limit yourself to an ugly online tracking site when you can have the Deliveries iPad app ($5) show you in beautiful detail where your package is, and how long it will take to get your grubby hands on your new purchase.

Predictive Car Rides

In 2019, Uber will be valued at $120 billion because it is disrupting the world of transportation, threatening taxi drivers around the world. In New York, a sale of seven taxi medallions in January 2018 generated, on average, $184,500. In 2013, those same medallions sold for nearly $1 million. [1] In San Francisco, only 17% of taxi drivers earn a sustainable level of income. [2] What do Uber and Lyft offer that taxis don't? A prediction of arrival, or ETA. Could control enthusiasm be the reason for their success?

1. Paul Berger, "Is the Market for New York City Taxi Medallions Showing Signs of Life?," *The Wall Street Journal*, 17-Jan-18.
2. Michael Cabanatuan, " Reviving SF's taxi industry: The city is looking at solutions," *San Francisco Chronicle*, 02-May-18.

negative, so inspired by that National Car Rental advertising campaign the trend is labeled Control Enthusiast.

National's ads feature former *Seinfeld* actor, Patrick Warburton, who, in his inimitable style, plays a very demanding car rental customer. In one television commercial, Warburton proclaims, "control is so, what's the word…sexy." In another, he concludes, "control suits me."

The first commercial also makes this apt observation, "And I don't have to talk to any humans unless I want to, and I don't." Who wants to talk to irritating human beings when one can avoid it? Avoiding humans is part of the control enthusiast's repertoire.

The trend also manifests itself in other ways. Old-school luxury meant having someone else deal with your luggage. The control enthusiast way is rolling your own wheeled bags. I'm fine thanks…I don't need any help!

Jazzed by technology's ability to free users from wires and to instantly gratify, people are gradually demanding greater control over transactions. Shoppers used to avoid self-check-out registers. "Who wants to talk to a machine?" the old thinking went. Today, we're more aligned with Warburton, "I don't want to waste my time talking to fools."

Another technology that echoes this undercurrent is package tracking. On any given business day, UPS handles 143 million package tracking requests. [51] FedEx processes another 6.5 million. [52] That's *150 million* control enthusiast commands submitted each day.

One company that has leveraged the control enthusiast trend is Domino's Pizza. In 2008, Domino's launched the food delivery industry's first pizza order tracking mechanism. [53] Available initially only via the Domino's website, the company added pizza tracking to its mobile app in 2011 and smartwatches in 2014.

The pizza maker's strategy of making tracking central to its marketing message is catching on. One San Francisco florist, Rossi & Rovetti, announced delivery tracking in 2013, mentioning Domino's in its press release. [54] The company no longer appears to promote that feature, a big mistake. San Francisco-based BenchMade Modern tags each sofa with a tracking device so you can follow its route to you. [55] Meanwhile, Amazon has one-upped both UPS and FedEx by showing an approaching delivery on a map.

Air Canada was one of the first airlines to offer luggage tracking back in 2004. It was a smart move because who wants to deal with the person staffing the luggage service desk after losing a bag? Delta upped the ante by letting passengers track luggage in realtime using its mobile app. The company spent $50 million on an RFID system that uses a chip embedded in luggage tags to keep track of bags. [56] Delta, you're hearing us!

In 2014, Burger King abandoned its 40-year-old slogan, "Have It Your Way," for an ostensibly more personal "Be Your Way." [57] Was that the right move?

51. "UPS Fact Sheet," *UPS*, ret. 04-Jan-19.
52. "FedEx Fact Sheet," *FedEx*, Jan-14.
53. "Pizza Tracker Tech Allows Domino's Customers to Track Orders from Store to Door," *Hospitality Technology*, 05-Feb-08.
54. "San Francisco Florist is now doing for online flower delivery like Domino's did for online pizza ordering," *PRNewswire-*, 05-Feb-13.
55. Abigail Stone, "The Best Online Sofa," *The Wirecutter*, 05-Mar-18.
56. Ashton Kang, "Delta introduces innovative baggage tracking process," *Delta News Hub*, 28-Apr-16.
57. "Burger King scrapping 'Have It Your Way' slogan," *CNBC*, 19-May-14.

Pushbutton Society

On March 31, 2015, Amazon.com launched Dash — a small, branded Wi-Fi pushbutton that, when pressed, instantly places an order for the product in question. Dash represents the ultimate convergence of Unwired's Connected Home and Control Enthusiast subtrends.

Amazon's Dash button joins other retailers and restaurants who have introduced buttons that offer consumers instant gratification. In 2012, Red Tomato Pizza in Dubai launched the VIP Fridge Magnet — a pizza box-shaped magnet that could place a pizza order by relying on the user's smartphone Bluetooth connection. [58]

Advertising agency TBWA Dubai described the results of this innovative strategy as follows, "In just four weeks, on a total marketing budget of $9,000, deliveries increased by 500% with 3,240 requests from existing customers and 97,133 requests from new customers." [59]

In June 2014, Paris, France-based Darty, a consumer electronics retailer, launched Bouton Darty, a 7-cm (2.75-inch) square magnetic button that once pressed connects via Bluetooth or Wi-Fi to Darty's support center. Subscribers then receive a call back in less than a minute. Bouton Darty costs € 25 ($28.50) plus a monthly subscription of € 2. [60]

Instant gratification and precise control is the motivation behind Hilton Worldwide installing voice controls in selected hotel properties, probably welcoming the same control enthusiasts targeted by National Car Rental. The launch campaign says it all: "Room Controls At Your Fingertips."

IMAGE COURTESY: HILTON WORLDWIDE HOLDINGS INC.

Hilton's Message Is Crystal Clear: Room Controls at Your Fingertips

Hilton is rolling out a connected room experience to its hotels, allowing guests to control and personalize aspects of their room, such as lighting and temperature using their mobile Hilton Honors app.

58. Samanta Murphy, "Refrigerator Magnet Lets You Order a Pizza in One Tap," *Mashable*, 26-Mar-12.
59. "VIP Fridge Magnet," *Welovead*, ret. 16-Aug-18.
60. Gaël Weiss, "Bouton Darty : un bouton connecté pour les aider tous," *FrAndroid*, 05-Jun-18.

Amazon Dash Button: Instant Gratification on Demand

Amazon's Dash buttons let users instantly buy products from Amazon at the touch of a button. The order is placed untethered and unfettered via Wi-Fi. Now that's what some would call dream shopping.

There is no more prominent, shinier button than the Nest Learning Thermostat — a beautifully designed click-wheel that invites you to click it. Tony Fadell, who is called "one of the fathers of the Apple iPod," founded Nest Labs in 2010 and launched its innovative smart thermostat in October 2011. [61] That explains Nest's use of the click wheel, a feature of the first iPod.

In a world where 30% admit never agreeing about room temperature with other household members, and 27% reportedly take matters into their own hands, the Nest Learning Thermostat is welcome news indeed. [62] Nest and other smart thermostat makers introduced a neutral, digital third party to solve temperature disagreements.

As this generation and future ones become reliant on instant-gratification, solutions like these, our pushbutton society will increasingly become more demanding. Push a button and your inventory of Red Bull is replenished. Push a button and track your Uber. Push a button, and your garage door opens. Push a button and receive an instant call back. Push a button and curtains close, lights dim, and your flat panel rises out of its TV lift cabinet at the foot of the bed. Is everything to your liking, Mr. Bond? And now, thanks to Logitech Pop, we have the ultimate pushbutton, which can be placed anywhere, ready at your connected home's beck and call. [63]

Bouton Darty Provides Technical Support on Demand

Need instant tech support satisfaction? Darty, a French consumer electronics chain, offers subscribers a button that wirelessly submits tech support requests. Button pushers are promised a call back in one minute.

The ability to wield all this power has, unsurprisingly, led to a culture of impatience. A survey from Edison Research found that 67% of complaining social media users expect to hear back within a day of pushing that message submit button. Four out of 10 want to hear *within an hour*. [64] And among millennials that impatience is even more pronounced. [65]

Google reports that searches for "open now" have tripled in the past two years, while searches for "store hours" dropped. [66]

As Queen famously sings, "I want it all, and I want it now."

61. "Tony Fadell," *Wikipedia*, ret. 17-Aug-18.
62. Chris Taylor, "Couples fight for control in Battle of the Thermostat," *Reuters*, 29-Jul-14.
63. Micah Singleton, "The Logitech Pop is the smart home button you've always wanted," *The Verge*, 11-Aug-16.
64. Jay Baer, "42% of Consumers Complaining in Social Media Expect 60 Minute Response Time," *Convince & Convert*, 2012.
65. "Big Banks Show Significant Gains in Customer Satisfaction as Midsize Banks Decline and Regionals Plateau, J.D. Power U.S. Retail Banking Study Finds," *J.D. Power*, 28-Apr-16.
66. Lisa Gevelber, "Micro-Moments Now: Why expectations for 'right now' are on the rise," *Think With Google*, Aug-17.

Singles Nation

They were first spotted during the 1970s in that ahead-of-the-curve state California. No, not yuppies, bumper stickers proclaiming, "Happiness Is Being Single." Whoever came up with that slogan was acutely aware of a big wave washing ashore. America, and the rest of the world for that matter, is becoming a nation of singles.

The proportion of married couples has been shrinking for decades. In 1930, married couples accounted for 84% of households. [67] In 2008, married couples as a proportion of American households slipped into a minority for the first time, dipping below 50% (chart). The Singles Nation trend took off during the 1970s and continued its ascendance with 48% of the nation's 126 million households in 2017 made up of married couples, according to the Census Bureau. [68]

Many contemporary phenomena fuel the trend. A significant factor is couples postponing marriage. More people are also living with their parents, in part because they're burdened by student loan debt. Out-of-the-closet gays have also had some impact. More women in the workforce mean a decreased dependence on financial support.

Another influence is the Unwired Ubertrend, which has fostered an untethered generation, one that greatly treasures the value of freedom,

IMAGE COURTESY: CREATIVE COMMONS LICENSE.

Happiness Is Being Single License Plate Frame Sends Loud Message

Could a subtle cultural message from the 1970s be responsible for accelerating a trend that began in the 1950s? Only time will tell, but "control enthusiasm" appears to be accelerating Singles Nation.

67. Sam Roberts, "To Be Married Means to Be Outnumbered," *The New York Times*, 15-Oct-06.
68. "Family Households with Married Couples," *U.S. Bureau of the Census*, 20-Dec-17.

and also bolsters the growing control enthusiast syndrome seen earlier.

The difficulty of pleasing a modern partner is illustrated by a University of Texas study, whose author concluded that "What it boils down to is that a [beautiful] woman who has it all, wants it all." [69] Did we really need a survey to confirm that?

Our overly indulgent culture has made everyone wishing for more. Hollywood's flitting-about ways are rubbing off on Joe Six Pack, leading many to think that "the next one" will be better.

Celebrity ogling magazines have many wishing for an Eva Longoria-style wedding, complete with rings donated by Piaget. But while they wait for that better one, many men and women end up living alone or, worse, with their parents.

The Census Bureau reports that one-third of young adults lived in their parents' home in 2015. [70] The *Failure to Launch* group was larger than those living with a spouse or romantic partner, living alone or with roommates, or living as single parents.

The trend is global. In Australia, one in four households is headed by a single person. And the trend Down Under has increased sharply since the 1970s, paralleling the U.S. experience. [71] In such large cities as Paris, 50% of dwellings are inhabited by just one person.

In Japan, 54% of Japanese women in their late 20s are single, up from 31% in 1985. [72] And about half of single women ages 35 to 54 have no intention to marry.

Not that there's anything wrong with marriage. Despite their new-age attitudes, most young people still want to marry and settle down.

The reality is that more millennials seem to be concluding that being single and waiting for that better next one is a preferable pastime, with far-reaching consequences. Is it time to revive that 1970s bumper sticker?

Single Tapete: A Wallpaper Designed for Single People

Invented in Germany by Andrea Baum and designed by Susanne Schmidt, Single Tapete shows attractive, life-size images of fictitious persona, like "Christine" above, designed to help single people feel less lonely.

Co-Viewing

Our growing solitude goes beyond single households. A 2004 Knowledge Networks study found that 45% of primetime viewers now watch TV by themselves, versus 31% a decade earlier. Researchers now consider familial television viewing so remarkable that they have coined a new term for it: "co-viewing." [1] You can't make these things up. Enjoy your TV show.

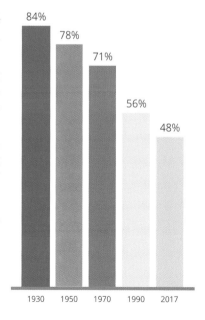

Married Households Share of Total

- 84% — 1930
- 78% — 1950
- 71% — 1970
- 56% — 1990
- 48% — 2017

2018 U.S. Census Bureau

1. "Co-Viewing with Kids," *WETA*, ret. 04-Jan-19.

69. Lee Dye, "Study: Beautiful Women Want It All," *ABC News*, 26-Mar-08.
70. Jonathan Vespa, "Jobs, Marriage and Kids Come Later in Life," *U.S. Census Bureau*, Aug-17.
71. David De Vaus and Lixia Qu, "Demographics of living alone," *Australian Government*, Mar-15.
72. Paul Wiseman, "No sex please — we're Japanese," *USA Today*, 02-Jun-04.

The faceless masses of today's society, emboldened by an anonymous internet culture, have lowered the barrier of civilized behavior. An undesired side effect of the Casual Living Ubertrend, which breeds informality, is the evaporation of decorum.

6

Casual Living

The Evaporation of Decorum

Warning signs abound: road rage, vicious online comments, drunken football louts, surveillance videos that graphically capture incredible incidents, including police beatings, child cruelty, and other uncouth behavior. It's an ignominious list that keeps growing daily. The Casual Living Ubertrend starts innocently enough with "Casual Friday" — a trend that ushered in informal wear in business settings. As the dress-down trend spread, however, it also coincided with a series of frightening parallel phenomena, including violent videos, trolling and cyberbullying, plus many other manifestations that can only be attributed to a culture that cares less and less about human decency, while flaunting a casual disregard for civility. Society's cesspool is deepening. And social media is its vortex.

Casual Friday

In the 1940s, a prominent Hawaiian surfer, Duke Kahanamoku, approached the management of the Royal Hawaiian Hotel and proposed that staff begin wearing Hawaiian shirts every Friday. [1] The trend, initially called Aloha Shirt Friday, was renamed Aloha Friday in 1966.

Typical Aloha (Hawaiian) Shirt: Diamond Head Lighthouse

A tropical patterned Aloha shirt ($40) sold by Shaka Time, "Hawaii's trendiest fashion retailer," is representative of the eye of the storm that ignited the Casual Living Ubertrend.

On August 21, 1959, Hawaii became the 50th U.S. state, causing the number of visitors to jump from 296,000 per year to 1.7 million between 1960 and 1970. [2] The popularity of the Hawaiian islands among U.S. travelers was responsible for a mainland boom in Hawaiian cultural artifacts, from tiki lounges to surfing to Aloha, or Hawaiian, shirts.

What made Duke Kahanamoku so influential with Royal Hawaiian Hotel management was his prominent role in popularizing an ancient Hawaiian sport, surfing, beginning in Southern California in 1912. [3] How could one individual be so instrumental in kickstarting both surfing and a casual office dress trend? Kahanamoku had help from the Hawaiian garment industry, which came up with the idea to rechristen the trend Aloha Friday in 1966. [4]

By 1985, Hawaii tourist arrivals approached 5 million, exposing many visitors to the islands' more casual lifestyle. [5] In the 1970s, Aloha Friday slowly began spreading east to California, and by the 1990s it had made its

IMAGE COURTESY: DIAMOND HEAD LIGHTHOUSE/SHAKA TIME INC.

1. Maleko McDonnell, "When did we first start celebrating Aloha Friday?," *KITV*, 27-May-16.
2. Landess Kearns, "5 Reasons America Became Obsessed With Hawaii In The 1960s," *HuffPost*, 06-Dec-17.
3. "Duke Kahanamoku," *Wikipedia*, ret. 23-Aug-18.
4. Krissy Clark, "Dress code: The history of 'business casual,'" *Marketplace*, 17-Aug-12.
5. "Tourism Looks to the Future," *Hawaii's Economy*, Jul-99.

way to New York, acquiring a new moniker along the way, Casual Friday. [6]

Casual Friday spurred a dominant office fashion, business casual, a 1980s apparel trend that sprang from Silicon Valley's freewheeling ways. Thanks to brands as such Gap and Levi's Dockers, and backed by such Silicon Valley stalwarts as Apple, Intel and Sun Microsystems, business casual came to stand for khaki pants and button-down plaid shirts.

In 1994, Electronic Arts Co-Founder Bing Gordon told *FORTUNE*, "If you don't have anything to say, wear a suit." [7] To this day, "suits" is a derogatory term used to describe staid, old-school executives living in the past. "t-shirts," on the other hand, denote cool cats, usually techy types.

As University of Nevada, Las Vegas Associate Professor of History Deirdre Clemente tells it, khaki pants and a button-down collar shirt became the baseline for dressing down because both garments were designed for practicality. British soldiers in mid-19th-century India wore khaki for its durability. The button-down shirt originated on England's polo fields where it prevented the collar from flapping up during a match. [8]

Women joined the trend by ditching their pseudo-men's suits, sweater sets, and most of their jewelry, makeup and shoulder pads, instead favoring simpler monochromatic outfits matched with more sensible shoes.

One of the earliest, non-Silicon Valley adopters of business casual was Pittsburgh-based Alcoa in 1991, *Wall Street Journal* fashion columnist Teri Agins writes in her book *The End of Fashion*. But Alcoa employees could only dress casually for two weeks after donating to the United Way. At the opposite end of the spectrum was J.P. Morgan Chase, which did not loosen its dress code until June 2016. [9]

By 1996, nearly 75% of American businesses had introduced a Casual Friday policy, up from 37% just four years earlier. [10] In the early aughts, Rowenta reported that only 12% of U.S. companies would ever consider returning to a more formal dress code.

The business casual impact on traditional office apparel, including suits and ties, continues to this day. A Travelodge study of 2,000 workers found that only one in 10 U.K. employees still wears a suit to work. [11]

NPD observed a brief uptick in tailored clothing sales in 2011, with men's suits and sports coats jumping 10.8%, ties and other neckwear rising 10.3%, and men's shirts gaining 2.3%. [12] Another short rebound took place in the first half of 2013 when sales of sports coats rose 14%, and suit separates jumped a remarkable 55%. [13]

But by 2017 sales of men's tailored clothing resumed its steady decline. [14] That downtrend is the result of another substantial cultural change brought about by the Casual Living Ubertrend, the popularity of activewear.

Revenge of the Suit

In 2002, sales of men's tailored clothing, including suits and sportcoats, had fallen 1% to $4.7 billion, after declining 0.8% in 2000, reported NPD. Suit makers received good tidings that year when Bear Stearns and Lehman Brothers reinstituted a formal business dress code, designed to sharpen their image. [1] The joy didn't last long. In 2008, both investment banks collapsed in the wake of a self-inflicted credit crisis. [2] Many suits were filed in the aftermath, proving that sharp suits can't hold a candle to lawsuits.

1. Cheryl Lu-Lien Tan, "The Office Coverup," *The Wall Street Journal*, 05-Aug-06.
2. Lauren Ezell, "From Bear to Lehman: Documents Reveal an Alternate History," *Frontline*, 01-May-12.

6. "Casual Friday," *Wikipedia*, ret. 23-Aug-18.
7. Lauren Goldstein, "What We Wore Simply put, the history of office attire for men goes something like this: suits, suits, suits, suits, khakis," *FORTUNE*, 22-Nov-99.
8. Deidre Clemente, "Why American Workers Now Dress So Casually," *The Atlantic*, 22-May-17.
9. Emily Glazer, "J.P. Morgan Says Employees Don't Always Have to Wear Suits," *The Wall Street Journal*, 03-Jun-16.
10. Linda Himelstein, "Levi's Vs. The Dress Code," *Bloomberg BusinessWeek*, 31-Mar-96.
11. "The death of the business suit?," *Business Traveler*, 11-Feb-18.
12. Andria Cheng, "Men's Apparel Turns Alpha," *The Wall Street Journal*, 17-Nov-11.
13. "NPD Reports Tailored Is Back And Driving The Growth In Apparel Sales," *The NPD Group*, 24-Sep-13.
14. Dorothy Crouch, "According to The NPD Group, Athleisure Is Here To Stay—For Now," *California ApparelNews*, 23-Aug-18.

The New Daily Wardrobe — "Caj"

The three pillars of the "going caj" trend that dispenses with formality and that has been adopted by people worldwide, stresses easy-to-care-for fabrics and comfort above all. Pictured, left to right: Silver "pre-distressed" jeans, a replica of the original Colchester sneaker ($95) and an "Overdressed" t-shirt from PrettyLittleThing ($18).

Formal Entertaining Decline

The preference for less formality has also led to less formal entertaining. On February 27, 2003, *USA Today* reported that formal china sales have been flat in the past 10 years due to an "overwhelming trend" toward casual entertaining. Most people now entertain and live in the kitchen, which has caused a decline in the value of formal dining room furniture, because people don't use dining rooms anymore. [1]

1. Scott Reyburn, "Why Are Antiques So Cheap? Because Everyone Lives in the Kitchen," *The New York Times*, 26-Oct-18.

The Global Uniform

Ever wonder why the U.S. has been so successful at unifying the world's wildly diverging clothing fashions? If there is one enduring fashion statement America has exported globally, it's blue jeans. Then came t-shirts and sneakers, both of which have become part of a de facto global uniform. Now, people around the globe are getting ready to adopt yet another North American fashion trend, athleisure.

In 1853, San Francisco was in the midst of the gold rush and well on its way to becoming America's largest city west of the Mississippi River. [15] A Bavarian immigrant and astute merchant, named Levi Strauss, noticed the need for clothes that could withstand the rigors of mining. His first creation was a pair of miner's overalls made from brown cotton tent canvas. [16]

For the next pair, Strauss and tailor Jacob Davis decided to switch to denim, which was shorthand for *serge de Nimes*, a twill fabric produced in the south of France. To make the pants less susceptible to dirt, Strauss dyed the fabric an indigo blue. By the 1860s, Levi Strauss' blue pants had become the daily wear of choice of miners, farmers and cattlemen throughout the West.

In 1873, Strauss paid $69, the price of a patent application, to buy an idea from a Russian tailor living in Reno, Nev. who had developed a technique for making miner's pants stronger by riveting critical seams. The riveted pants were reportedly nicknamed "jeans" after the city of Genoa, where sailors wore blue cotton canvas. However, they were still referred to as "overalls" until the 1950s, when teens started calling them jeans. That led Levi's to update its ads and packaging to reflect this change.

15. "San Francisco Gold Rush," *SF-info.org*, ret. 24-Aug-18.
16. Jan Adkins, "A History Of Blue Jeans: From Miners' Wear to American Classic," *Mother Earth News*, Jul-90.

Over the next century, Levi Strauss' invention would become a global sensation, an item worn by many citizens of the western world, and even leading to a "designer jeans" market. In 2016, 143 years after the official introduction of Levi's jeans, the Cotton Inc. Lifestyle Monitor reported that consumers now own nine denim garments on average, including six pairs of jeans. [17]

The story is much the same for t-shirts. The U.S. Navy first used them around the 1898 Spanish American War.[18] Today, the world buys more than 10 billion t-shirts each year. [19] And the t-shirt market, with or without promotional messages, has become a $20 billion industry. Not too shabby for underwear.

The Casual Living Ubertrend also impacted footwear. In 1892, the Colchester Rubber Co., based in Colchester, Conn., introduced the world's first basketball sneaker, a five-inch high-top. [20] That same year, the United States Rubber Co., one of the original Dow Jones 12 companies, acquired Colchester Rubber. [21] In 1916, U.S. Rubber consolidated its 30 footwear companies under one brand name, Keds. They eventually were nicknamed sneakers because they were so quiet, allowing a wearer to sneak up on someone.

As we all know, fashion directions come and go. While 64% of women surveyed two decades ago chose denim jeans as their favorite apparel item, today consumers are moving to athleisure. Still, the global denim jeans market is predicted to generate $130 billion in sales in 2021, up from $52 billion in 2007. [22]

Athleisure

Consumers are signaling that they want casual clothing that can be worn both for exercising and general use. Hip-hop and yoga initially fanned the flames of the athleisure look. Now a host of manufacturers are riding the wave of comfort with athletic style.

In the past, it was considered appropriate to dress up for travel or when going out. Now it's commonplace to see people wearing sweatpants on planes or having dinner in what once deemed underwear, leggings.

Casual Living has been a boon to athleisure apparel, a contraction of athletic and leisure, which blends comfort with function. Consumers want activewear items that can transition easily from Zumba to social settings. Athleisure is part of the activewear market, which increased 2% to reach $48 billion in 2017. [23] In comparison, the overall U.S. apparel market *declined* 2% to $215 billion in 2017.

The athleisure trend extends to footwear. The "sport leisure" style has become the largest category in the U.S. sneaker market, beating performance-oriented footwear. Sales of sport leisure style sneakers increased 17% in 2017 to $9.6 billion. [24]

This trend was foreseen by many science fiction movies, which often feature form-fitting "catsuits" as the apparel of choice of the future.

Athleisure: Fabletics Salar Mesh PowerHold Leggings

With the market opting for the convergence of gym and leisure wear, apparel and footwear manufacturers now deliver both comfort and function in "athleisure" wear. Leggings, in particular, have become very popular with consumers, ditching their mostly monochromatic past and adopting colorful patterns. In 2017, U.S. imports of women's elastic knit pants surpassed those of jeans for the first time, according to the U.S. Census Bureau.

17. "A Perennial Favorite," *Cotton Inc. Lifestyle Monitor*, 20-Oct-16.
18. "T-shirt," *Wikipedia*, ret. 16-Dec-18.
19. Jeremy Howell, "How the T-shirt became a million dollar idea," *BBC News*, 27-Oct-17.
20. "Colchester Rubber Co.," *Wikipedia*, ret. 16-Dec-18.
21. "United States Rubber Company," *Wikipedia*, ret. 16-Dec-18.
22. "Retail sales of the denim jeans market worldwide from 2012 to 2021,' *Statista*, ret. 16-Dec-18.
23. "Millennials, Athleisure, and E-commerce Continue to Drive Apparel Sales, But Growth Has Slowed," *The NPD Group*, 21-Feb-18.
24. Andria Cheng, "The Athleisure Trend Isn't Taking A Rest," *Forbes*, 09-Feb-18.

Rude Behavior

"I'm sorry, Sir, but I do not believe we've been properly introduced," is a classic cartoon and movie punch line that exemplifies British politeness. But the way U.K. football fans behave nowadays has given the British a reputation for acting like drunken louts rather than being well-mannered.

Society has shed its stiff upper lip and is evolving into a culture that is far more casual and relaxed, but also much more unruly, as courtesy and good manners have become a thing of the past. A major side effect of the Casual Living Ubertrend is the evaporation of decorum.

Evidence of this undesirable phenomenon is cropping up everywhere. On Broadway, badly behaving audiences are all too common, reports the *New York Post*.[25] Ringing phones, glowing screens as people text, crinkling wrappers are par for the course in theaters these days. The situation has been exacerbated by theatergoers who can now drink alcohol during many shows, which results in fidgeting, rattling ice cups, and even patrons nodding off and snoring, or laughing inappropriately.

To challenge unruly behavior, actors have been forced to respond more aggressively too. In the 2015 revival of *She Loves Me*, a cellphone went off as Laura Benanti was singing *Will He Like Me*. "I'll wait," Benanti said. The phone continued to ring. "We'll all wait," she added, and the orchestra stopped playing until the phone was silenced.

Broadway is not the only to suffer; sports fan behavior has become spectacularly bad in the past four decades. The Bleacher Report produced a summary in 2011 of the worst fans in sports history, a list topped by a Philadelphia Phillies fan, a city notorious for poor fan behavior. [26]

> "The Casual Living Ubertrend is fueled, in part, by the rapid growth of the world's urban populations, which has turned cities into faceless masses of people. Anonymity encourages offensive behavior because there is no shame when acting irresponsibly."
>
> **Michael Tchong**
> Ubertrends

25. Michael Riedel, "Actors say rude audiences are destroying Broadway," *New York Post*, 04-Nov-17.
26. Ed Novelo, "The 30 Absolute Worst Fans in Sports History," *Bleacher Report*, 24-Aug-11.

The fan in question, Matthew Clemmens, 21, was harassing an off-duty cop and his 16- and 11-year-old daughters when he stuck his finger in his mouth and vomited on the younger girl and her father.

The people who should know better, parents, are behaving equally poorly. In one youth basketball game, parents charged the court to throw punches at the referee. Harassment is so bad that 70% of new referees quit within three years, according to the National Association of Sports Officials. [27]

The trend is not limited to the U.S. In Denmark, a soccer fan ran on the field in 2007 and tried to throw a punch at the referee. [28] Thanks to the wonders of YouTube, fans around the world can now enjoy these sordid spectacles. The role YouTube plays in disseminating all these graphic examples of uncivilized behavior is covered in the next chapter, Voyeurgasm.

In 2004, one of the worst brawls in U.S. sports history took place near the end of an Indiana Pacers-Detroit Pistons game. Fans and players threw punches, while one spectator even threw a chair. Nine players were suspended more than 140 games by the NBA for the fracas commissioner David Stern called "shocking, repulsive and inexcusable."

The Casual Living Ubertrend is fueled, in part, by the rapid growth of the world's urban populations, which has turned cities into faceless masses of people. Anonymity encourages offensive behavior because there is no shame when acting irresponsibly. The fact that spectators are now actively and aggressively getting involved in public events is just the latest twist in this unsettling Ubertrend.

The lack of courtesy has spilled over into politics. During a heated healthcare bill debate, Texas Republican Rep. Randy Neugebauer is heard yelling "baby killer" while fellow Michigan Congressman Bart Stupak speaks. [29]

The lack of etiquette infects not only Washington. Over on MSNBC, Chris Matthews hosts a four-member panel during *Hardball* — a cacophony of rising voices, struggling to be heard over the competitive din. Matthews has the less than appealing habit of rarely letting anyone finish a point. The *Hardball* spectacle is not alone. Many of these panels have become ugly slugfests, marred by name calling and even cursing.

The incidences of moral turpitude are not limited to the New World. In Italy, a fist fight broke out in 2010 in an Italian newsroom behind a seemingly clueless anchor. [30] Fist fights among elected officials now happen regularly.

Anonymity was certainly not involved in an incident that had Faith Hill berating a fan for grabbing her husband's private parts during a Soul2Soul 2007 tour stop at the Cajundome in Lafayette, Louisiana. The incident shows just how brazen society has become. [31]

The list of incidents is endless. Congressman gets spat on, Kanye West interrupts Taylor Swift's VMA acceptance speech, babies are routinely left out in 100-plus-degree car heat. The lack of sensibility and courtesy appears bottomless. Human indecency and cruelty have lost their boundaries.

Wild Plassen

In Holland, *wild plassen*, "wild peeing" or public urination, has caused a national outcry. One Dutch company, called Urilift, marketing under the Pop-Up Toilet Co. brand, has developed a creative solution, which lets municipal governments rapidly deploy and neatly store away its space-age urinoirs. [1] As its name implies, these urinoirs actually lower to the ground to

hide the receptacle of this unsavory habit. San Francisco chose to install an open-air urinal to tackle the problem. [2] The Paris version, dubbed *Uritrottoir* (uri-sidewalk; photo), is a urinal cleverly disguised as a planter box with a capacity of 180 *pipis*, as the French put it. [3]

1. "Dag en nacht, voor man en vrouw," *Straat Beeld*, 25-Jan-18.
2. Robin Abcarian, "Open-air urinal in San Francisco park has no designs on privacy," *Los Angeles Times*, 01-Apr-16.
3. Mymy, "Le pipi des mecs est bienvenu dans la rue, celui des femmes reste un tabou," *madmoiZelle*, 13-Aug-18.

27. Bill Pennington, "Parents Behaving Badly: A Youth Sports Crisis Caught on Video," *The New York Times*, 18-Jul-18.
28. "Football spectator hit referee," *YouTube*, 02-Jun-07.
29. Jake Sherman and Meredith Shiner, "GOP lawmaker: I yelled 'baby killer,'" *Arizona Republic*, 22-Mar-10.
30. "Epic Newsroom Fight Behind Anchor Caught On Camera," *HuffPost*, 04-May-10.
31. "Faith Hill Confronts Fan From Stage for Groping Husband Tim McGraw at Louisiana Show," *Associated Press*, 01-Aug-07.

Raging Against The Machine

Casual Living

In 1988, Los Angeles news station KTLA coined the term "road rage" after a string of shootings on the city's freeways. [32] According to the *St. James Encyclopedia of Popular Culture*, the term was inspired by "roid rage," which refers to the sudden, violent outbursts people experience after taking steroids. [33]

It should be stated that "aggressive driving" — including speeding, tailgating, weaving, red light running and rapid lane changes — was around long before 1988. In a 1950 Walt Disney cartoon, *Motor Mania*, mild-mannered character Goofy experiences a radical transformation: "Once behind the wheel, a strange phenomenon takes place. Mr. Walker [Goofy] is charged with an overwhelming sense of power, his whole personality changes, he becomes an uncontrollable monster."

Uncontrollable monster is an apt description of what many of today's drivers have become. Road rage received broad media coverage during the 1990s, a decade that saw the number of cars increase by 30 million, which traveled an additional 600 billion miles each year by 2000. [34]

Besides crowded roads, anonymity is also a factor in aggressive driving. The NHTSA paints this picture of the uncontrollable monster: "Shielded from the hostile outside environment by tinted windows and a micro-climate that defies the seasons, a driver can develop a sense of anonymity and detachment." As Villanova University Social Psychologist Erica Slotter says, "When we feel anonymous, we lose focus of our moral compass

Chevrolet Colorado ZH2 Epitomizes Darth Vader SUV Trend

Have visions of *Mad Max: Fury Road* dancing through your head? Preparing for a world like in *The Book of Eli*? Then the Chevrolet Colorado ZH2 is for you. The "Darth Vader" phenomenon, promoted by limousine companies, police, rappers, and security forces, makes it look cool to be ensconced in massive, black vehicles that readily intimidate the public. GM calls the Colorado ZH2 "physically imposing." Yea, right.

IMAGE COURTESY: GENERAL MOTORS CO.

32. "Aggressive Driving and Road Rage," *SafeMotorist.com*, ret. 25-Aug-18.
33. "Tips for coping with Road Rage and Aggressive Driving," *Denver Public Library*, ret. 25-Aug-18.
34. "Aggressive Driving Enforcement," *National Highway Traffic Safety Administration*, Mar-04.

Road Rage in Santa Clarita, Calif.

In June 2017, one of the most spectacular cases of road rage occurred when a motorcyclist was caught on video kicking a car that then hit the median and careened across the 14 Freeway and struck a passing truck. The motorcyclist, Andrew Flanigan, 45, was arrested in February 2018.

and are more likely to behave badly." [35] The AAA Foundation for Traffic Safety conducted a study of more than 10,000 traffic accidents linked to aggressive driving between 1990 and 1996 and found a 51% increase in serious incidents, but more frequent media reports may have influenced that jump. [36] However, according to an analysis of NHTSA data by *The Washington Post*, the number of fatal accidents increased nearly tenfold between 2004 and 2013, rising from 26 to 247 deadly crashes. [37] But that's a drop in the bucket compared to the 32,719 traffic fatalities in 2013. [38]

AAA's *Prevalence of Aggressive Driving* report cites that 56% of fatal crashes "involved at least one driver who was reported to have performed at least one potentially aggressive action." [39] Applying this barometer, the actual aggressive driving fatality number may be much higher.

That hunch is also supported by the self-reported jump in aggressive driving behavior. A 2002 Public Agenda study backed The Pew Charitable Trust reported that 35% of Americans admit to aggressive driving. [40] In AAA's 2014 report that figure is now 78%, with tailgating (51%) and yelling at other drivers (47%) being the leading aggressive behaviors mentioned. Although these study methodologies are certainly not comparable, anecdotal evidence suggests that road rage is becoming a bigger issue.

AAA's July 2016 *Aggressive Driving* report also found that nearly two in three drivers believe that aggressive driving is a bigger problem today than three years ago. Our escalating lack of manners is such an ignominious part of the fabric of life that 79% of Americans surveyed say lack of respect and courtesy is a serious problem, according to Public Agenda.

Now contrast those opinions with the 78% who report having engaged at least once in aggressive driving in the past year, and you can readily see Goofy's uncontrollable monster metaphor jumping to life.

Air Rage

United Airlines Flight 857 from was proceeding smoothly on its way to Shanghai from San Francisco. Everything was quiet in row 55, where identical twins Cynthia and Crystal Mikula, 22, of Buckley, Mich., were enjoying a movie and lunch. But after having too many drinks, they started calling each other profane names, got into a physical altercation and used the aircraft restroom to smoke. [41]

Then things turned really ugly. The crew tried to restrain Cynthia, who wanted Crystal to open the aircraft's door, and got punched in the face. The pilots decided to fly the plane to Anchorage, Alaska, 1,100 miles away where the raging twins were arrested. As you might expect, the April 19, 2001 fracas was caught on video and can be viewed at ABC News.

It was not the first U.S. air rage incident. That honor belongs to Washington

35. George Dvorsky, "Why We Become Such Assholes When We're Behind the Wheel," *Gizmodo*, 14-Jan-16.
36. Louis Mizell, Matthew Joint, et al., "Aggressive Driving: Three Studies," *AAA Foundation for Traffic Safety*, Mar-97.
37. Christopher Ingraham, "Road rage is getting uglier, angrier and a lot more deadly," *The Washington Post*, 18-Feb-15.
38. "2013 Motor Vehicle Crashes: Overview," *NHTSA*, Dec-14.
39. "Prevalence of Self-Reported Aggressive Driving Behavior: United States, 2014," *AAA Foundation for Traffic Safety*, Jul-16.
40. "Aggravating Circumstances," *Public Agenda*, 2002
41. Kim Murphy, "Terror Twins Cool Their Jets in an Alaskan Jail," *Los Angeles Times*, 13-May-01.

Air Rage: Cynthia Mikula Being Removed from United Flight 857

On April 19, 2001, Cynthia Mikula and her twin sister Crystal caused such a commotion that United had to fly back two hours to Anchorage, Alaska, to have the "Terror Twins" removed. In a video, Mikula is heard screaming, "Why don't you tell them I didn't do nothing wrong?"

radio talk show host Julianne Malveaux, 42, who called a 9-year-old girl who accidentally bumped her while she asleep "a little savage" and what *The Washington Post* describes as "a particularly foul four-syllable word." [42]

She also swore at a flight attendant who accidentally sprayed her with a can of soda when it opened and grabbed another flight attendant's arm when asked her to put away her laptop before the plane landed. As a result, she was arrested on landing and charged with assault and sentenced to probation. [43] Malveaux' altercation took place on October 22, 1994.

According to the International Air Transport Association, which represents 265 airlines and 83% of global air traffic, there were 10,854 worldwide cases of unruly passengers in 2015, or one in every 1,205 flights, a 14% increase compared to the year before. [44]

The leading cause of air rage, at 23%, was alcohol or drug intoxication; followed by physical aggression in 11% of the cases. Verbal abuse and failure to follow flight crew instructions were cited in a majority of the incidents.

A horrifying example of such a scenario was an incident involving Wall Street investment banker Gerald Finneran, 59, who was flying from Buenos Aires to New York on October 20, 1995. Already overserved, Finneran was harassing and assaulting flight attendants trying to get more wine. When they refused to serve him, he defecated on a service cart in first class in full view of other passengers, then began wandering around the cabin, leaving feces in his footprints and smearing some of it on the walls.

This is undoubtedly one of the worst cases of air rage ever to occur, and graphically illustrates the accelerating collapse of human decency and civility.

A fascinating finding is that part of the problem is the design of airplanes, specifically the inclusion of a first-class section. A recent study by two Harvard professors, Katherine DeCelles and James Collins discovered that the chances of an air rage incident happening in economy are 3.84 times greater when there is a first-class section.

Of course, not all aircraft rage happens in the air. Many altercations occur right on the ground. The United Airlines incident involving a doctor who was forcibly removed from his seat by ground personnel, losing two teeth in the process, was shocking. [45]

In another notorious case of ground rage, a passenger was removed from an American Airlines to Dallas at New York's La Guardia after creating a commotion. It all started when a gate agent welcomed passengers with a Yuletide greeting while boarding. The passenger barked at the agent, "You shouldn't say that because not everyone celebrates Christmas."

The agent responded, "Well, what should I say then?" He shouted, "Don't say, 'Merry Christmas!'" as he brushed by the agent. Once on the plane, he was greeted by a flight attendant who also wished him a "Merry Christmas." That was the last straw as he proceeded to launch into a tirade that only ended when he was escorted off the plane. [46]

Casual Living is turning some into an abusive, modern-day Scrooge.

42. Phil Matier and Andy Ross, "Unfriendly Skies," *San Francisco Chronicle*, 17-Sep-95.
43. "List of air rage incidents," *Wikipedia*, ret. 26-Aug-18.
44. Kate Silver, "Air rage incidents are on the rise. First-class sections aren't helping," *The Washington Post*, 24-Jan-17.
45. Don Babwin, "Lawyer: Doctor Dragged Off United Flight Has Concussion, Lost Teeth," *CBS Boston*, 13-Apr-17.
46. Michael Liss et al., "Passenger tossed after flipping out over staff's 'Merry Christmas,'" *New York Post*, 25-Dec-14.

Suicide Killer

Another mass shooting just took place. This time in Jacksonville, Fla., where a sore videogame loser killed two people and injured nine. [47] The shooter was killed in what is another case of revenge and suicide. The Suicide Killer trend, also known as "going postal" is the ultimate expression of the growing disdain for human values.

David Katz, 24, of Baltimore, Md., killed two innocent people at the GLHF Game Bar in Jacksonville, and permanently changed the lives of nine. He then committed his last cowardly act, taking his own life at the scene. [48]

Going postal came in use during the 1980s to describe a violent workplace slaying that took place in a U.S. Postal Service facility. Current or former postal employees have killed a total of 65 people in 22 workplace rage incidents between 1975 and 2017. The term surfaced in print on December 17, 1993 in the *St. Petersburg Times*: "The symposium was sponsored by the U.S. Postal Service, which has seen so many outbursts that in some circles excessive stress is known as 'going postal.'" [49]

The worst slaying took place in Edmond, Okla. in 1986 when Patrick Sherrill, a part-time letter carrier, entered the Edmond Postal Office and fatally shot 14 employees and wounded six. He subsequently committed suicide.

Today, going postal has been subsumed by mass shootings that happen with such frequency that Americans have become numb to the news. The modern mass shooting trend began in Austin, Tex. on Aug. 1, 1966, where Charles Whitman killed 16 until police shot him.

Since then more than 154 shootings have taken place in which a lone shooter killed four or more people. [50] A total of 1,102 people have been killed in these shootings, 185 of were children and teenagers. Of those children, 20 were first-graders between six and seven years old.

In the early history of America, the killing was a necessary evil. It was done to eliminate enemies, rivals and adversaries. Today's mass shootings involve the murdering of many innocent bystanders. People who happen to be in the wrong place at the wrong time. The goal has become to eliminate as many people as possible on your way to your own grave. It's the ultimate act of selfishness. In 2017, nearly 40,000 people died from guns in the U.S., the highest in 50 years. [51]

And yet despite overwhelming evidence offered by virtually every other country in the western world that controlling gun ownership and sales reduces murder, the U.S. government prefers to stand by and do nothing.

As long as there is no direction from the government, many citizens will continue to believe it's OK to kill just for the hell of it. Selfishness and zero moral leadership have given us the Suicide Killer trend. It's a trend that can be reversed. Hopefully sooner, rather than later.

#VegasStrong

It was the worst mass shooting in U.S history, with 58 people killed and 851 people injured. The shooter, a 64-year-old Floridian, was someone with no criminal history, no history of mental disorders, no beef with country music or musicians, and no financial problems (he had spent $95,000 before the slaughter on firearms purchases). [1] Yet, he committed the vilest act in U.S. history. Like most mass shootings, the perpetrator just wanted "to be known as having the largest casualty count," according to his brother. Killing this many people would permanently etch his otherwise forgettable life in many people's memories. What is most remarkable about this pinnacle of egotistic selfishness is that it was matched in no small measure by the company, MGM Resorts International, that hosted this individual at its Mandalay Bay hotel. MGM Resorts sued 1,000 victims of the shooting rampage to prevent them from holding the company liable for the incident. [2] If ever there was an example of the emblematic callousness of Casual Living, MGM Resorts must be it.

1. David Montero, "Las Vegas gunman was a loner and gambler, but motive behind mass shooting remains unclear, police report says," *Los Angeles Times*, 03-Aug-18.
2. Richard Oppel, "MGM Resorts Sues 1,000 Victims of Las Vegas Shooting, Seeking to Avoid Liability," *The New York Times*, 17-Jul-18.

47. Chris Kitching, "David Katz: All we know so far after Jacksonville shooter "snapped" during video game tournament killing two," *Mirror*, 27-Aug-18.
48. KC Baker and Greg Hanlon, "Chaos, Panic and Screams as Jacksonville Mass Shooting Is Captured on Live Video," *People*, 26-Aug-18.
49. "Going postal" and "List of postal killings," *Wikipedia*, ret. 16-Dec-18.
50. Bonnie Berkowitz, Denise Lu and Chris Alcantara, "The terrible numbers that grow with each mass shooting," *The Washington Post*, 29-Jun-18.
51. Sarah Mervosh, "Nearly 40,000 People Died From Guns in U.S. Last Year, Highest in 50 Years," *The New York Times*, 18-Dec-18.

Cyberbullies, Flames & Trolls

Internet boosters trumpeted interactivity as its chief benefit. That two-way conversation supposedly set it apart from traditional, unidirectional media. Of course, that was before comments like the thoughtfully composed, "Ur ugly u suk and u should die," appeared beneath a video posted on YouTube.

> **"**Nasty comments, sometimes even death threats, have become ubiquitous on virtually any site that seeks to engage readers in discussion"
>
> **USA Today**
> 30-Jul-07

That comment was cited in a 2007 *USA Today* story by Janet Kornblum who further wrote: "Nasty comments, sometimes even death threats, have become ubiquitous on virtually any site that seeks to engage readers in discussion." [52] She correctly surmised that anonymity was a significant driving force behind the growing rudeness of society. A decade later, things have gotten much worse.

In 2008, NPR launched its commenting system with much fanfare. NPR's former managing editor for digital news, Scott Montgomery, wrote this in his 2016 farewell-to-comments announcement: "After much experimentation and discussion, we've concluded that the comment sections on NPR.org stories are not providing a useful experience for the vast majority of our users," [53] So much for user interaction.

The decline in etiquette started in the early 1980s in internet chat rooms, where "flaming wars" and a growing incidence of "trolling" were the earliest forms of anti-social behavior. In 1983, *The Hacker's Dictionary* defined flaming, derived from "inflaming," as "to speak rabidly or incessantly on an uninteresting topic or with a patently ridiculous attitude."[54] Both

52. Janet Kornblum, "Rudeness, threats make the Web a cruel world," *USA Today*, 30-Jul-07.
53. Matthew Green, "No Comment! Why More News Sites Are Dumping Their Comment Sections," *KQED News*, 24-Jan-18.
54. "Flaming," *Wikipedia*, ret. 02-Jan-19.

The Participatory Blues

Michael Crawford's not-so-humorous take on interactivity shows the hazards of a two-way conversation in a world dominated by the casual disregard for civility. It's a cynical, but accurate, point of view on what happens when human beings are asked to engage with others today.

Pepe the Frog

Internet memes have long been a popular way of convey- ing a message, often humor- ous, but always pointed. In the dark alleyways of the internet, a once simple cartoon charac-

ter, Pepe the Frog, was hijacked by nefarious forces to use as an avatar to promote

hateful and offensive ideas of the alt-right. [1] Things took such a nasty turn that the Anti-Def- amation League had to add the cartoon to its online database of hate symbols. Isla Vista shooter Elliot Rodger reported- ly announced his shooting in a post that used the Pepe meme. Cartoon creator Matt Furie was forced to serve cease-and-de- sist orders to several alt-right personalities and sites. [2] It's a story that makes you want to say, "People grow up."

1. Jessica Roy, "How 'Pepe the Frog' went from harmless to hate symbol," *Los Angeles Times,* 11-Oct-16.
2. Matthew Gault, "Pepe the Frog's Creator Goes Legally Nuclear Against the Alt-Right," *Motherboard,* 18-Sep-17.

trolling, which involves making random unsolicited and/or controversial comments designed to enrage discussion forum members, and flaming are widely practiced today in all social media. Trolls are the loudest voices in the room, the ones who write "crazy, nasty things just to get people all riled up." Their singular mission is to subvert a conversation by hijacking the topic and creating a war of sorts with incendiary comments.

Cyberbullies

One afternoon in October 2006, 13-year-old Megan Meier received a message from a boy she had befriended on MySpace, that read, "The world would be a better place without you." That same afternoon, Meier, who had a history of depression and suicidal impulses, hanged herself in her bedroom.

It turned out that the "Josh Evans" MySpace account was set up by Lori Drew, the mother of Sarah Drew, who was Meier's arch-nemesis. [55] What self-respecting parent does this? Only one who believes that cyberbullying is a cure for what ails society.

Then there is the case of 12-year-old Gabriella Green who was cyberstalked by two 12-year-old middle-school students. Green died from hanging on January 10, 2018. The police have charged the cyberbullies in Panama City Beach, Fla. [56]

So-called "attack videos" are also part of the psychological terror being inflicted on society today. One such video shows a young girl from San Mateo, Calif. being viciously attacked by a schoolmate, leading the despondent victim to abandon high school due to fear and depression.

55. Jennifer Steinhauer, "Verdict in MySpace Suicide Case," *The New York Times,* 26-Nov-08.
56. Jamiel Lynch, "Police accuse two students, age 12, of cyberbullying in suicide," *CNN,* 24-Jan-18.

Future Of An Uncivilized World

Book of Revelation

To predict the future, it's sometimes useful to dig up the past. The Bible's *Book of Revelation*, written circa 95, contains some revelatory predictions. It foresees the presence of a "beast" and "false prophet." Revelation 20:15-20: "And the devil, who deceived them, was thrown into the lake of burning sulfur, where the beast and the false prophet had been thrown." [1] It also features an apocalyptic vision for the followers of the beast. Revelation 21:6-8: "But the cowardly, the vile, the murderers, the sexually immoral, those who practice magic arts, the idolaters and all liars — their place will be in the fiery lake of burning sulfur." There are many parallels with today's world as it moves towards this dark vision of the future. It should be an early distant warning for all true believers for "Nothing impure will ever enter [heaven], nor will anyone who does what is shameful or deceitful."

1. Jack Wellman, "Revelation Summary, Commentary and Key Verses," ret. 16-Dec-18.

The candidate exclaimed, "I could stand in the middle of Fifth Avenue and shoot someone, and I wouldn't lose any voters, OK?" [57] A mobster turned politician? No, the President of the most powerful nation on earth. In an almost too logical twist, the U.S. now has a Casual Living President.

His rallies have been marked by violence, including a punch that landed squarely on the jaw of a protester, mainly because he invites violence: "I'd like to punch him in the face." [58] He has repeatedly used profanity, like when he proposed taxing Chinese imports, "Listen, you motherf... ers, we're gonna tax you 25%." [59]

President Donald Trump personifies an increasingly unsavory aspect of society, one that is increasingly in-your-face, unscrupulous and severely lacking in etiquette. This Casual Living Ubertrend chapter documents the many phenomena being carried by a wave that is inundating society. Pay heed, because it portends the growing likelihood of the end of civilized behavior unless incisive action is taken on the part of government, business, education *and* parents.

It's the result of a mostly anonymous society where old-school values are rapidly heading toward the exit, trampling everything else on the way out. The Casual Living Ubertrend is not solely responsible for the decline of civility. The trend is also being propelled by the Digital Lifestyle, Unwired and, in particular, the Voyeurgasm Ubertrends, covered in the next chapter.

"The Donald" is merely an outgrowth of a trend that took off in the 1980s.

57. Jeremy Diamond, "Trump: I could 'shoot somebody and I wouldn't lose voters'," *CNN*, 24-Jan-16.
58. Jeremy Diamond, "Donald Trump on protester: 'I'd like to punch him in the face'," *CNN*, 23-Feb-16.
59. "Donald Trump - "Listen you motherfuckers, we're gonna tax you 25%," *YouTube*, 29-Apr-11.

EXTRA EDITION

Chicago Tribune

TUESDAY, DECEMBER 9, 2008 | The Midwest's largest reporting team | 24 hours at chicagotribune.com

© CHICAGO TRIBUNE

ARRESTED

U.S.: Blagojevich tried to sell Senate seat in 'political corruption crime spree'

Historic day in Illinois politics

6 a.m.
Two FBI agents arrive at Gov. Rod Blagojevich's Northwest Side home with an arrest warrant.

11 a.m.
U.S. Atty. Patrick Fitzgerald details the charges against Blagojevich and his chief of staff, John Harris.

CHARGE 1: Conspiracy to commit fraud. Blagojevich and Harris allegedly sought to defraud the state by, among other things, selling the vacant U.S. Senate seat of President-elect Barack Obama.

CHARGE 2: Solicitation of bribery. Blagojevich allegedly sought to have Chicago Tribune editorialists fired in exchange for assistance with Wrigley Field sale.

12:30 p.m.
Sen. Dick Durbin calls for a special election to fill Obama's seat, saying, "No appointment by this governor could produce a credible replacement."

12:45 p.m.
Lt. Gov. Pat Quinn calls for Blagojevich to step aside, saying the governor is "seriously impeded from carrying out his oath of office."

1:30 p.m.
Blagojevich and Harris appear in federal court. After a 15-minute hearing, each is released on his own recognizance.

1:56 p.m.
Obama tells reporters at his Chicago transition office that "I had no contact with the governor..."

Gov. Rod Blagojevich was arrested at his home about 6 a.m. after asking, "Is this a joke?" Joel Worth/Tribune photo

8 PAGES OF COVERAGE

Lt. Gov.: Blagojevich should step aside

By Jeff Coen, Rick Pearson and David Kidwell
Tribune reporters

state and the fate of the open Senate seat—which the governor alone has the power to fill under the state law.

Today's Modern Values Headline: Corruption and Greed

The media are brimming with stories about greed and corruption, signaling to members of society far and wide that it's OK to cheat and steal, just don't get caught.

It erupted on TV where Morton Downey was infamous for blowing smoke in the face of guests while hosting his unique brand of "trash TV," a show that, worryingly, also encouraged fist fights among its guests. The writing was on the video wall.

Against all logic, save for those familiar with the undercurrents of this Ubertrend, Trump's followers and his party have turned a deaf ear to the lies, his sexual immorality and his continuous belligerence towards anybody who crosses his path.

Trump's favorite tool of choice to berate perceived enemies and opponents is Twitter, a medium designed initially for positive social engagement, not bullying and personal threats. In another perverse twist of fate, Twitter CEO Jack Dorsey believes that the world is better served by allowing the President's vitriolic attacks on the social network.

That allows Trump free rein to instigate havoc directly from his mobile device, further cultivating the vagaries of the Casual Living Ubertrend.

It would take a monumental effort on the part of government, educational institutions and business to counter this tsunami — a distinct possibility should things worsen considerably, but highly improbable in today's could-care-less world.

After all, many of society's cultural leaders are also steeped in corruption and greed, and show little compunction about cheating, lying and stealing. The Bernie Madoffs, Enrons and Blagojeviches of the world have cast a long shadow that is darkening the moral landscape.

Corporate leaders feel free to cheat by sneakily charging fees that are not included in the published price. They work very hard to make sure that consumers can't get easily cancel a subscription but make it very easy to sign up or upgrade. They sink their tax windfalls into stock repurchases without considering the welfare of their employees. And Wall Street condones this behavior by compensating the wrongdoers with higher share prices while punishing those who reward their underpaid workers.

Can there be a return to a more morally just society? Highly unlikely. Fully 74% of Americans believe society today is generally more ill-mannered than it was 30 years ago and that civility in politics is notably lacking. [60] Imagine what they will say in 2050.

The outrageous acts of the Casual Living Ubertrend are part of a growing pattern of abuse and dystopia. And it's all due to a severe lack of education and moral leadership on the part of both parents and society's heads of state. Expect to encounter more air- and road-rage perpetrators dressed in Hawaiian shirts and sweatpants hurling epithets at you in the near future.

60. "Americans believe civility is on the decline," *The Associated Press-NORC Center for Public Affairs Research*, 22-Apr-16.

Voyeurgasm has created a society obsessed with celebrities, reality shows, surveillance and other voyeuristic pursuits. Fueled by an insatiable curiosity, the need to watch will usher in a highly transparent future where the innermost workings are revealed in ultra high definition.

7

Voyeurgasm

I Like to Watch

Rodney King's 1991 beating was a watershed moment. Not only was it the most important capture of police violence on video at the time but it helped entrench the Voyeurgasm Ubertrend, which points to a future where just about everything will be captured digitally. Voyeurgasm promises to completely upend media and entertainment, much as the current generation of visually oriented social networks, including YouTube and Instagram, together with billions of smartphones, digital cameras and ultra-high-definition video and surveillance gear, have coalesced to create a bold new world of graphically explicit experiences. Driving this Ubertrend is an endless stream of increasingly sophisticated imaging technologies that capture microcosmic details in eye-watering resolutions.

The Beating Of Rodney King

Voyeurgasm

> On Sunday, March 3, 1991 at 12:30 am, Rodney King was going 115 mph (185 kph) in the westbound lanes of Los Angeles' Foothill Expressway in his white Hyundai. After a brief car chase, King was ordered to lie on the ground.

As King laid on the ground, at least four Los Angeles Police Department officers began beating and kicking him. Unbeknownst to the police, one of the many witnesses watching from the balconies of Mountainback Apartments on Foothill Boulevard was George Holliday, who used his brand-new Sony Handycam video camera to record the incident. [1] In the 81 seconds of video footage captured by Holliday's camcorder, police are seen kicking and clubbing King 56 times. [2]

Holliday, the owner of an L.A. plumbing company, sent the video to local news station KTLA and it ended up being broadcast by CNN the next day. [3] Holliday's video was a milestone, widely considered the first example of citizen journalism. [4] It was also the first "viral video," although it would be another 14 years before YouTube would see the light of video.

It was the first time excessive police force and brutality received extensive media coverage. That was partly due to the graphic nature and brutality of the content but also because Holiday made his video available to the press. It was the departure point of the Voyeurgasm Ubertrend, which is ushering in a future where just about everything will be captured by smartphones, action-, dash- or security-cam video.

> " People, I just want to say, you know, can we all just get along?"
>
> **Rodney King**
> *Commenting on the Los Angeles Riots*
> 01-May-92

1. Hector Tobar and Richard Lee Covin, "Accounts of Rodney Glen King's arrest describe repeated striking and kicking of the suspect," *Los Angeles Times*, 07-Mar-91.
2. Chelsea Matiash and Lily Rothman, "The Beating that Changed America: What Happened to Rodney King 25 Years Ago," *Time*, 03-Mar-16.
3. "Rodney King," *Wikipedia*, ret. 16-Dec-18.
4. Dimas Sanfiorenzo, "How the Rodney King Beating Became the First Viral Video + Changed America Forever," *Okayplayer*, 29-Aug-17.

Rodney King Police Brutality Video

Rodney King's 1991 beating was a groundbreaking event. Not only did it capture police violence on video, but it helped propel a new Ubertrend, Voyeurgasm, which points to a highly transparent future where just about everything will be captured on video.

MAR. 3 1991

Police Officer Convictions

In an extremely rare outcome, former Texas police officer Roy Oliver was convicted of murder for the shooting of unarmed, 15-year-old Jordan Edwards in April 2017. According to The Associated Press, fewer than 90 officers have been charged with murder or manslaughter for police shootings since 2005. [1] Based on "The Counted," that number would be significantly higher (main story). Less than half were convicted or pleaded guilty to lesser charges. Even rarer is a guilty verdict: That has happened only five other times in the past 13 years in cases involving non-federal law enforcement officers — and four of those convictions were overturned, according to Bowling Green State University criminologist Phil Stinson.

1. "Experts: Unusual factors in ex-Texas cop's murder conviction," *The Associated Press*, 30-Aug-18.

When the four accused officers were tried a year later, a jury found them not guilty despite the videotaped evidence. A TIME/CNN survey conducted shortly after the verdict found that 57% of those polled felt the outcome was the result of racism. The acquittals ignited the 1992 Los Angeles riots, the worst U.S. rioting since the 1960s.

In six days of violence, including arson, assaults, looting and murder, beginning April 29, 63 people were killed, 2,383 injured, more than 12,000 arrested, and property damage topped $1 billion. Local police, supported by Governor Pete Wilson's California National Guard, was unable to control the situation. On May 1, President George H. W. Bush deployed the 7th Infantry Division and the 1st Marine Division to restore peace and order.

Incredibly, the U.S. does not maintain a comprehensive public database of police shootings. A report by Anthony Bui and colleagues of the David Geffen School of Medicine at UCLA used "The Counted," a compilation of media reports of police killings by *The Guardian* to arrive at 1,146 police killings in 2015 and 1,092 in 2016. [5] Not surprisingly, African-Americans are twice as likely to die at the hands of police compared to whites — a rate of 7.2 per million compared to 2.9 per million, respectively.

It's impossible to estimate how many police shootings have been captured on video in the past 28 years, but that figure has increased significantly since the arrival of the smartphone. Mother Jones compiled a graphic tally in 2015 of 13 police killings captured on video during the past year. [6] Newsone published a list of 46 black men and boys, who all except one, Trayvon Martin, were killed by police from December 2011 to July 2018. [7] Of that list, nine killings, or 20%, were captured on video: Eric Garner, Laquan McDonald, Tamir Rice, Charly Keunang, Walter Scott, Brendon Glenn, Alton Sterling, Philando Castile and Terence Crutcher.

5. Maggie Fox, "Police killings hit people of color hardest, study finds," *NBC News*, 07-My-18.
6. Jaeah Lee and AJ Vicens, "Here Are 13 Killings by Police Captured on Video in the Past Year," *Mother Jones*, 20-May-15.
7. "46 Black Men And Boys Killed By Police," *Newsone*, 14-Jul-18.

Best Known and All-Time Most Expensive Viral Movie

Abraham Zapruder filmed an 8mm movie of the assassination of John F. Kennedy, the 35th president of the United States, as he rode in a motorcade in Dallas, Tex., on November 22, 1963. The U.S. government purchased the 26-second movie clip for $16 million in 1999.

Bystander Recordings

Rodney King's beating was not the first high-profile event captured by a citizen journalist, or "bystander recording" as they came to be known. [8] That credit belongs to Ukrainian-born Abraham Zapruder, co-founder of Dallas-based clothing manufacturer Jennifer Juniors. [9] In 1963, as John F. Kennedy's motorcade was passing by, Zapruder used his top-of-the-line, 8-mm Bell & Howell Model 414 PD Zoomatic movie camera to capture the moment Kennedy was assassinated.

Life magazine purchased the rights to the 26.3-second film clip for $150,000, paid in six annual installments of $25,000, in today's inflated dollars that would be equal to $1.5 million. [10] In 1975, five years after Zapruder had passed away, Time-Life sold the rights to the footage back to the Zapruder family for $1. The U.S. government paid $16 million in 1999 for the 494-frame film; the highest price ever paid for a bystander recording.

> "Little Brother is watching Big Brother."
>
> **Clayton Patterson**
> Bystander Video Recording Artist

Much less financially successful was artist Clayton Patterson, who in 1988 used a VHS camcorder to capture video of New York City's Thompkins Square Riots, which gained notoriety due to police attacks on residents and protesters. Patterson's bystander recording was the most damning evidence yet of police brutality, according to *The New Yorker*. His feat led to an appearance on *The Oprah Winfrey Show*.

Twenty years earlier, another New Yorker, Andy Warhol, had uttered this famous line, "In the future, everyone will be world-famous for 15 minutes." Now Patterson had his 15 minutes. Despite the evidence captured by his video leading to 14 police officers being tried on police brutality charges,

8. Emily Raboteau, "The Long, Vital History of Bystander Recordings," *The New Yorker*, 11-Aug-16.
9. "Abraham Zapruder" and "Zapruder Film," *Wikipedia*, ret. 31-Aug-18.
10. Larry Mcshane, "How film taken by Abraham Zapruder, a garment maker, launched family into spotlight and became its greatest burden," *New York Daily News*, 17-Nov-13.

plus the removal of the precinct's captain, Patterson never gained much recognition for his scoop, primarily because he elected not to release the video publicly. But he did add an incisive observation to the lexicon of Voyeurgasm: "Little Brother is watching Big Brother."

Early bystander recordings did not have the benefit, or detraction, of social media engagement on YouTube or Facebook. Still, the growing number of camcorders caused a surge in high-profile events captured on video that made the evening news or were shared in online forums and via e-mail.

One of the most prominent of the early Voyeurgasmic videos was O.J. Simpson's infamous 1994 White Bronco car chase along the San Diego 405 freeway. Millions watched mesmerized as the drama unfolded in what, at times, seemed like a slow-motion dream sequence.

New York witnessed another major bystander video incident during the National Puerto Rican Day Parade on June 11, 2000. Dozens of young men went on a "wilding" rampage in New York's Central Park, robbing, fondling or stripping 47 women during the incident. [11] Critics charged that NYPD officers looked the other way to avoid confronting minority groups.

A few bystanders used their camcorders to record the incident. Some of these videos wound up at Spectrum News NY1, a 24-hour cable news channel then owned by Time Warner. Despite a policy of not identifying crime victims, NY1 aired clips without blurring the faces or uncovered body parts of women involved, a no-no in today's social-media-patrolled world.

But nothing could prepare viewers for the highly graphic videos showing the destruction of New York's World Trade Center on September 11, 2001. People everywhere sat in stunned silence as broadcast news reports repeatedly showed videos of the two airliners crashing into the twin towers and the subsequent nightmarish collapse of these massive structures.

The Mirror

Voyeurgasm dates back to the beginning of humanity but the invention of innovative tools over the past few centuries have turned this Ubertrend into a significant cultural force. The 1835 invention of the common mirror by Justus von Liebig was such a milestone.

Liebig, a German chemist, developed a process for applying a thin layer of metallic silver to one side of a pane of clear glass. [12] The mirror was a major breakthrough: it let people easily see at themselves for the very first time. To this day, mirrors play an essential role in the Voyeurgasm Ubertrend by helping shape the cult of narcissism ("Selfies-R-Us," page 256).

Two decades before the invention of the mirror, Nicéphore Niépce built the first camera in 1816. Niépce had coated a paper with silver chloride, which darkened when exposed to light. [13] That same period produced the Kinetograph "movie" camera in 1891, thanks to William Dickson, a Scottish inventor and employee of Thomas Edison. [14]

Crash Video Rubbernecking

On July 20, 2000, Air France Concorde Flight 4590 suffered a tire blowout as it was taking off from Charles de Gaulle runway 26R. [1] A poorly installed titanium alloy strip that had fallen off a Continental Airlines DC-10 on the same runway five minutes

earlier, plus a missing spacer in the left main landing gear beam contributed to the blowout. Tire debris caused a leak in fuel tank five and an engine fire. The crash of Concorde Flight 4590 less than two minutes later was caught on video by a Spanish truck driver's wife. Of the many air crash videos on YouTube, the most spectacular one was captured with a dashcam: National Airlines Flight 102 — a Boeing 747 crash near Bagram Airfield in Afghanistan on April 29, 2013.

1. "Air France Flight 4590," *Wikipedia*, ret. 17-Dec-18.

11. "Puerto Rican Day Parade attacks," *Wikipedia*, ret. 17-Dec-18.
12. Joseph Castro, "Who Invented the Mirror?" *Live Science*, 28-Mar-13.
13. "History of the camera" *Wikipedia*, ret. 17-Dec-18.
14. "Movie Camera," *Wikipedia*, ret. 17-Dec-18.

Sony Portapak AVC-3400

Introduced in 1969, the Sony Portapak AVC-3400 was the workhorse camera of the 1970s. It had a 2/3-inch vidicon — the cathode ray tube (CRT) used to capture images before the introduction of charge-coupled devices (CCDs) in the 1980s — an electronic viewfinder and a 6x zoom lens. The Portapak had a 30-minute recording capacity.

First Consumer Camcorder

In 1983, Sony launched a break-through: the first consumer camcorder, a contraction of camera and recorder, the Betamovie BMC-100P.[1] Sony was able to miniaturize its recording head, allowing the use of a standard Betamax cassette, but had to sacrifice video playback. JVC overcame that shortcoming when it debuted the JVC GR-C1 VHS-C camcorder in 1984. Betamovie weighed 5.5 pounds (2.5 kg) so it had to rest on a shoulder, but it was capable of recording up to 3½ hours of baby's first steps.

1. "Betamovie," *Wikipedia*, ret. 17-Dec-18.

Early still and movie cameras were revolutionary recording tools but were also cumbersome to use. Zapruder's 8-mm film of Kennedy's assassination, for example, posed an immediate challenge: There was no facility in Dallas capable of quickly developing the film. The FBI had to ask Kodak officials to open their local lab to process the footage.

That all changed with the invention of the video camera, in particular, the development of mobile, user-friendly gear. The 1963 Neiman Marcus Christmas catalog featured the first "home video system," made by Ampex, which included a large camera, 100-pound VR-1500 video recorder, separate TV monitor, plus custom-made furniture. It was priced at $30,000, which included an Ampex engineer to set it all up in the buyer's home.[15]

In 1967, Sony introduced its first generation of "Portapak" video systems, the Sony DV-2400, which consisted of a black-and-white video camera and a record-only ½-inch video tape recorder (VTR) unit. The Portapak revolution helped create two new Voyeurgasm waves, video art and "guerrilla video," or low-budget video.

An example of guerrilla filmmaking was 1999's *The Blair Witch Project*, which was produced for $60,000 and generated $250 million at the box office.[16] This movie, which debuted at Sundance in 1999, used Hi8 video cameras in addition to regular film cameras and was one of the first to apply the novel technique of viral marketing.

Portapak video gear helped fuel the activism of the late 1960s and early 1970s when society was challenged by a new counterculture and faced much political upheaval. It provided an inkling of disruptions to come.

Many more video innovations were in the offing, a total of 54 formats have been introduced since the invention of "quad" tape (quadruplex) by Ampex in 1956. Too many to cover in this cursory examination of the history of video, but the first big waves included U-matic (1971), Betamax (1975), VHS (1977) and Betacam (1983).

The miniaturization of video recording devices, however, would spur the true arrival of the bystander recording trend. After the 1983 introduction of the consumer camcorder (sidebar) came another wave of new video formats. Kodak launched the 8-mm Video8 format in 1984, which Sony capitalized on with its first Handycam in 1985. The next format, Hi8, featured improved resolution and a provision for digital audio.

In 1995, JVC, Panasonic and Sony, and other video camera manufacturers launched DV, Digital Video, which became the de facto standard for home video production. Eleven years later, a startup called Pure Digital, launched the Flip video camera in February 2006, aimed at an eager community of video bloggers and social media users.

It was named after its flip-out USB plug, a first among camcorders and a testament to its computer-centric design. Pure Digital was sold to Cisco for $580 million in March 2009, which folded the company two years later.[17]

The introduction of digital video technology and the Flip provided the stepping stones for the next major video revolution, the smartphone.

15. Mark Shapiro, "The History of Camcorders," *Electronic Component News*, 28-Aug-14.
16. "The Blair Witch Project," *Wikipedia*, ret. 02-Sep-18.
17. Marguerite Reardon, "Cisco buys Flip Video maker for $590 million," *CNET*, 19-Mar-09.

Smartphones

Camcorders revolutionized civilization, but it's the smartphone that completed the virtuous video cycle by allowing any captured event to be instantly uploaded to the internet or social media, without the need of wires, thanks to the Unwired Ubertrend.

The retail launch of the iPhone on June 29, 2007 was the single most momentous occasion in the history of technology, as described in the Unwired Ubertrend chapter (page 206). While the first iPhone featured a camera good enough to turn one into a pixel paparazzi (see "Celebrity Worship Syndrome, page 252), it wasn't until 2009, when the iPhone 3GS added the ability to record video, that the wheels were set in motion for the convergence of ease of use and bystander video recording.

The iPhone 3GS offered VGA-quality video resolution, 640x480 pixels, at 30 frames-per-second. That's a far cry from today's iPhone Xs, which records at 4K resolution, 3840x2160 pixels, and *60 fps*. That's six times as much horizontal resolution and 4.5 times as much vertical resolution. That explains why Cisco shuttered the Flip camera, or why neither Panasonic or Sony introduced a traditional camcorder at the 2017 Consumer Electronics Show in Las Vegas, the first time that had happened in decades. At the 2018 CES, Panasonic took one last stab with three new camcorders.

The iPhone 3GS was, of course, not the first mobile phone with a video camera. The Nokia 6600 (6620 in the U.S.), a feature phone, could record 27-second videos in 2003. [18] The first smartphone with video recording was the Nokia N95, which debuted the same year the first iPhone did. [19]

Smartphones unleashed the citizen journalist in all of us. According to InfoTrends, the world took 100 billion more photos in 2017 than it did in 2016 — 85% of those images were made with smartphones. [20] The same ratio probably holds true for video as well.

What makes smartphones so essential to life is that Digital Lifestyle value of convergence. The smartphone is the ultimate convergence device, as a RadioShack ad from the 1990s, left, vividly illustrates. Having a computer in one's pocket makes the direct upload of videos to the internet and social media seamless. Its wireless connectivity, available anywhere, anytime has made the smartphone the darling of today's video crowd in just 11 years. In the U.S., 87% of households own one, second only to television. [21]

The Screensucking trend described on page 184 is being driven by a massive variety of fascinating video content contributed by billions of internet users and media brands. Each day, Facebook's 2.3 billion users consume more than 100 million hours of videos. [22]

In real life, or IRL as technocrats put it, road traffic is often halted by rubberneckers. You might label the online video trend "digital rubbernecking."

Early 1990s RadioShack Ad

This RadioShack ad features a clock radio, earphones, calculator, personal computer, cellular telephone, CD player, radar detector, desktop scanner, CB radio, answering machine, landline telephone, and cassette tape recorder. Except for the CB radio and radar detector, a smartphone can handle *all* these functions, either directly or via a third-party app.

18. "Nokia 6600," *Wikipedia*, ret. 02-Sep-18.
19. "Nokia N95," *Wikipedia*, ret. 02-Sep-18.
20. Caroline Cakebread, "People will take 1.2 trillion digital photos this year — thanks to smartphones," *Business Insider*, 31-Aug-17.
21. "Smartphones Approaching TVs as Americans' Most-Frequently Owned Tech Product, Says New CTA Study," *Consumer Technology Association*, 25-Jun-18.
22. Josh Constine, "Facebook Hits 100M Hours Of Video Watched A Day, 1B Users On Groups, 80M On Fb Lite," *TechCrunch*, 27-Jan-16.

YouTube

Voyeurgasm

On July 15, 2014, a largely unknown artist uploaded a music video to YouTube about the lifestyle of a popular Seoul, South Korea neighborhood. You couldn't have asked for a darker horse. Luckily, PSY scored an amusing hit in *Gangnam Style*, which racked up 1.5 billion video views in less than a year.

That a medium that only came in existence in February 2005 would be able to vault a virtually unknown South Korean to the top of world's cultural consciousness is indicative of the power YouTube now wields. In its 13 years of existence, YouTube has become a medium that serves as the world's primary outlet for video fans and citizen journalists.

YouTube has elevated the Voyeurgasm Ubertrend to an entirely new level. Not since the early days of MTV has any medium done more for the art of short-form video. And lately, it's begun to show designs on the long-form video market too, although it has a lot of catching up to do to Netflix.

Its ride to the zenith of video has shaken up the media landscape and established a new marketing world order, one powered by YouTube influencers. These influencers together with others upload more than 300,000 videos to YouTube each day. [23] That's equivalent to more than 500 hours of video uploaded *each minute*. [24]

Consumption figures for the pioneer of video viewing on the internet are equally staggering. *The Wall Street Journal* reports that "YouTube viewers worldwide are now watching more than 1 billion hours of videos a day,

Fatal (Streaming) Attraction

The combination of smartphone videos and social media have inspired a scary new trend, live streaming one's death. Obdulia Sanchez, an 18-year-old California woman, was arrested after live-streaming a fatal car crash on Instagram that killed her sister. [1] In another Instagram live-streaming incident, Ukrainian beauty queen Sofia Magerko and her friend are seen drinking in the car just before it smashes in a light pole killing them both. [2] There are at least 10 of these livestream YouTube videos, including one showing a Finnish couple drinking heavily before their high-speed car crash kills them both.

1. Sontaya Rose, "Parents reeling after live streamed crash leaves one daughter dead and other in jail," *ABC30 News*, 24-Jul-17.
2. Caroline Mortimer, "Teenage beauty queen livestreams her own death in drink-drive accident on Instagram," *Independent*, 04-July-17.

23. Bobby Owsinski, "YouTube By The Numbers: 1 Day, 300,000 New Videos + More Surprising Stats," *Hypebot*, 09-Dec-16.
24. Mark Robertson, "500 Hours Of Video Uploaded To Youtube Every Minute [Forecast]," *Tubular Insights*, 13-Nov-15.

PSY *Gangnam Style* Viral Video

Uploaded in July 2012, *Gangnam Style* by South Korean pop icon PSY has been viewed more than 3.2 billion times. *Gangnam Style* was the YouTube views record holder until July 2017, when Wiz Khalifa's *See You Again* surpassed it. Luis Fonsi's *Despacito* passed both in August 2017. It took Khalifa two years to achieve that feat and just seven months for *Despacito*, suggesting an acceleration in YouTube's influence sphere.

> **"**YouTube is poised to eclipse U.S. television viewership fueled by [its] aggressive embrace of artificial intelligence."
>
> **The Wall Street Journal**
> 27-Feb-17

threatening to eclipse U.S. television viewership, a milestone fueled by the Google unit's aggressive embrace of artificial intelligence to recommend videos." [25] AI and video...and you thought the term "boob tube" was awful.

There is no question about it, YouTube is reshaping the way the world shares and consumes video. That lofty position has made YouTube the perfect conduit for any sensational visual reportage, from police brutality to road-rage incidents. It has also become the go-to medium for how-to videos, music videos (photo) and, let's not forget, humorous baby, dog and cat videos.

Since most social media influencers use video content when marketing on behalf of brands, they are a perfect match for video-oriented media, like YouTube, Instagram and Facebook. Top YouTube influencer, based on her $1 million fee per post cost, is Beyoncé. [26] But when it comes to toys, Beyoncé is no match for six-year-old Ryan who reportedly makes $11 million a year reviewing toys on YouTube. [27]

The burgeoning beauty market is a perfect hunting ground for social media influencers. How-to videos from 34-year-old, Dubai-based Huda Kattan have attracted more than 26 million followers on Instagram and 2 million-plus subscribers on YouTube. That leverage has allowed her to create Huda Beauty, a billion-dollar cosmetics brand. [28] Now think of what the storytellers of tomorrow will be able to do with their voyeurgasmic 8K videos. The revolution will be streamed.

25. Jack Nicas, "YouTube Tops 1 Billion Hours of Video a Day, on Pace to Eclipse TV," *The Wall Street Journal*, 27-Feb-17.
26. Kristine Solomon, "Beyoncé Becomes 1st Influencer Valued at More Than $1 Million Per Social Media Post," *Yahoo! Lifestyle*, 03-Apr-17.
27. Bill Murphy, "This 6-Year-Old Makes $11 Million a Year on YouTube. Here's What His Parents Figured Out," *Inc.*, 12-Dec-17.
28. Susannah Hutcheson, "How I became a makeup mogul: Beauty influencer Huda Kattan talks about business, life," *USA Today*, 21-Aug-18.

Ultra High Definition

Voyeurgasm

In 1970, Gil Scott-Heron recorded a poem accompanied by congas and drums, called *The Revolution Will Not Be Televised*. Scott-Heron's groundbreaking rap was intuitively on the money because, as it turns out, the revolution is being streamed via the internet in 4K.

Inventing the Action Camera

In 2002, while on a surfing trip to Australia, Nick Woodman wanted to record his Aussie surfing adventure. Realizing that nothing on the market met his specific needs, Woodman singlehandedly created the innovative GoPro action camera, which established a new Voyeurgasm market. Proving just how much people like recording their own sports activities, GoPro cameras were at one time the best-selling digital cameras on Amazon.com. That's quite a feat considering that shooting sports action footage is a relatively small niche market.

In the middle ages, oil paintings and sketches were among the first media that helped budding voyeurs catch glimpses of others, clothed or disrobed. In 1839, Louis Daguerre introduced the daguerreotype, ushering in the photographic revolution that let anyone record images on film.

It was the invention of the video tape recorder in 1951 by Charles Ginsburg and his Ampex research team that would eventually enable the world of video as we know it today. [29]

Fast forward this history tape to the 1990s. In a noteworthy occurrence, the U.S. government's Federal Communications Commission (FCC), legislated a new trend, HDTV in December 1996, officially called the ATSC (Advanced Television Systems Committee) standard for terrestrial DTV/HDTV broadcasting. The adoption of HD video technology would ripple through the television market for decades to come.

The first regularly scheduled U.S. broadcasts in high definition included NBC's *The Tonight Show,* starting on April 26, 1999, followed in the fall by CBS' primetime movies and ABC's *Monday Night Football*. [30] CBS also broadcast the Final Four in HD for the first time in 1999. [31]

While HD, with a 1920 x 1080-pixel resolution, used to look good, the

29. "Video," *Wikipedia*, ret. 04-Sep-18.
30. "The Tonight Show," *Wikipedia*, ret. 05-Sep-18.
31. Ted Kritsonis, "NCAA Final Four the first major U.S. sports event in 4K," *Digital Trends*, 13-Apr-18.

World's First 8K OLED TV

LG: World's First 88-Inch OLED TV

LG Electronics shows off the world's first 88-inch 8K OLED TV at IFA 2018 in Berlin, which boasts an eye-watering resolution of 7680 x 4320 pixels, generated by 33 million self-emitting pixels. Bigger is indeed better.

IMAGE COURTESY: LG ELECTRONICS USA INC.

Far Bigger Is Better

The funny thing about flat panels is that they're never big enough. In 2004, bulky CRTs kept TVs to under 27 inches. By 2020, the average video display sold in the U.S. will be more than 52 inches (132 cm).[1] As the above OLED TV shows, your room wall is the limit.

1. Luigi Lugmayr, "Chinese Buy Bigger Tvs Than Americans," *I4U News*, 25-Jan-18.

market is moving to "ultra high definition" or "UHD," which doubles the number of pixels to 3840 x 2160, explaining its more popular name, "4K."

At the 2018 Consumer Electronics Show in Las Vegas, LG launched an 88-inch, 8K OLED TV, offering double the resolution of 4K TV, 7680 x 4320 eye-bleeding pixels (photo).[32] Devices like these will provide endless hours of voyeurgasmic entertainment in the very near future, particularly for entertainment venues like sports bars.

The 4K trend is not limited to television. Resolution fever has spread to the smartphone market. The 2015 iPhone 6s and 6s Plus were the first iPhones to offer 4K video.[33] Action cameras (sidebar), camcorders, dashcams and surveillance cameras increasingly provide the feature as well.

Unfortunately, while consumers are eagerly adopting the 4K standard, and consumer electronics manufacturers are already looking ahead to 8K, television broadcasters still have their feet firmly planted in the HD world. Luckily, top internet streaming outfits, including Amazon, Netflix and YouTube, have accepted the 4K challenge.

The 4K revolution will not be televised any day soon.

32. Adi Robertson, "LG kicks off CES's giant, expensive TV race with an 88-inch 8K OLED display," *The Verge*, 01-Jan-18.
33. J. D. Biersdorfer, "Recording 4K Video on an iPhone," *The New York Times*, 01-Feb-18.

Celebrity Worship Syndrome

Voyeurgasm

Our voyeuristic obsession with celebrities led *New Scientist* to conclude in 2003 that one-third of Americans were suffering from something it dubbed "Celebrity Worship Syndrome" or CWS. [34] It was a diagnosis a long time in the making.

How did society become so obsessed with all things celebrity? For an answer to that question, one has to travel back to Chicago in the year 1911. That's when a new publication called *Photoplay* debuted. Initially conceived as an insider business magazine, it soon shifted focus to capitalize on the public's growing interest in the private lives of celebrities. [35]

By 1918, *Photoplay*'s circulation had surpassed 200,000, an exceptional feat in a day and age when the largest consumer publication, *Ladies Home Journal*, had just north of 1 million readers. [36] One notable story offered a hint of things to come. The February 1928 *Photoplay* featured a "true confession" article by Brooklyn-born flapper Clara Bow. [37] Many of Bow's contemporaries were shocked by the story's honesty and transparency, suggesting that the early symptoms of CWS had begun to set in. *Photoplay* ceased publishing on April 15, 1980 and its six-person staff began a new chapter of celebrity watching at *Us* magazine.

While some might classify CWS as merely an advanced case of idle curiosity, outside forces have continued to fuel the burning itch of society's nosiness. In 1967, the *National Enquirer* refocused its editorial on celebrities, which some believe may well have been a CWS inflection point. [38] Others suggest the 1974 debut of *People* magazine, which became Time Inc.'s most

IMAGE COURTESY: HURLEY INTERNATIONAL.

Brands Also Worship Celebrities

Costa Mesa, Calif.-based Hurley described its CWS symptoms as follows, "Hurley Aligns with Bar Refaeli the Ultimate Embodiment of their Beach & Youth Culture. Bar will bring her experience, enthusiasm and charisma to collaborations, initiatives and events for which she and Hurley share a passion, as well as star in the Young Contemporary campaigns." Amen.

34. Kate Douglas, "When you wish upon a star," *New Scientist*, 16-Aug-03.
35. "Photoplay," *Wikipedia*, ret. 18-Dec-18.
36. Marco Santana, "Ladies Home Journal to cease monthly publication," *Des Moines Register*, 24-Apr-14.
37. Pamela Hutchinson, "Photoplay magazine: the birth of celebrity culture," *The Guardian*, 26-Jan-16.
38. "National Enquirer," *Wikipedia*, ret. 18-Dec-18.

Pixel Paparazzi 2007: Courtney Love in SoHo, New York

Courtney Love captured with a smartphone outside The Mercer Hotel in New York's SoHo district on Friday, July 13, 2007 at 6 pm. This picture, shot by yours truly, is the first paparazzi photo ever taken with an iPhone. Notice the artifacts in this first-generation iPhone image.

IMAGE COURTESY: MICHAEL TCHONG.

profitable property, with annual revenues of $1.5 billion at its peak. [39]

The September 14, 1981 debut of *Entertainment Tonight* (ET) introduced daily, tabloid-style journalism to television. *ET* became a true Voyeurgasmic treat on September 8, 2008, when it began broadcasting in HD. [40]

The Celebrity Worship Syndrome trend was ratcheted up at least 10 notches when celebrity news and gossip site TMZ launched on November 8, 2005. TMZ, a joint venture between AOL, at the time owned by Time-Warner, and Warner Brothers division Telepictures International, symbolizes the global institutionalization of celebrity watching. [41]

Within two years, TMZ had become the fifth most popular news site, with 10.5 million unique U.S. visitors, thanks to its chatty, and stalker-like, coverage of the Hollywood set. [42] At the time, TMZ dwarfed its entertainment-news rivals, besting all non-portals, save for CNN and MSNBC.

The future of Celebrity Worship Syndrome can only be imagined, but if society's current interest in digital rubbernecking is any indication, many more will soon be infected by CWS.

39. "People," *Wikipedia*, ret. 18-Dec-18.
40. "Entertainment Tonight," *Wikipedia*, ret. 06-Sep-18.
41. "TMZ," *Wikipedia*, ret. 18-Dec-18.
42. Jon Fine, "TMZ: Cleaning Up By Dishing Dirt," *BusinessWeek*, 19-Nov-07.

Reality Television

An American Family

In 1973, PBS broadcast 12 one-hour episodes of *An American Family* — a groundbreaking sociological experiment that shocked the U.S.[1] Widely regarded as the birth of reality television, the series peeked in on an affluent real-life Santa Barbara, Calif. household and

starred a philandering father, Bill Loud, and his wife, Pat. The show was both addictive and hard to watch, especially when Pat openly discusses Bill's adultery with her brother and sister-in-law, or when she tells Bill to move out. *An American Family* also shattered another taboo — it provided a startling account of oldest son Lance's openly gay life in New York. Voyeurgasm at its earliest and, arguably, best.

1. William Yardley, "Bill Loud, the Father of TV's 'An American Family,' Is Dead at 97," *The New York Times*, 27-Jul-18.

The scene is set in New York City, where seven complete strangers are brought together to live in a SoHo loft while having their daily lives videotaped. It's all part of the May 21, 1992, MTV Networks premiere of *The Real World* — a TV show that ignites the reality show trend. [43]

There is no more exuberant expression of Voyeurgasm than reality television, *The Real World*, or *Real World* as it was later called, was in fact based on a 1973 PBS documentary, *An American Family*, widely considered the first reality TV show (sidebar). [44]

The late 1980s ushered in another television spectacle, appropriately enough dubbed "Trash TV," that would exert a significant influence on future reality TV programming — *The Morton Downey, Jr. Show*. This talk show featured screaming matches among Downey, his guests and audience members, which, on a few occasions, even resulted in physical confrontations.

Another pioneer of reality TV programming, albeit often all too real, was *Cops*, which premiered in 1989. This half-hour, quasi-documentary, reality TV show followed police officers, sheriff's deputies, federal agents, and state troopers, as they conducted narcotics raids and prostitution stings.

The popularity of peeping-tom internet webcams in the 1990s, like JenniCam, got creative juices flowing around the globe. In the Netherlands, Van der Mol Studios developed *Big Brother* in 1999, which lived up to its promise of constant surveillance. After the show reached the U.S. on July 5, 2000, a review in *The New York Times'* called it "The Electronic Fishbowl." [45]

43. "Real World (TV series)," *Wikipedia*, ret. 18-Dec-18.
44. "An American Family," *Wikipedia*, ret. 18-Dec-18.
45. Marshall Sella, "The Electronic Fishbowl," *The New York Times*, 21-May-00.

Reality TV Show: Keeping Up With The Kardashians, Season 14

When KUWTK debuted in October 2007, many believed the show was going to crash and burn quickly. *The New York Times* said it was a show about "desperate women climbing to the margins of fame." Fourteen years and billions of dollars later, everyone, it seems, is paying closer attention to the Kardashians.

IMAGE COURTESY: E!.

The impact of reality TV has been staggering. *Big Brother* was followed by more than 300 reality TV shows, including *Survivor* (2000), *The Amazing Race* (2001), *American Idol* (2002), *The Bachelorette* (2003), *Project Runway* (2004), *Hell's Kitchen* (2005) and *The Real Wives of Orange County* (2006), proving that people do indeed like to watch. The season one finale of *Survivor* drew a staggering 50 million viewers who tuned in to see Richard Hatch win $1 million after living on an island with strangers for weeks. [46]

Some shows pushed the Voyeurgasm envelope to the limit. In 2001, NBC introduced a vomit-inducing reality show, *Fear Factor*. Discovery joined the game in 2013 with a show called *Naked and Afraid* that features, what else, a completely naked cast with intimate body parts strategically blurred.

Combining reality TV with the public's celebrity obsession produced a new viral strain, celebrity reality shows, popularized by the MTV's 2003 reality show, *Newlyweds*. A deluge of copycats followed, including *The Simple Life*, *The Osbournes*, *Celebrity Fit Club*, *The Surreal Life*, *Hogan Knows Best* and, of course, the most long-lived one, *Keeping Up With The Kardashians*.

Our look-at-me Hollywood culture fueled a dizzying array of offshoots, ranging from the bizarre to the outrageous. VH1's *Flavor of Love*, starring Public Enemy's Flavor Flav, featured a "spitting incident" that set a temporary standard for a voyeurgasmic low.

Will the onslaught of reality TV shows continue to clog the airwaves? Doh, with production costs low and curiosity at an all-time high, for sure!

46. Emily Yahr, Caitlin Moore and Emily Chow, "How we went from 'Survivor' to more than 300 reality shows: A complete guide," *The Washington Post*, 29-May-15.

Selfies-R-Us

Voyeurgasm

It was a shot seen around the world. At the 2014 Academy Awards, Ellen DeGeneres had Bradley Cooper take a selfie, surrounded by Hollywood's elite. The image was retweeted 3.4 million times, setting a Twitter record. It was the most potent expression of a new social custom, the selfie.

Sexting a Mirror Selfie

Mirrors continue to play a crucial role in our narcissistic world, as this selfie shows. Because rear-facing cameras usually produce superior results, taking selfies in mirrors has become popular. Some selfies, much racier than this one, are shared by picture takers with others, a trend dubbed "sexting." Some really brave souls even post them on image-sharing networks.

The trend began inauspiciously enough with the 2010 debut of the Apple iPhone 4, which boasted two new features: a high-resolution screen, dubbed Retina, plus a front-facing camera. The combination of a hi-res screen and user-facing camera helped spark a huge trend that actually exposes ourselves: Taking pictures of one's self in various states of dress, or undress. The ability to use a phone's large display to compose a photograph makes the phone a unique imaging device, reminiscent of the view camera.

The phenomenon took off so quickly that by 2013, just three years later, Oxford University Press paid the trend the ultimate compliment by naming selfie "word of the year." [47] That was even faster than emoji, which took five years to become word of the year. At the time, the Oxford Dictionaries editors offered an eye-opening metric of the term's surging popularity: Its use had jumped 17,000% compared to the year before.

These self-portraits are the latest manifestation of a growing culture of narcissism. But selfies are also a perfect tool for self-accreditation. Who doesn't want to take a selfie with the Pope, as three people did in 2013? It's a great way to prove that you were there *and* with someone important. Then again, Pope Francis believes that our selfie culture leads to alienation and a departure from reality. [48]

47. Bryan Bishop, "'Selfie' is the 2013 Oxford Dictionaries Word of the Year," *The Verge*, 18-Nov-13.
48. Junno Arocho Esteves, "'Selfie' culture leads to alienation, says Pope Francis," *America – The Jesuit Review*, 15-May-18.

IMAGE COURTESY: REDDIT SCREENSHOT.

Bradley Cooper Selfie Was the Most Retweeted Tweet of 2014

At 3.4 million retweets, the selfie Ellen DeGeneres had Bradley Cooper take at the 2014 Oscars was the most retweeted tweet ever until the record was broken in 2017 by Carter Wilkerson who needed his Wendy's chicken nuggets fix.

IMAGE COURTESY: BRADLEY COOPER.

Selfies quickly became a nuisance at public venues, especially when combined with another exponent of this cultural tide, the selfie stick. Ellen DeGeneres made a global call to arms when her Academy Awards tweet lamented, "If only Bradley's arm was longer" (photo). By fall 2014, there were more than half a dozen selfie-stick competitors. BuzzFeed caught President Obama clowning around with one just before Valentine's Day 2015. [49] Their unwieldiness quickly led to selfie-stick bans around the world, ranging from Apple's Worldwide Developers Conference to Coachella to the Kentucky Derby to the Museum of Brisbane in Australia. [50]

And speaking about sticks, who was the early poster child of sexting selfies? Say it out loud: Anthony Weiner! The former Democratic congressman created quite a stir when he sexted a 21-year-old female college student in Seattle (sidebar). Jokes about Anthony's Weiner, bazinga, became fodder for much late-night show slapstick humor. [51]

Selfies impacted traditional camera design, with many makers adopting articulating LCD screens that can be swiveled 180 degrees to better take that one-of-a-kind shot. Now stop saying that we're being selfie-ish.

49. Andrew Gauthier, "Things Everybody Does But Doesn't Talk About, Featuring President Obama," *BuzzFeed*, 12-Feb-15.
50. Roger Fingas, "Apple bans selfie sticks, monopods from WWDC 2015," *AppleInsider*, 14-Apr-15.
51. "Anthony Weiner Resigns: Timeline Of Photos, Twitter Scandal Fallout," *HuffPost*, 16-Jun-11.

Surveillance

Big Brother watches over London with 500,000 eyes that track every citizen's movement. That's more surveillance cameras than any other city in the world. [52] On a given day, a Londoner can expect to be recorded more than 300 times. [53]

In a world that actively pursues voyeurism, there is a no more practiced art than training a battery of surveillance cameras all over your terrain to help catch the unwitting prey.

The U.K. landscape is now dotted by 5.9 million cameras, a sliver of the global installed base of 245 million video surveillance cameras in 2014. [54][55] The U.K.'s mass surveillance practice has been repeatedly called into question by famous street artist Banksy, whose biting commentary on this state of affairs is frequently the subject of his artwork (photo).

The city's highly visible cameras are posted on corners of many buildings, on new buses and in every underground station. And since 2003, the license plate of every car driving into central London during weekdays has been recorded as part of a program to reduce traffic congestion and charge drivers fees, but also to track criminals and terrorists.

Voyeurgasm has been a boon for law enforcement, catching an endless string of people red-handed while committing a crime. Madeline Toogood beating her daughter in 2002 was one of the earliest examples of child abuse captured on surveillance video. [56] Another was that of an Orlando woman who was caught "power-washing" her child in a car wash.[57]

Security Footage Shocks Brazil

Scenes captured by security cameras on the night of July 22, 2018 are gruesome indeed: Luís Felipe Manvailer can be seen assaulting his wife, Tatiane Spitzner, in the garage of their building. [1] She tries to flee, but he forces her into the elevator. They go up to their fifth-floor apartment. Less than 20 minutes later, he takes the elevator back down to fetch her bloody, lifeless body, which had plummeted to the sidewalk below. The video, first broadcast on the television program Fantástico, caused outrage in Brazil. Manvailer is currently on trial. [2]

1. Shasta Darlington, "Domestic Abuse, Shown Blow by Blow, Shocks Brazil," *The New York Times*, 07-Aug-18.
2. Sabrina Coelho, "Luis Felipe Manvailer, acusado de matar a advogada Tatiane Spitzner, chega ao Fórum de Guarapuava para acompanhar audiências," *Globo*, 11-Dec-18.

52. "How many CCTV cameras in London?," *Caught on Camera*, ret. 07-Sep-18.
53. Jordan Teicher, "Gazing Back at the Surveillance Cameras That Watch Us," *The New York Times*, 13-Aug-18.
54. Niall Jenkins, "245 million video surveillance cameras installed globally in 2014," *IHS*, 11-Jun-15.
55. James Temperton, "One nation under CCTV: the future of automated surveillance," *Wired U.K.*, 17-Aug-15.
56. Lloyd Vries, "Videotaped Mom: I'm Not A Monster," *CBS News*, 23-Sep-02.
57. "Women Caught On Tape Power Washing Little Girl," *WFMY News*, 06-Mar-08.

Banksy: One Nation Under CCTV

The Royal Mail granted permission for the creation of artwork on a Newman Street post office yard wall in London, without knowing what the work would look like. Once the scaffolding was removed, one of Banksy's many digs aimed at Big Brother was revealed to much consternation.

IMAGE COURTESY: OXYMAN/WIKIMEDIA COMMONS.

News reports now frequently include the silent videos of security cameras playing back criminal acts. An elevator camera recorded a man assaulting his wife in Brazil, causing an uproar when it became known that the assault led to her death (sidebar). The U.S. witnessed a similar incident involving the attack of Jay Z by Beyoncé's sister Solange.

Security cameras have recorded countless acts of reprehensible behavior, from FedEx drivers carelessly tossing delivery packages to three girls taking a bath in an industrial KFC sink, or, worse, a West Virginia Pizza Hut district manager urinating in a Taco Bell sink. [58]

Each incidence posted on YouTube helps sell more security cameras. According to Stratistics MRC, the size of the global video surveillance industry in 2015 was estimated at $20 billion and is expected to triple to $63 billion by 2022. [59]

Ruled by the Voyeurgasm Ubertrend, and spurred by a global surveillance and security camera frenzy, it looks like Big Brother is poised to gain many more eyes. Expect just about everything to be digitally recorded one day by billions of surveillance cameras.

58. "Pizza Hut Manager Caught Peeing in Sink," *NBC News*, 21-Feb-14.
59. "Global Video Surveillance Market 2017 Analysis, Segmentation, Competitors Analysis," *Reuters*, 15-Jun-17.

Transparency

Voyeurgasm

It's crystal clear that the Voyeurgasm Ubertrend is shape-shifting the world as we know it by injecting transparency into everything it does. The after effects are already rippling through society. Heightened visibility has reshaped accountability, crime, the social dialog, and much more.

The U.S. crime rate has plunged dramatically over the past 25 years. [60] Many theories have been proffered, but no explanation is widely accepted. Yet it's evident that technology advances, including burglar alarms, computers, the internet, nationwide crime databases, internet protocol (IP) surveillance cameras and DNA profiling have all become significant crime deterrents.

Social media has turned the world into a glass box. Nothing escapes the social media posse, and the posse cannot avoid social media. The impact of this glass box has already had substantial repercussions, often in unpredictable ways. But that's before the next transparency wave hits.

Two technologies will pace that wave. Blockchain will bring greater transparency to the supply chain, encouraging more ethical behavior and ensuring the authenticity of the product being supplied. Its smart contracts will help combat fraud while its third-party verification process will speed up transactions and reduce cost. Facial recognition will further discourage cheaters and liars from entering the system at will, as they do today. eBay had an opportunity to make its "Power Sellers" system be part of a global, third-party verified marketplace. I told the company's CMO about this possibility in 2005, but he ignored my advice. Today, eBay is

Shower Transparency: SoHo Metropolitan Hotel, Toronto

Toronto's SoHo Metropolitan Hotel, designed by the architecture firm of Page and Steele, shows how Voyeurgasm has even infiltrated hotel room design: a growing number of hotels now feature transparent showers and bathrooms.

IMAGE COURTESY: MICHAEL TCHONG.

60. Dara Lind and German Lopez, "16 theories for why crime plummeted in the US," *Vox*, 20-May-15.

Kitchen Transparency: Ku Noodle

Ku Noodle at Las Vegas' SLS hotel features a transparency trend that is bound to experience increasing future adoption: see-through kitchens. What better way to keep an eye on the kitchen staff than have your customers do it for you?

IMAGE COURTESY: MICHAEL TCHONG.

an increasingly marginal player in the e-commerce game.

The physical impact of greater transparency already permeates architecture, from glass-walled bathrooms to see-through restaurant kitchens (photos). Businesses will increasingly adopt glass walls to let patrons monitor the staff and vice versa. The 2007 financial crisis was primarily due to opaque transactions that brought the global economy to its knees. Advanced machine learning-based applications will reduce non-transparent processes by bringing glass walls to business and government.

Improved 4K video surveillance technology will induce more ethical behavior. Billions of these cameras backed by billions of more smartphones will ensure that just about everything will be captured digitally. AI-driven recording modes will eliminate the need to interact with a device to record an event. Sensory-based panic codes, either spoken or detected due to a lack iris contact, will report personal assaults immediately.

Society is hurtling towards a future that answers a favorite cliché, often used by financial analysts but applicable to everyone, "I have no visibility." Before this transparency nirvana can come to be, another massive crash will be required to drive home the need for greater transparency and visibility. We all want more visibility. Voyeurgasm will provide an eyeful.

WAF, the Woman's Acceptance Factor Ubertrend, is leading to an increasingly female-centric society. It's being driven by more highly educated women, female entrepreneurs and politicians, whose social media influence, is helping to shape-shift the order of humanity.

8

WAF

Ascent of Woman

The term "WAF" sprang from an internet discussion forum aimed at men seeking advice on how to obtain their better half's approval before, or after, acquiring new gear. Humorously entitled "The Wife Acceptance Factor — Not in my house!" — this forum was dedicated to a contemporary phenomenon and used a moniker that was semi-onomatopoeic code for man's "better half." What their banter hinted at, however, was the inherent power wielded by women, especially those who control the purse strings. The WAF Ubertrend uses these candid confessions as a proxy for the ascent of woman. One that has been slow in the making, and rife with resistance and obfuscation. As this chapter shows, the WAF Ubertrend marches on and could provide the spark for a matriarchal society.

Seneca Falls

Situated in Upstate New York's idyllic Finger Lakes region, Seneca Falls is a prototypical American village. Director Frank Capra was so taken that he based his mythical Bedford Falls in the movie *It's a Wonderful Life* on Seneca Falls. [1] This little town would be in the spotlight much earlier for an entirely different reason.

In the 1840s, rustic Seneca Falls was home to about 4,300 inhabitants. [2] It was in this part of Western New York that on July 18, 1848, the first Women's Rights Convention was held, a momentous event that would later become to define the global suffrage movement. [3]

Why Seneca Falls? A community of abolitionists and their relatives, joined by Quaker women, had started businesses in Seneca Falls and nearby Waterloo in the 1830s and 40s. Among the reformers was 32-year-old Elizabeth Cady Stanton, who together with Lucretia Mott, her sister Martha Wright, Jane Hunt, and Mary Ann M'Clintock organized the convention. [4]

The group hammered out a formal list of grievances, which was called the "Declaration of Sentiments" and was based on the Declaration of Independence. It denounced inequities in property rights, education, employment, religion, marriage and family, and suffrage. The demand for voting rights was framed as follows, "He has never permitted her to exercise her inalienable right to the elective franchise." [5] This was such

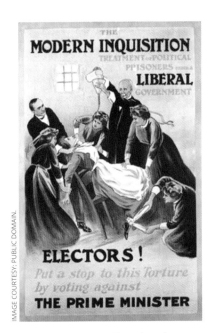

IMAGE COURTESY: PUBLIC DOMAIN.

1910 U.K. Poster Showing the Force-feeding of a "Suffragette"

U.K. suffragettes were members of the WSPU — Women's Social and Political Union — formed on 10 October 1903. The organization fought for women's suffrage, or the right to vote in public elections, under the banner "Votes for Women" by participating in marches, heckling, civil disobedience and hunger strikes. The *Daily Mail* coined the term "suffragette" in 1906, which was immediately embraced by the WSPU.

1. "It's a Wonderful Life," *Wikipedia*, ret. 18-Dec-18.
2. "Seneca Falls," *Wikipedia*, ret. 18-Dec-18.
3. "Suffragette," *Wikipedia*, ret. 18-Dec-18.
4. "Women's Rights Convention in Seneca Falls, NY," *University of Rochester Susan B. Anthony Center*, ret. 12-Sep-18.
5. Elizabeth Cady Stanton, "Declaration of Sentiments," *History Is A Weapon*, ret. 18-Dec-18.

Women's Suffragists Parade Down New York's Fifth Avenue in 1917

Started in 1910, the eight Annual Women's Suffrage Parade on Fifth Avenue, featured suffragists carrying placards with signatures of more than 1 million women. The parade was led by Carrie Chapman Catt, president of the National American Woman Suffrage Association, which was dissolved in 1920 after women received the right to vote.

IMAGE COURTESY: THE NEW YORK TIMES PHOTO ARCHIVES.

IMAGE COURTESY: UNITED STATES MINT.

Susan B. Anthony Silver Dollar

The United States Mint introduced the Susan B. Anthony silver dollar in 1979. It was the first time that a woman appeared on a circulating coin. The Anthony coin was minted from 1979 to 1981, and again in 1999.

a controversial statement that Mott protested vigorously, but Stanton prevailed. On July 19, the declaration was presented before an audience of 300 at the convention featuring Stanton, Lucretia Mott and Frederick Douglass, an escaped slave, abolitionist and dyed-in-the-wool supporter of women's rights who, as *The New York Times* writes, "was on his way to becoming one of the most famous speakers of the century." [6]

Stanton opened the convention with these famously historic words, "We hold these truths to be self-evident: that all men and women are created equal." However, showing the value of a truly integrated society, were it not for Douglass' oratory, historian Lisa Tetrault writes in *The Myth of Seneca Falls*, the "controversial" resolution demanding women's voting rights might actually have failed. [7]

The suffrage movement suffered a set back in 1869 when two competing organizations were formed, one led by Susan Anthony and Elizabeth Cady Stanton and the other by Lucy Stone. Stone was a was a prominent U.S. orator, abolitionist and vocal advocate of women rights. In 1855, she became the first woman to keep her own name after marriage. [8]

After two decades of rivalry, the two organizations merged in 1890 as the National American Woman Suffrage Association (NAWSA) with Anthony as its leading force. By the turn of the century, the suffrage movement enlisted armies of women to march for equal rights (photo). This activist movement led to the 19th Amendment, ratified in 1920, which barred U.S. states from denying voting rights based on gender.

The suffrage movement was a critical element in the struggle for women's rights and signaled the start of the WAF Ubertrend — a slowly gathering force that would ripple through society for generations to come.

6. Brent Staples, "How the Suffrage Movement Betrayed Black Women," *The New York Times*, 28-Jul-18.
7. Lisa Tetrault, "The Myth of Seneca Falls: Memory and the Women's Suffrage Movement, 1848-1898," *The University of North Carolina Press*, 01-Feb-17.
8. Diana Boxer, "American Women, Changing Their Names," *NPR*, 13-Jun-06.

Holy Crud, Didn't Tell Wife!

"Holy crud! Got a new plasma, didn't tell wife!!! Any good excuses?" read the cry for help from "exsilio," which was posted to the AVS Forum on August 30, 2003. Obviously, exsilio did not seek approval from the "WAF" before his big purchase.

WAF Origin

In September 1983, Larry Greenhill first used the term "Wife Acceptance Factor," writing for *Stereophile* magazine. [1] Graciously, Greenhill credited fellow *Stereophile* reviewer Lewis Lipnick with inventing the term, which is also loosely described as "wife approval factor," "wife appeal factor" or simply WAF. The term refers to the assessment of design elements that either increase or diminish the likelihood of a wife approving the purchase of expensive consumer electronics gear, such as speakers, home theater systems and personal computers. Stylish, compact forms and appealing colors are commonly considered to have a high WAF. It has been modernized and updated as the Woman's Acceptance Factor — a meaningful definition for this Ubertrend.

1. "Wife acceptance factor," *Wikipedia*, ret. 05-Jan-19.

WAF

In the mid-1990s, a new word cropped up on the Home Theater Spot discussion forum. The term, semi-onomatopoeic code for man's "better half," was used by men seeking advice on how to obtain their spouse's or girlfriend's approval before, or after, acquiring new consumer electronics gear. [9] Soon enough a dedicated forum was established for sharing tips and excuses, humorously entitled "The Wife Acceptance Factor — Not in my house!"

The internet's anonymous nature lets men pour out their hearts in ways the real world rarely sees: "My wife calls the shots in the entire house except for my home office, home theater and kitchen when I'm in there cooking. The living room has to meet her specs 100%."

"Go ahead for plasma!" read another forum posting's subject line. "I have the WAF on my side for a new plasma after the first of the year. We're moving into a classic 1917 bungalow and had issues with where the TV stuff would go," continued the post.

Online chat sites and forums provide an unusually intimate glimpse into society's evolving values. Men were once widely considered the "head of household," but the Wife Acceptance Factor phenomenon shows just how much decision-making power women have gained, particularly those who control a household's finances.

"Men like toys, electronics, sports cars, golf memberships. Then they get married, and wives have a say, even veto power. Torn between their own desires and preserving their marriages, the men of the new millennium are learning about WAF," Kimberly Blanton wrote in *The Boston Globe*. [10]

The phenomenon has gone global, judging by many similar types of posts written in different languages. And the arrival of same-sex marriages has even given the concept a new namesake among gay and lesbian couples: SAF, or Spouse Approval Factor.

Given that wife-persuasion tactics continue to be frequently discussed in chat rooms with men grumbling, anonymously, of course, about their difficult partners, many consumer electronics manufacturers have started to focus their design strategies on gaining quick WAF approval.

Martha Barletta, author of *Marketing to Women*, notes "It would be a great idea for manufacturers to design a whole suite of consumer electronics

9. "wife acceptance factor," *Word Spy*, ret. 18-Dec-18.
10. Kimberly Blanton, "WAF (Wife Acceptance Factor) — Men learn to listen to their spouses on big purchases," *The Boston Globe*, 28-Jun-04.

products aimed at women. If they're aiming for a high WAF rating that may well be the only way to go."

The unusual display of emotional intelligence on the part of male forum dwellers was the inspiration for using the WAF moniker for this particular Ubertrend, while subtly renaming it the "Woman's Acceptance Factor."

Chief Financial Controller

Evidence of the financial influence of women is everywhere. NPR reports that in many Asian countries husbands hand their earnings to women who give them a small allowance. The phenomenon even has a saying: "A woman is a slave before marriage but a general after." Anecdotal observations like these confirm the influence of women on household spending, which continues to rise.

One of the most frequently cited statistics is "women control 80% or more of spending." No one is quite sure where that statistic originated but many point to Barletta's 2002 book, *Marketing to Women*, in which she claims that women "handle 80% to 90% of spending and purchasing for the household." Barletta recently admitted to *The Wall Street Journal* that she has no specific source for the data. [11]

While this widely quoted figure of women's influence on household spending can't be attributed to any specific study, Barletta tells me that "Most marketers don't recognize the power of indirect influence."

One 2010 study of nearly 4,000 Americans 16 and older by London consulting firm Futures Co. did, however, find that 37% of women say they have *primary responsibility* for shopping decisions in their household, while 85% say they have primary or shared responsibility. The figures for men were similar: 31% and 84%.

A 2008 online survey by the Boston Consulting Group, which is *not projectable* to the U.S. population, asked women what percentage of household spending they *control or influence*. The average U.S. answer was 73%. By comparison, men said they control or influence 61% of spending on average.

The data about actual outlays controlled by women are similarly frequently used without research attribution. In his 2003 book *Re-imagine!*, Tom Peters got things started by suggesting that U.S. women now control about $3.3 trillion in annual consumer spending and $1.5 trillion more in business outlays. [12] According to Peters, American women are the largest national economy on earth, larger than all of Japan's.

In 2010, Muhtar Kent, Chairman and former CEO of The Coca-Cola Company stated that "women control over $20 trillion in worldwide spending." [13] While Kent did not attribute the data to any specific study, the figure has been widely cited on the internet.

Whatever the real figure is, it's indisputable that women today wield a great deal of power over spending. Moreover, that influence will only grow.

> " 37% of women say they have primary responsibility for shopping decisions in their household, while 85% say they have primary or shared responsibility"
>
> Futures Co. Study
> 2010

11. Carl Bialik, "Who Makes the Call at the Mall, Men or Women?," *The Wall Street Journal*, 23-Apr-11.
12. Tom Peters, "Re-imagine!: Business Excellence in a Disruptive Age," *Dorling Kindersley Publishing*, 2003.
13. "Statistics On The Purchasing Power Of Women," *Girlpower Marketing*, ret. 18-Dec-18.

Glass Ceiling

In her June 7, 2008 Democratic party concession speech, Hillary Clinton used a beautiful metaphor to describe the ascent of women: "Although we weren't able to shatter that highest, hardest glass ceiling this time, thanks to you, it has about 18 million cracks in it and the light is shining through like never before."

Clinton was referring to the votes she had received during the primaries, many from women who viewed her presidential aspirations as a testament to the new-found power of women. That speech she gave that night, now commonly referred to as the "Glass Ceiling Speech," was one of Clinton's most lauded and memorable moments.

The glass ceiling reflects the widely experienced invisible barrier women encounter as they climb the career ladder. The term dates back to 1979, with two women claiming they invented it.

The Washington Post reports that Marilyn Loden, then a 31-year-old mid-level manager at New York Telephone Co., was asked to join four other women on a panel entitled "Mirror, Mirror on the Wall." [14] The name was fitting, Loden recalled, because the discussion centered on how women, and their self-image, were to blame for their lack of advancement in the workforce. Mirrors are also made of glass, which inspired her to call the invisible barrier to advancement "glass ceiling."

The Wall Street Journal confirms that the term was popularized in the 1980s, but says it was coined by former Hewlett-Packard employee, Katherine Lawrence, at a July 1979 conference of the Women's Institute for the

IMAGE COURTESY: KHURAL OF THE TUVAN REPUBLIC.

First Female Head of State: Khertek Anchimaa-Toka

Born in a poor peasant family, Anchimaa learned to read and write in Mongolian, and later was one of the first to learn the national Tuvan alphabet. In 1940, she became Chairwoman of Little Khural of the Tuvan People's Republic — the first non-hereditary female head of state in the modern world. The Soviet Union annexed the Tuvan People's Republic in 1944.

14. Theresa Vargas, "She coined the term 'glass ceiling.' She fears it will outlive her," *The Washington Post*, 01-Mar-18.

> ❝ From now on, it will be unremarkable for a woman to win primary state victories, unremarkable to have a woman in a close race to be our nominee, unremarkable to think that a woman can be the president of the United States."

Hillary Clinton
07-Jun-08

Global Growth of Women Heads of State by Decade

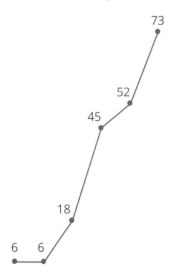

Oct-18 Wikipedia

Freedom of the Press. [15] Whoever invented the term, the glass ceiling is cracking in more places than ever before. As Clinton stated in her 2008 concession speech, "You can be so proud that, from now on, it will be unremarkable for a woman to win primary state victories, unremarkable to have a woman in a close race to be our nominee, unremarkable to think that a woman can be the president of the United States," she said. "And that is truly remarkable, my friends." [16]

While Clinton shattered one of those "highest, hardest ceilings" when she became the first female presidential candidate nominated by a major party, she was not, however, the first female presidential candidate. That accomplishment belongs to Victoria Woodhull whose 1872 presidential candidacy preceded suffrage for women in the U.S. [17]

At each of her concession speeches, Clinton has urged her young followers not to give up on their dreams. That message has resonated among women, who are leading a "Pink Wave" that is set to transform government.

Pink Wave

Energized by Clinton's defeat and the inappropriate behavior of men, a record number of women are now running for office, buoyed by a wave of enthusiasm among women voters. The U.S. is actually trailing other nations when it comes to female heads of state who have been leading governments since the 1940s.

India gave the world Indira Gandhi, who served as prime minister starting in 1966. Israel's Golda Meir became prime minister in 1969. In 1974, Isabel Peron became the first female president of any republic on the American continent. The U.K. followed with Margaret Thatcher in 1979. The pace quickened in the 1980s (chart). First up, Iceland's Vigdís Finnbogadóttir — the world's first democratically, directly elected female president. She was followed by Jeanne Sauvé in Canada (1984), Corazon Aquino, Philippines (1986) and Benazir Bhutto, Pakistan (1988). Many more female leaders would follow, the notable ones including Angela Merkel of Germany (2005), Michelle Bachelet, Chile (2006), Cristina Fernández de Kirchner, Argentina (2007), Dilma Rousseff, Brazil (2011) and Theresa May, U.K. (2016).

Despite lagging economies and *machismo* cultures, Latin America, in particular, has elected more women to the highest office than any of its northern cousins. In Chile, Michelle Bachelet was chosen twice to serve as President. And the latest, Carrie Lam, sworn in as Hong Kong's first female leader, sends a loud message to Beijing's all-male leadership. [18]

The 2019 freshman class of women in U.S. Congress has set a record, with 102 female representatives and 25 female senators, which raises female representation in Congress from 20% to 24%. It presages a change in the public debate on such issues as healthcare, immigration, abortion rights, education and gun control.

15. Ben Zimmer, "The Phrase 'Glass Ceiling' Stretches Back Decades," *The Wall Street Journal*, 03-Apr-15.
16. Claire Landsbaum, "Hillary Clinton Just Shattered the 'Highest, Hardest Glass Ceiling'," *The Cut*, 06-Jun-16.
17. "List of female United States presidential and vice-presidential candidates," *Wikipedia*, ret. 18-Dec-18.
18. Austin Ramzy, "Carrie Lam Is Sworn In as Hong Kong's First Female Leader," *The New York Times*, 30-Jun-17.

IMAGE COURTESY: U.S. AIR FORCE/STAFF SGT. MARLEAH ROBERTSON.

Alpha Moms

There it was, the umpteenth TV commercial featuring a woman doing housework. The year is 2009, and you might as well be living in a different age. You fill in the name of the brand: PAM Cooking Spray, Tide, McCormick's, even hip Target — all relegating women to the subsidiary role of "happy homemaker." You would think the Renaissance men and women of advertising could come up with something a little bit more enlightening. Thank goodness many did.

Ad agencies have slowly been getting the message that it's not OK to always portray women in a "chief cook and bottle washer" role. One Whirlpool television commercial even starts with a man cleaning an oven pan. Unfortunately, research shows that most household work still rests with women (sidebar), even though many women now work in addition to shouldering the duties of childcare and household maintenance.

Part of the issue is that advertisers remain intent on reaching a market segment identified as "Alpha Moms" ("Alpha Mums" in the U.K.). ABC's *Good Morning America* first described this group as "a generation of college-educated mothers who channel their experiences from the workplace and apply them to parenting with the same level of intensity." [19] Alpha Moms are educated, tech-savvy Type A moms with a common goal: mommy excellence. They are multitaskers, kid-centric and hands-on.

With those outstanding qualities, it's easy to see why marketers are drawn to this audience and its potential circle of influence. After all, if they're impressing neighbors and friends with their use of technology, child rearing, and household organization skills, and posting those experiences on social media, they're exactly the type of people you would want to associate

19. Jennifer Satterwhite, "Alpha Moms, Beta Moms and rest of us Greek alphabet moms," *Blogher*, 09-Apr-07.

your brand with. Christine Mau, the first woman to fly a Lockheed Martin F-35A Lightning II Joint Strike Fighter, one of the Air Force's newest fifth-generation jets, is a perfect example of an Alpha Mom (photo).

And more women are following in Mau's footsteps after she broke through the female sound barrier. There are now three Air Force women in active duty flying the F-35A Lightning II. [20]

Multitasking Females

Multitasking is a skill mothers are well-versed in due to their packed home schedules. A 2011 study by two sociologists found that mothers spend 10 hours more a week multitasking than fathers and that these additional hours are mainly related to time spent on housework and childcare. [21]

So it's not surprising that a study conducted by U.K. psychologists and sponsored by the British Academy found that women outperformed men in two multitasking experiments, one involving computer-based task-switching and another focused on paper-and-pencil multitasking tests. [22] In the latter test, men and women did not differ significantly at solving simple arithmetic problems, searching for restaurants on a map, or answering general knowledge questions on the phone. However, women were significantly better at devising strategies for locating a lost key.

Two other studies produced contradictory results. One experiment in China confirmed that women outperform their male counterparts when it comes to multitasking. [23] By contrast, a study of Swedish twentysomethings found that men may actually be better than women at multitasking when spatial tasks are involved. [24] This study relied on the Vandenberg and Kuse Mental Rotations Test, which gauges the ability to rotate mental representations of two-dimensional and three-dimensional objects. Preschool-age children are known to be capable of representing complex temporal patterns by using spatial "timelines" as retrieval aids.

One particularly notable finding of the Swedish study was that the male advantage was eliminated when female study participants were in their menstrual cycle, disputing the widely held notion that a woman's biology can befuddle her brain. [25]

It turns out that women are more adept at certain skills, such as spatial awareness, after their period. And three weeks later, they become noticeably better communicators, and, oddly, particularly good at detecting when others are feeling fearful.

As society learns to multitask more (See "Multitasking," page 186), expect women to be at the forefront of this ultra-valuable skill.

Doing Gender

Despite decades of advancements since the founding of the Women's Liberation Movement in 1967, little real progress has come in one area, the division of household chores. A study by sociologists Judith Treas and Sonja Drobnic confirms that the lion's share of domestic responsibilities still rests with women, even as more of them work outside the home. [1] As Treas tells *UCI News*, "There has been some change, but we're a long way from full equality." [2] Even in households where wives earn bigger paychecks than their husbands, women often wind up doing a larger share of the housework. Whether they realize it or not, few can resist showing off how "feminine" or "masculine" they really are to a heterosexual audience in the home. Sociologists have a term for this charade: "doing gender."

1. Judith Treas and Sonja Drobnic, "Dividing the Domestic," *Stanford University Press*, 25-Feb-10.
2. Heather Wuebker, "Domestic duties still largely 'women's work'," *UCI News*, 07-Mar-11.

---

20. Tom Demerly, "Meet the U.S. Air Force Reserve's First Female F-35A Lightning II Pilot," *The Aviationist*, 08-Sep-18.
21. Shira Offer and Barbara Schneider, ."Revisiting the gender gap in time- use patterns: Multitasking and well-being among mothers and fathers in dual-earner families," *American Sociological Review*, p. 76, 01-Dec-11.
22. Gijsbert Stoet et al., "Are women better than men at multi-tasking?," *BMC Psychology*, 24-Oct-13.
23. Dongning Ren et al., "A Deeper Look at Gender Difference in Multitasking: Gender-Specific Mechanism of Cognitive Control," *IEEE Explore*, 28-Dec-09.
24. Timo Mäntylä, "Gender Differences in Multitasking Reflect Spatial Ability," *Psychological Science*, 05-Mar-13.
25. Zaria Gorvett, "How the menstrual cycle changes women's brains – for better," *BBC Future*, 07-Aug-18.

Female Liberation: Heading South

This 2005 French-Canadian movie tells the story of three women who visit Haiti in the late 1970s to enjoy a romp in the sun with local teenage gigolos, an emancipated female version of sex tourism. Male sex workers in the Caribbean are called "Sanky Panky," just in case you need to know.

IMAGE COURTESY: HAUT ET COURT.

Hysteria

Increasing self-awareness has been a boon to women around the globe. The unshackling of outdated societal norms, including the gaining of voting, birth control, women's liberation and abortion rights, have instilled women with a sense of confidence to push themselves, and generations to come, to the limit.

One such unshackling happened when, what was once considered a medical device, the vibrator, became freely available at stores everywhere. The vibrator was developed in Victorian times to help relieve the symptoms of "hysteria" — chronic anxiety, irritability and abdominal heaviness. More plainly stated, these "patients" were suffering from sexual frustration.

The invention of the vibrator is the subject of the movie *Hysteria*, which stars Maggie Gyllenhaal as a "spirited, young Victorian lady" and love interest of doctor Mortimer Granville, who invents the vibrator in the name of medical science. [26]

As history tells us, the only effective remedy for hysteria was a treatment

26. Decca Aitkenhead, "The buzz: how the vibrator came to be," *The Guardian*, 07-Sep-12.

that had been practiced by physicians for centuries, consisting of a "pelvic massage," which was performed manually until the patient reached a "hysterical paroxysm" — after which she was miraculously healed. Granville, a respectable Victorian doctor, grew tired of bringing female patients to orgasm using his dexterity alone, so he dreamed up a device to do the job.

Today, vibrators come in a variety of shapes and sizes, both powered or non-powered, that have saved many a woman from the ravages of hysteria. Seven startups, all led by women, have shaken off the stigma of marketing a sex toy and are seeking approval of a solution for your enjoyment. [27]

Gyllenhaal is but one actress in a long line of women whose roles have helped women better grasp the long and sorrowful history of women under the yoke of society. She tells *The Guardian*, "I've done a lot of 'out there' sexual movies but this one pushed even my boundaries." Pushing boundaries is the first step to cracking open the glass ceiling.

Another boundary pusher that showed women that they are their own bosses is *Heading South* — a movie about older, single women visiting 1970s Haiti in a female version of sex tourism. This French-Canadian film drew big audiences to theaters in 2006. The star of the film is Charlotte Rampling, surprise, another British actress, who plays Ellen, a single 55-year-old professor of French literature at Wellesley. Ellen spends her vacation at a resort where poor local teenagers serve as holiday gigolos, devoting themselves to "nourishing the women's starved libidos in exchange for food, gifts and temporary refuge from the perils of the island's repressive regime," as *The New York Times* delicately put it. [28]

The Times quotes a retired, 63-year-old schoolteacher, Marjorie Solovay, who raves, "The whole notion of women's sexuality fading away has disappeared. Women's sexuality carries on." It does indeed.

Female sexuality has been weaponized by FEMEN, a Ukraine-based radical feminist activist group (sidebar). FEMEN members bare their graffiti-riddled breasts in high-profile locations, such as the World Economic Forum in Davos, Switzerland to bring attention to women's rights.

That women are quickly reworking their sexual identity is a foregone conclusion. *Heading South* was preceded by the "cougars" trend, which reared its ugly cat head in 1999 when Canadian site Cougardate.com was established. [29] Not to overstate the case, but a cougar is an older woman who actively pursues casual, and quite often sexual, relationships with younger men. [30]

In 2001, Valerie Gibson authored the book *Cougar: A Guide for Older Women Dating Younger Men*, which gave the concept eager wings. According to a March 3, 2001 *Toronto Globe and Mail* article, Cougardate.com was inspired by a nephew of one of the two female founders, who told the ladies that they were like cougars in search of small, defenseless animals. The nephew said he got the term from members of his hockey team.

From hysteria to cougars, if there's any doubt that the WAF Ubertrend is hard at work to shatter the glass ceiling, it should be dispelled by now.

27. Suzannah Weiss, "7 Women-Led Start-ups That Want to Change How You Think About Sex," *Glamour*, 16-Jun-17.
28. Elizabeth Hayt, "Libidos of a Certain Age," *The New York Times*, 16-Jul-06.
29. Grant Barrett, "Time for a cougar?," *The Toronto Star Online*, 17-Oct-07.
30. "Cougar (slang)," *Wikipedia*, ret. 15-Sep-18.

No Testosterone

If women are to conquer the world and shatter the glass ceiling, it has to be another one of those cliché "win-win" situations for all involved. Luckily, plenty of evidence is emerging that having women in key positions will make this a much better world.

And speaking of feeling much better, public health researchers at Harvard University waded through three years of records of U.S. patients, ages 65 and up, and discovered that the lucky ones treated by female doctors had significantly lower mortality rates than patients treated by male physicians. [31] As more research data like this becomes available, the difference between male and female physician salaries should decline from its deplorable current level of $51,315. [32]

This data should also help dispel the notion that female physicians provide lower quality care, particularly given the finding that among married or partnered women physicians with children, after adjustment for work hours, spousal employment, and other factors, women spent 8.5 more hours per week on domestic activities. [33]

That same job quality standard has also surfaced in business. In 2014, Credit Suisse released the results of the CS Gender 3000 study, which tracks 27,000 senior managers at more than 3,000 of the largest global corporations. The study, entitled *The Credit Suisse Gender 3000: Women in Senior Management* was followed by a 2016 research update, *The CS Gender 3000: The Reward for Change*. Both studies are so multi-faceted that they are summarized below:

- **Female directors** – A survey of companies with a market cap larger than $10 billion found that those with at least one woman on their board of directors outperformed corporations that had no female directors by 26% over a period of six years ending 2011. More importantly, this group of companies would also have outperformed global equities as measured by MSCI's ACWI (All Country World Index).

- **Female management representation** – From year-end 2013 through mid-2016, companies where women accounted for 25% of senior leadership outperformed the ACWI index at a compound annual growth rate of 2.8%. At companies where women comprised 33% of senior leadership, the outperformance was 4.7%. The figure jumped to 10.3% at companies where more than 50% of senior leaders were women, compared with a 1% annual decline for the MSCI ACWI index over the same period.

- **Top countries with female board representation** – The top five countries with the highest percentage of women represented on corporate boards are all European and include Norway (47%), France (34%), Sweden (34%), Italy (31%) and Finland (31%).

1. Maurie Backman, "Here's Why Women Make Great Investors," *The Motley Fool*, 26-Jul-17.
2. Stan Choe, "Many women think men are the better investors; they're not," *The Associated Press*, 23-May-17.

31. Yusuke Tsugawa et al., "Comparison of Hospital Mortality and Readmission Rates for Medicare Patients Treated by Male vs Female Physicians," *JAMA Internal Medicine*, 19-Dec-16.
32. Anupam Jena, "Sex Differences in Physician Salary in US Public Medical Schools," *JAMA Internal Medicine*, 11-Jul-16.
33. Shruti Jolly et al., "Gender Differences in Time Spent on Parenting and Domestic Responsibilities by High-Achieving Young Physician-Researchers," *Annals of Internal Medicine*, 04-Mar-14.

- **Queen Bee myth** – There is a widespread "Queen Bee" notion that argues that women in senior positions actively exclude other women from top management promotions. Credit Suisse debunks this myth by reporting that female CEOs are 50% more likely than male CEOs to have a female CFO, and 55% more likely to have women running business units.

Female performance is not just limited to high-paying jobs. Want to get out of the supermarket line fast? Look for female cashiers, recommends *The New York Times*. [34] That opinion comes from Robert Samuel, founder of Same Ole Line Dudes, a New York-based service that will stand in line for you. His highly qualified opinion on the matter: "This may seem sexist, but I prefer female cashiers. In my experience, they seem to be the most expedient at register transactions and processing."

Of course, that Queen Bee notion does have its roots somewhere. The same mentality that produces superior workers and investors is also likely to create friction among other female staffers. In 2011, UCLA lecturer Kim Elsesser analyzed responses to a study of more than 60,000 people and found that women, even those who were managers themselves, were more likely to want a male boss than a female one. [35] That stings. It also, surprisingly, suggests that female manager sensitivity training is in order.

34. Christopher Mele, "How to Pick the Fastest Line at the Supermarket," *The New York Times*, 07-Sep-16.
35. Olga Khazan, "Why Do Women Bully Each Other at Work?," *The Atlantic*, 03-Aug-17.

Motivated Reasoning

On Saturday, August 5, 2017, media reports surfaced about a 3,300-word online manifesto, entitled "Google's Ideological Echo Chamber," written by 28-year-old James Damore, a Google engineer. His core argument: Men and women have psychological differences that are a result of their underlying biology. Those differences make them differently suited to and interested in the work that is core to Google. [1]

In the manifesto, Damore questioned the company's diversity policies and claimed that scientific data backed up his assertions. In a company-wide e-mail written the following Monday, with the subject line, "Our Words Matter," Google CEO Sundar Pichai wrote that Damore's manifesto crossed the line "by advancing harmful gender stereotypes in our workplace." Pichai added that "To suggest a group of our colleagues have traits that make them less biologically suited to that work is offensive and not OK." [2]

Damore was fired that same day. Before being fired, Damore submitted a complaint to the National Labor Relations Board claiming that Google's upper management was "misrepresenting and shaming me in order to silence my complaints." Damore also charged that he was being smeared and that he was a victim of political correctness.

In a 3,000-word analysis, *Wired*'s Megan Molteni takes the Manifesto apart piece by piece, citing a typical smart person's "incoherency problem." Another takedown comes from *The Economist*, which drafted an e-mail Larry Page's should have written: "Your interpretation is wrong. Your memo was a great example of what's called 'motivated reasoning' — seeking out only the information that supports what you already believe. It was derogatory to women in our industry and elsewhere. Despite your stated support for diversity and fairness, it demonstrated profound prejudice. Your chain of reasoning had so many missing links that it hardly mattered what your argument was based on. We try to hire people who are willing to follow where the facts lead, whatever their preconceptions. In your case we clearly made a mistake." [3] *The Economist* artfully crystallized what most people felt about this divisive matter.

1. Megan Molteni, "The Actual Science Of James Damore's Google Memo," *Wired*, 15-Aug-17.
2. Daisuke Wakabayashi, "Google Fires Engineer Who Wrote Memo Questioning Women in Tech," *The New York Times*, 07-Aug-17.
3. "The e-mail Larry Page should have written to James Damore," *The Economist*, 19-Aug-17.

Mind The Gap

Women have traditionally trailed men when it comes to college degrees. However, that gap is narrowing. In Oxford's fall 2017 class, women outnumbered men for the first time. As *The New York Times* notes, "It only took 1,000 years. [36]

> **As recently as the 1970s, men attending college outnumbered women, 58% to 42% — the ratio has now almost exactly reversed."**
>
> **U.S. Department of Education**

According to data released by the Universities and Colleges Admissions Service, 1,070 women won undergraduate places to start at Oxford in fall 2017, compared with 1,025 men. Moreover, the trend throughout the British university system appears to be accelerating.

The U.S. tipping point occurred in 1981-82, when women first exceeded men in gaining a bachelor's degree, according to the U.S. Department of Education. [37] By 2011, women for the first time also passed men in obtaining advanced degrees, according to the U.S. Census Bureau. [38]

Today, men, whatever race or socioeconomic group they belong to, are less likely than women to earn a bachelor's degrees. Among those who do, men tend to get worse grades than women, while fewer complete their degrees in four or five years, Department of Education statistics show. [39]

That's due to college men studying less and socializing more than their female classmates. [40] As a result, at colleges nationwide, women are walking off with a disproportionate share of honors degrees, ranging from elite schools, such as Harvard University, to large public universities, such as UCLA, and smaller colleges like Florida Atlantic University.

36. Stephen Castle, "Women Outnumber Men in Oxford's Newest Class. It Only Took 1,000 Years." *The New York Times*, 26-Jan-18.
37. "Degrees conferred by degree-granting institutions, by level of degree and sex of student: Selected years, 1869-70 through 2021-22," *National Center of Education Statistics*, ret. 28-Sep-18.
38. "In a First, Women Surpass Men in Advanced Degrees," *Associated Press/The Wall Street Journal*, 26-Apr-11.
39. Tamar Lewin, "At Colleges, Women Are Leaving Men in the Dust," *The New York Times*, 09-Jul-06.
40. Jillian Kinzie, "The Relationship between Gender and Student Engagement in College," *Indiana University Center for Postsecondary Research*, 2005.

As recently as the 1970s, men attending college outnumbered women, 58% to 42% — the ratio has now almost reversed with women comprising 56% of students on campuses nationwide in the 2017-18 school year, according to the U.S. Department of Education. [41]

Some 2.1 million fewer men than women were enrolled in college in 2017. By 2026, women will make up 57% of college students, the U.S. Department of Education estimates. [42] Women constitute, overall, the majority in graduate schools and professional schools too.

If this trend continues, women will one day occupy the majority of mission-critical jobs requiring a college degree. While that day lies on the horizon, that is, unfortunately, not the case today.

Unstacking the Deck

For almost 40 years, women have outnumbered men on U.S. college campuses; have been accepted to the same schools as men; have studied in the same degree programs and have graduated at higher rates than men. Despite those achievements, women are less likely than men to have careers aligned with their field of study. [43]

According to a Bloomberg analysis of American Community Survey data of educational attainment, occupation and income, many women end up accepting jobs that have lower career earning potential.

While male psychology graduates are more likely to be psychologists and managers, female psychology graduates typically end up as social workers and counselors. Male sociology graduates tend to become managers and lawyers, whereas female sociology graduates commonly choose to become, once again, social workers and counselors. Also, while teaching is the top occupation for men and women in both majors, women end up as teachers at a much higher rate than men.

Despite these challenges, the milestone achievements of women obtaining greater numbers of advanced college degrees as well as bachelor's degrees, is slowly reshaping traditional roles of who goes to work and who stays home with the kids. By 2016 the share of stay-at-home dads who were the primary caregivers for their children rose from 4% to 7%, reaching nearly 1.9 million. [44]

That trend is propelled by the record number of women in the workforce, which reached 57% of females 15+ in 2016. [45]

Their incomes have experienced a similarly sharp rise. In the past four decades, the median income of women has risen 87% compared to just 6.8% for men. [46]

Jennifer Doudna

The CRISPR genetic editing breakthrough represents a significant leap forward in medical science. Jennifer Doudna, a biochemist and a professor in the Departments of Chemistry and Chemical Engineering, and Molecular and Cell Biology at the University of California, Berkeley, is a prominent figure in the CRISPR revolution. Her fundamental work and leadership in developing CRISPR-mediated genome editing is remarkable. In 2012, Doudna and Emmanuelle Charpentier were first to propose that CRISPR/Cas9, enzymes from bacteria that control microbial immunity, could be used for programmable editing of genomes, which is now considered one of the most significant discoveries in the history of biology. [1]

1. "Jennifer Doudna," *Wikipedia*, ret. 05-Jan-19.

41. "Total undergraduate fall enrollment in degree-granting postsecondary institutions, by attendance status, sex of student, and control and level of institution: Selected years, 1970 through 2027 (2017)," *National Center of Education Statistics*, ret. 28-Sep-18.
42. Jon Marcus, "Why Men Are the New College Minority," *The Atlantic*, 08-Aug-17.
43. Jackie Gu, "Women Lose Out to Men Even Before They Graduate From College," *Bloomberg*, 15-Mar-18.
44. Gretchen Livingston, "Stay-at-home moms and dads account for about one-in-five U.S. parents," *Pew Research Center*, 24-Sep-18.
45. Esteban Ortiz-Ospina and Sandra Tzvetkova, "Working women: Key facts and trends in female labor force participation," *Our World in Data*, 16-Oct-17.
46. Jonathan Rothbaum, "Looking at All Workers Paints a Different Picture," *U.S. Census Bureau*, 24-Oct-17.

Social Media Influencers

The Digital Lifestyle unleashed the social media revolution, altering the way society engages. The WAF Ubertrend is driving women to social media's front lines of, turning them into the most potent force online.

Women are the top users of social media. Except for YouTube, more adult U.S. women use Facebook, Instagram, Pinterest, Snapchat and Twitter, than their male counterparts, and they are tied with men in the usage of professional networking site LinkedIn. [47]

Women are also more engaged, with 30% checking their social media multiple times per day, compared to 26% of men. [48] That elevated social media use and engagement level have vaulted women to the top echelon of marketing's hottest new discipline, social media influencer outreach. Influencer campaigns rely on social media personalities who can reach out to their circles of influence to impact purchase habits.

These campaigns leverage influencers in certain markets, such as fashion, beauty, food, entertainment, travel, automotive or technology, by having them create posts that appeal to their constituencies. The U.S. Federal Trade Commission (FTC) requires that sponsored posts be identified as paid advertising by including either a #sponsored or #ad hashtag. [49]

Despite that requirement, influencer marketing is predicted to reach $5 billion at a minimum by 2022, according to BI Intelligence. [50] Moreover, Klear reports that women posted 84% of #ad posts in 2017. [51]

47. Aaron Smith And Monica Anderson, "Social Media Use in 2018," *Pew Research Center*, 01-Mar-18.
48. "Women Dominate Every Social Media Network -- Except One," *Entrepreneur*, 04-Mar-14.
49. Benjamin Chacon, "How to Properly Disclose Sponsored Instagram Posts According to the FTC," *Later*, 15-Oct-17.
50. Keving Gallagher, "The Influencer Marketing Report: Research, strategy & platforms for leveraging social media influencers," *Business Insider*, 24-Sep-18.
51. Yuval Maoz, "The State of Influencer Marketing," *Klear*, 15-Jan-18.

Social Media Influencer Selena Gomez Hawking Coca-Cola

A September 2016 Instagram post featured an image of Selena Gomez sipping a Coke and waxing poetically, "when your lyrics are on the bottle." The post, which lacked the requisite #ad hashtag, drew some 6.3 million likes and reportedly cost Coca-Cola $550,000.

IMAGE COURTESY: THE COCA-COLA COMPANY.

Facebook popularized the term "social graph" on May 24, 2007 at its F8 Developer Conference, when Facebook CEO Mark Zuckerberg outlined the company's ambitious plans to map people's relationships and subjects they value.

The value of the social graph is well documented. Social media users are not only more likely to recommend and buy brands, but their friends are also likely to follow suit. Nearly six out of 10, or 57%, of millennials say they "spent money they hadn't planned to because of what they saw on their social media feeds," reports Allianz Life's Generations Ahead Study. [52]

Voyeurgasmic social networks like Instagram tend to have even more impact, with 72% of Instagram users reporting making fashion, beauty or style-related purchases after seeing something on Instagram, with the most-purchased categories being clothing, makeup, shoes and jewelry. [53] Since women dominate these shopping categories, the value of their social graph has skyrocketed.

Predictably, female celebrities are influencer megabrands, lead by Beyoncé, whose social media posts are said to be worth $1 million each, based on her 121 million followers and brand authenticity. [54]

Before Kim Kardashian, who now boasts 122 million Instagram followers, achieved fame with *Keeping Up With The Kardashians* (page 253), she was reportedly charging a mere $10,000 for each sponsored post. [55] That was six years ago, an eon in social media terms.

In between, much one-upwomanship has taken place. In September 2016, Selena Gomez attracted a whopping 6.3 million likes for a sponsored post of her downing a Coke (photo). Beyoncé's February 2017 pregnancy announcement trashed that record when her baby bump post drew a staggering 11.2 million likes. [56]

One year later, Kylie Jenner took the crown away from Beyoncé with a pic of her newborn baby girl Stormi Webster, which got more than 14 million likes. [57] If it's any consolation to Selena Gomez, she remains Instagram's most popular user with 144 million followers. Yet, Gomez readily admits that she doesn't even like Instagram. [58]

52. "Millennials Making Financial Progress, but Efforts Thwarted by Influence of Social Media," *Allianz*, 06-Feb-18.
53. Cara Salpini, "Study: Instagram influences almost 75% of user purchase decisions," *Retail Dive*, 23-Aug-17.
54. Kristine Solomon, "Beyoncé Becomes 1st Influencer Valued at More Than $1 Million Per Social Media Post," *Yahoo! Lifestyle*, 03-Apr-17.
55. Jo Piazza, "How Much Can a Celebrity Make for Tweeting?," *Vulture*, 28-Jan-12.
56. Lizzie Plaugic, "Beyoncé's pregnancy announcement is the most-liked Instagram post of all time," *The Verge*, 01-Feb-17.
57. Cady Lang, "Here's the Instagram Post That Just Dethroned Queen Beyoncé From the Top Spot," *Time*, 07-Feb-18.
58. Kaitlyn Tiffany, "Instagram's most-followed user doesn't like Instagram," *The Verge*, 16-Mar-17.

The power of social media is not limited to female celebrities. According to USC's Annenberg School for Communication and Journalism Marketing Professor Jeetendr Sehdev, female YouTube stars carry more clout than even their traditional Hollywood counterparts. [59] Sehdev's findings suggest that female YouTubers, including Zoella, Jenna Marbles and Bethany Mota, are 90% more genuine, 17 times more engaging and 11 times more extraordinary than mainstream celebrities in the eyes of their teenage fans.

That is much influence for new-age women to wield.That influence sphere will inevitably extend beyond advertising and starstruck YouTube teens one day. Influencers can also have a disproportionate amount of political clout, as detailed in a 2005 study produced for Blue Shield and Chevron, *Communicating With Congress*. [60] It describes their influence as follows:

> *"A 2004 report by The George Washington University Institute for Politics, Democracy, and the Internet (IPDI) found that people who use the Internet to become politically engaged are far more likely than average citizens to be 'Influentials.' Influentials, a term coined by the RoperASW market research firm, are people who 'tell their neighbors what to buy, which politicians to support, and where to vacation.' Influentials are thought leaders in their communities. They join organizations, attend meetings, try to persuade others of their points of view, and become engaged in political action. Typically, about 10% of the general public can be considered Influentials. Among Internet users, 13% can be considered Influentials."*

It's the political influence of half of those internet influentials, the female 6.5%, that will push the WAF Ubertrend squarely onto society's main stage.

#GamerGate

As one gender grows in power and the other sees its influence diminishing, escalating friction will inevitably arise. The Casual Living Ubertrend foreshadows a world steeped in anti-social behavior, so women should prepare for the risks and rewards of growing power. The #GamerGate saga provides a preview of such a future.

In August 2014, an ex-boyfriend accused game developer Zoë Quinn of having cheated on him. Because one of the alleged liaisons occurred with a reviewer of the prominent gaming site Kotaku, enraged gamers jumped to the erroneous conclusion that Quinn had traded sex for coverage. [61]

When several other high-profile members of the gaming community, including Boston-based game developer Brianna Wu, as well as feminist media critic Anita Sarkeesian, were drawn into the mêlée, the story quickly escalated. Both Sarkeesian, a frequent critic of female stereotyping in video games, and Quinn were forced to leave their homes after receiving numerous threats, some including graphic imagery of rape and death. [62]

> **“**Influentials, a term coined by the RoperASW market research firm, are people who 'tell their neighbors what to buy, which politicians to support, and where to vacation.' Among Internet users, 13% can be considered Influentials.”
>
> **Communicating With Congress**
> 2005

59. Tim Peterson, "Why Female Youtube Stars Carry More Clout Than Mainstream Celebs," *Ad Age*, 29-Oct-15.
60. Brad Fitch, Kathy Goldschmidt et al., "Communicating With Congress," *Congressional Management Foundation*, 2005.
61. "Gamergate controversy," *Wikipedia*, ret. 19-Dec-18.
62. Caitlin Dewey, "The only guide to Gamergate you will ever need to read," *The Washington Post*, 14-Oct-14.

Female Aggressors

Despite the widely held belief that women typically fall victim in domestic violence incidences, a study of 11,370 respondents reveals that half of violent relationships were reciprocally violent.[1] In non-reciprocally violent relationships, women were the perpetrators in more than 70% of the cases. A *Psychological Bulletin* analysis of 552 domestic violence studies found that men suffered 38% of physical injuries resulting from domestic violence disputes. Of course, that still means that 62% of those injured by a partner were women.[2] Evidence is emerging that social media is changing the way girls speak, making them seem more aggressive.[3] Ready for a tidal wave of change?

1. Daniel Whitaker et al., "Relationships With Reciprocal and Nonreciprocal Intimate Partner Violence," *American Journal of Public Health*, May-07.
2. John Archer, "Sex differences in aggression between heterosexual partners: A meta-analytic review," *Psychological Bulletin*, Sep-00.
3. Sarah Harris, "Watevs! Facebook and Twitter are making young girls more aggressive because of the way they write online," *Daily Mail*, 29-Jun-12.

Will online discourse become more or less shaped by bad actors, harassment and trolls?

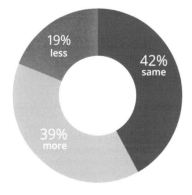

- 42% same
- 39% more
- 19% less

Source: 01-Jul-16 Pew Research Center and Elon University's Imagining the Internet Center

Quinn had already been a victim of "doxing" — the publication online of personal information, such as home and e-mail address, and phone number. The #GamerGate hashtag became a way for trolling participants to cheer egg on others on Twitter. Most Gamergaters congregated in the dark corners of the internet, at sites such as 4Chan, 8Chan, Reddit and other watering holes of the disenfranchised.

What is abundantly clear from this unsettling episode is that it was less about relationship ethics and more of a frontal attack on the critics of a male-dominated gaming culture. #GamerGate is just one manifestation of the struggle of reactionary forces fighting against inroads being made by the WAF Ubertrend.

Another beast that reared its ugly head was Elliot Rodgers, the Santa Barbara mass shooter who murdered six people because he blamed women for his inability to talk to girls and misery of being a virgin.[63]

Rodger and Alek Minassian, who intentionally drove a rental van onto a busy Toronto sidewalk in April 2018, killing 10 pedestrians and wounding 14, have a devoted following among "incels" — short for involuntary celibate.[64] These frustrated young men would gravitate to a now-banned Reddit group, where they would discuss their lack of sexual activity and blame women for their problems.

In the gaming community, the term "griefing" refers to repeatedly killing the same player so that the person can't move forward or messing with their play by disguising oneself with distressing images. "Griefing was a way to have power over other people without any repercussions since you can create multiple characters in the same game," former Cryptic Studios CEO Jack Emmert tells *The New York Times*. "When there are no repercussions, some people will start to do crazy things." Griefing has apparently moved to the real world, where gamers who enjoy violent games only see violence as a way to get even. Both Minassian and Rodger liked playing videogames, Halo 3 and World of Warcraft, respectively.

Luckily, women have decided to take matters in their own hands. Wu, who co-founded videogame studio Giant Spacekat in 2010, and was both a frequent target for threats and a prominent opponent of both Gamergate and online harassment, ran for a House of Representatives seat in 2018. "When I started speaking out about harassment, I thought something would change. But it hasn't — every single system failed us," Wu tweeted in 2016. "We're getting diminishing returns on writing and speaking out about harassment. I think the next step is running for office and passing laws." Unfortunately, Wu lost her bid, which she blamed on inadequate fundraising.

According to Pew Internet Research, trolls will continue to subvert social media. When Pew asked 1,537 tech experts, academics, government leaders, if future online discourse would become more or less shaped by bad actors, harassment and trolls, 42% said they expect things to stay the same, while 39% expect it to get worse (chart).

The only way to mitigate this trend is through better education and communication. Women, you have your jobs cut out for you.

63. Christian Durso, "I Read The Elliot Rodger "Manifesto" So You Don't Have To," *Medium*, 29-May-14.
64. "Alek Minassian Toronto van attack suspect praised 'incel' killer," *BBC News*, 25-Apr-18.

#metoo

It was a truly extraordinary occurrence, even by Hollywood's colossal standards. The downfall of one of Tinseltown's most powerful figures was a confluence of raging events, unified by a revealing social media hashtag: #metoo.

Sexual Harassment Origin

The term "sexual harassment" traces its origins to Cornell University in the mid-1970s, where journalist Lin Farley taught a course on women and work. [1] To best summarize the physical and emotional abuse women faced on the job, Farley and colleagues brainstormed the phrase "sexual harassment of women at work." The November 1977 issue of *Ms.* featured a story entitled, *Sexual Harassment On The Job And How To Stop It*. [2] Due to the sensitive nature of the topic, the cover illustration of the issue used a puppet. This phenomenon now had a name, signaling a significant inflection point in a growing national debate.

1. "By Kyle Swenson, "Who came up with the term 'sexual harassment'?," *The Washington Post*, 22-Nov-17.
2. Jessica Bennett, "The 'Click' Moment: How the Weinstein Scandal Unleashed a Tsunami," *The New York Times*, 05-Nov-17.

It all began with an October 5, 2017 article in *The New York Times* that detailed decades of allegations of sexual harassment against Hollywood movie mogul Harvey Weinstein. [65] The story was buttressed by the stunning admissions of actresses Rose McGowan and Ashley Judd, who set their fears aside to share their experiences valiantly. In less than three weeks, the *Times'* exposé snowballed into an avalanche of allegations involving Weinstein from no less than 87 accusers. [66]

The takedown of a high-profile, Hollywood studio boss emboldened many women to come forward with their own stories of sexual assault and abuse. By November 29, just 12 weeks after *The New York Times* broke the story, Business Insider compiled a list of 36 other powerful men who were caught in the downdraft of the #metoo movement. The list of alleged perpetrators ranges from actors to entertainers to media personalities and politicians, including Jeffrey Tambor, Steven Seagal, Kevin Spacey, Louis C.K., R. Kelly, Mark Halperin, Charlie Rose, President George H.W. Bush, Al Franken, Roy Moore and many others.

Prominent CEOs were not spared either. Wynn Resorts' Steve Wynn, Intel's Brian Krzanich and CBS' Les Moonves are just a few of the chief executives who left their companies after #metoo revelations cast a pall on their once sterling reputation. [67]

65. Jodi Kantor, Megan Twohey, "Harvey Weinstein Paid Off Sexual Harassment Accusers for Decades," *The New York Times*, 05-Oct-17.
66. Sara Moniuszko, Cara Kelly, "Harvey Weinstein scandal: A complete list of the 87 accusers," *USA Today*, 27-Oct-17.
67. "Post-Weinstein, These Are the Powerful Men Facing Sexual Harassment Allegations," *Glamour*, 27-Sep-18.

Wonder Woman: An All-Female Hit

Wonder Woman was the surprise global hit of Summer 2017, enjoying the largest-ever opening weekend for a film directed by a woman, Patty Jenkins. Starring Israeli actress Gal Gadot, *Wonder Woman* has grossed $821 million globally and was the third highest grossing film domestically in 2017.

IMAGE COURTESY: WARNER BROS. AND DC COMICS.

Dominoes fell in many other sectors, leading to the departure of 414 high-profile executives and employees who were outed by their accusers over 18 months. [68] Of the accused, all but seven were men or 98.3%.

The low ratio explains why female politicians rarely get caught up in sex scandals. Unlike former South Carolina Governor Mark Sanford, no female politician has had an Argentine soul mate; or has been caught by federal wiretaps arranging meetings with high-priced call girls, like Eliot Spitzer; or, as in the case of Anthony Weiner, shared lewd selfies on social media.

As Michigan Republican Representative Candice Miller told *The New York Times* during the Weiner scandal in 2011, "Every time one of these sex scandals goes, we just look at each other, like, 'What is it with these guys? Don't they think they're going to get caught?'" [69]

It's entirely conceivable that, as women gain power, more will follow in the footsteps of former Nashville Mayor Megan Barry, who illegally financed an affair with her chief of security detail through travel expense reimbursements, while both were married to other people. [70]

68. Jeff Green, "#MeToo Has Implicated 414 High-Profile Executives and Employees in 18 Months," *Time*, 25-Jun-18.
69. Sheryl Gay Stolberg, "When It Comes to Scandal, Girls Won't Be Boys," *The New York Times*, 11-Jun-11.
70. Ed Kilgore, "Nashville Mayor Resigns Over Using Taxpayer Money to Fund Affair With Bodyguard," *New York Magazine*, 06-Mar-18.

> **"People need to speak truth to power."**
>
> **Lynne Brookes**
> CEO, Synchrony Healthcare
> Communications

However, the likelihood that women will achieve parity with their male counterparts when it comes to sexual misconduct with employees or others runs counter to the intuition and judgment of most females.

During the confirmation hearings of Judge Brett Kavanaugh, one of his former Yale classmates, Synchrony Healthcare Communications CEO Lynne Brookes, a Republican, cited a powerful adage with a storied history, "People need to speak truth to power." [71] This non-violent political concept is said to have originated in a 1955 pamphlet "Speak Truth to Power: A Quaker Search for an Alternative to Violence." [72]

This saying may well hold the key in future turbulent times.

Wonder Woman

The #metoo movement has not only been a call for justice on the part of sexually harassed women. It's also drawing more attention to another female plight — the lack of women in high-profile positions. Less than 5% of companies in the Standard & Poor's 500 now have female chief executives. [73]

Worse, women account for 13% of startup founders but just 6% of founder equity, or $0.39 on the dollar. This equity gap is even larger than the $0.82 women earn for every dollar men make in similar positions. [74]

Captain Marvel: Brie Larson

Brie Larson will play Captain Marvel in Marvel Studios' first female-led superhero movie, which undoubtedly was spurred by the success of *Wonder Woman*. Set for a March 2019 release, *Captain Marvel* is co-directed by Anna Boden and is based on a script written by five women.

The story is much the same for female actors. An analysis conducted by *The New York Times*' Kevin Lee using Cinemetrics data found that the 2014 Academy Award lead actors averaged 85 minutes on screen, compared to just 57 minutes for lead actresses. [75] The 2013 Oscar results were even more biased towards men with nominated male stars averaging 100 minutes on-screen while lead actresses only had 49 minutes.

A new wave of straight-talking, millennial women could help reshape Hollywood. Emerging research suggests that social media is changing the way young women speak, making them seem more assertive. [76] University of Oxford Professor of Language and Communication Deborah Cameron says girls are at the forefront of language change, using such techniques as a rising tonal intonation and "vocal fry." These phenomena are more evident among girls since they tend to "communicate more than males." Adds Cameron, "Girls are the innovative ones, more than boys are."

The tide is turning, as Patty Jenkins' *Wonder Woman* suggests. It's now the highest-grossing live-action film directed by a woman in the world. Less than a month after its release, *Wonder Woman* overtook the U.S. box-office take of Warner Bros.' other DC Comics films. To date, *Wonder Woman* has earned $413 million at the domestic box office, compared to the previous record holder, *Batman v Superman*, at $330 million.

Could this signal the dawn of the age of Wonder Women?

IMAGE COURTESY: MARVEL STUDIOS.

71. "The Last Word With Lawrence O'Donnell," *MSNBC*, 28-Sep-18.
72. "Speaking truth to power," *Wikipedia*, ret. 03-Oct-18.
73. David Gelles, "Missing: Female C.E.O.s," *The New York Times*, 28-Sep-18.
74. Josh Constine, "The Gap Table: Women own just 9% of startup equity," *TechCrunch*, 18-Sep-18.
75. Kevin Lee, "The Gender Gap in Screen Time," *The New York Times*, 27-Feb-14.
76. Sarah Harris, "Watevs! Facebook and Twitter are making young girls more aggressive because of the way they write online," *Daily Mail*, 29-Jun-12.

Women Travel

With more women choosing to travel alone, or with other women, new services have cropped up aimed at this emerging niche. You can blame "Liz Gilbert," expertly played by Julia Roberts, who embarks on a post-divorce romp through Italy, India and Indonesia in *Eat Pray Love*.

In 2007, Beach No. 134 opened with much fanfare on a 50-mile stretch between Rimini and Riccione on Italy's Adriatic coast. The festivities featured model Karima Adebibe as Lara Croft, who was on hand to promote the new videogame *Tomb Raider: Anniversary* from Eidos Interactive. [1]

Dubbed the "Pink Beach," No. 134 featured a large sign of a macho man covered by a pink cross that warns "No Men." Food offerings ranged from healthy salads to fresh fish, while manicures, pedicures, keep-fit classes and cooking lessons from a well-known chef were also on the menu.

The timing of No. 134 was impeccable. Today, more women travel solo (Singles Nation, page 222), and indications are that solo female travel has a bright future, particularly adventure packages. According to the U.K.'s Abta Holiday Habits survey, one in nine holidaymakers reported vacationing on their own in the previous 12 months, double the six-year earlier number. [2]

The Georgian Court Hotel in Vancouver, British Columbia offers guests the Orchid Floor, which caters exclusively to female travelers. The Luthan Hotel in Riyadh, Saudi Arabia, bills itself as "the Sanctuary" — a women-only hotel with 25 rooms.

Demand has been met by a surge in the number of companies specializing in women-only travel. Sites like BookYogaRetreats.com, which targets an activity with a devoted female following, has seen a traffic surge. Hotels are starting to offer yoga, or at least information about nearby facilities, to their list of guest services. Now all you have to do is make sure to invite a female superhero to your world premiere.

1. Felix Lowe, "Italy opens first women-only beach," *The Telegraph*, 25-Jun-07.
2. Annabel Fenwick Elliott, "Why are so many of us now choosing to travel alone?," *The Telegraph*, 14-May-18.

WAF Timeline

1983
Larry Greenhill first uses "Wife Acceptance Factor" in the September 1983 issue of *Stereophile* magazine. Greenhill credits fellow reviewer and music professor Lewis Lipnick with coining the term. This Ubertrend uses a modern version: Woman's Acceptance Factor.

1981
Women exceed men for the first in gaining a bachelor's degree.

Selected by Ronald Reagan, Sandra Day O'Connor becomes the first woman appointed to the United States Supreme Court.

1974
Ella Grasso, the 83rd Governor of Connecticut, is first woman elected governor of a U.S. state without the benefit of a husband's incumbency.

1916
Margaret Sanger challenges New York's anti-contraception law by establishing a clinic in Brooklyn. She is credited with coining the term "birth control."

1920
The 19th Amendment is quietly signed into law by Secretary of State Bainbridge Colby. It declares: "The right of citizens of the United States to vote shall not be denied or abridged by the United States or by any State on account of sex."

1938
The Fair Labor Standards Act establishes a minimum wage without regard to sex.

1964
Title VII of the Civil Rights Act passes, which prohibits employment discrimination based on race, color, religion, national origin, or sex.

1870
First grand jury that includes women hears cases in Cheyenne, Wyoming.

1868
The Fourteenth Amendment is the first to define "citizens" and "voters" as "male."

1878
Susan B. Anthony amendment to grant women the vote is introduced in Congress.

1900

1950
There now are 18.4 million working women in the U.S., more than double the number from World War II.

1960
On May 11, 1960, the FDA announces the approval of G.D. Searle's oral contraceptive pill, Enovid.

1970
Representative Martha Griffiths files a discharge petition to demand that the ERA be heard by the full House. The Senate kills the bill.

1985
Wilma Mankiller becomes first female Principal Chief of The Cherokee Nation, originally a matriarchal society.

1848
July 18, 1848, the first Women's Rights Convention is held in Seneca Falls, New York.

1890
National American Woman Suffrage Association, led by Susan Anthony, is created from two competing organizations.

1900
There are now 5.3 million working women in the U.S.

All states have now passed laws modeled after New York's 1848 Married Women's Property Act, which grants married women some control over property and earnings.

Wyoming becomes the first state to grant women the right to vote in all elections.

1936
When Dr. Hannah Stone orders a new type of diaphragm ("pessary") from Tokyo, she's charged with importing "obscene matter." Attorney Morris Ernst wins "U.S. v. One Package of Japanese Pessaries," a victory for birth control.

1840	1860	1880	1900	1920	1930	1940	1950	1960	1970	1980	1990

Lucy Stone is first woman to keep her own name after marriage.

1855
Two competing women's organizations are formed, one led by Susan Anthony and Elizabeth Cady Stanton and the other by orator Lucy Stone.

First woman suffrage law is passed in the territory of Wyoming.

1869

U.S. Supreme Court rules states have right to exclude married women, in this case Myra Colby Bradwell, from practicing law.

1873
Through special legislation, Belva Lockwood becomes first woman to try a case before Supreme Court.

1879

Half a million watch 5,000 suffragists march down Pennsylvania Avenue in a D.C. Woman Suffrage Parade, led by lawyer Inez Milholland Boissevain riding on a white horse. Angry onlookers hurl cigarette butts and beat marchers, while police look on. The next day, the D.C. police chief is ousted.

1913

The largest parade ever held in New York City attracts 40,000 marchers, including the "Suffragette Mothers on the March."

1915

Seven million women take jobs during World War II, including 2 million "Rosie the Riveters."

1947

Jeannette Rankin of Montana, the first woman elected to Congress, is formally seated in the U.S. House of Representatives.

1917

1941
Daughters of Bilitis, the first lesbian rights organization, is co-founded in San Francisco by Del Martin and Phyllis Lyon.

Khertek Anchimaa becomes the first non-hereditary female head of state in the modern world.

1940

In Fay v. New York, the U.S. Supreme Court holds that women are equally qualified with men to serve on juries but are granted an exemption and may, or may not, serve as women choose.

Pharmaceutical company G.D. Searle files FDA application to license their drug Enovid for use as an oral contraceptive.

1959

On Sept. 4, 1969, Governor Ronald Reagan signs the Family Law Act of 1969, making California the first state to adopt "no fault" divorce law.

In Griswold v. Connecticut, the Supreme Court overturns one of the last state laws prohibiting the prescription or use of contraceptives by married couples.

1965

The U.S. Supreme Court declares that the Constitution protects women's right to terminate an early pregnancy, thus making abortion legal.

Billie Jean King beats Bobby Riggs in a tennis "Battle of the Sexes."

1973

The Seventh Circuit Court of Appeals rules that women meeting the physical requirements can work in many jobs that had been for men only.

"Glass Ceiling" is first mentioned at a conference.

The U.S. Mint puts Susan B. Anthony on the silver dollar. It's the first time that a woman appears on a circulating coin.

1955

1969
Chicago Women's Liberation Group organizes, becoming the first to use the term "liberation."

WOMEN'S LIBERATION

1979

1967

Top timeline

Katharine Graham is the first female CEO of a Fortune 500 company and publisher of *The Washington Post*.

1990

Commanding rescue ship Opportune, lene Iskra becomes first woman command a U.S. ry vessel.

1998

Mitsubishi Motor Manufacturing of America agrees to pay $34 million to settle an E.E.O.C. lawsuit contending that 350 women were sexually harassed at its Normal, Illinois auto plant. It is the largest such settlement on record in a corporate case.

2000

CBS Broadcasting agrees to pay $8 million to settle a sex discrimination lawsuit by the E.E.O.C. on behalf of 200 women.

The U.S. Supreme Court invalidates portions of the Violence Against Women Act, permitting victims of rape and domestic violence to sue their attackers in federal court.

2001

66 million U.S. working women.

2006

Heading South, a movie about older, single women visiting 1970s Haiti in a female version of sex tourism, creates a stir.

2008

Hillary Clinton gets 18 million votes in U.S. presidential race but concedes with "Glass Ceiling" speech.

Ukrainian artist Oksana Shachko establishes activist group FEMEN with friends Anna Hutsol and Alexandra Shevchenko.

2010

37% of women say they have primary responsibility for shopping decisions in their household, while 85% say they have primary or shared responsibility.

Kathryn Bigelow becomes the first woman to win an Oscar for best director in Academy Award's 82-year history for *The Hurt Locker*.

Elena Kagan is confirmed to the U.S. Supreme Court. Kagan is the fourth female to serve on the Supreme Court.

Credit Suisse reports that companies with at least one woman on their board of directors outperform corporations that have no female directors by 26%.

2012

Jennifer Doudna and Emmanuelle Charpentier propose CRISPR/Cas9r genome editing, one of the most significant discoveries in the history of biology.

2014

#GamerGate incident uncovers the brooding frustrations of young men who feel threatened by new-age women.

Elliot Rodger kills six people in Santa Barbara, drawing attention to the "incel" underground of sexually frustrated men who blame women for their lack of sex.

Female YouTubers, like Zoella, are 17 times more engaging than mainstream celebrities.

2016

57% of women ages 15+ are now in the workforce.

A Wells Fargo study discovers that women are better investors than men.

2018

The 2019 freshman class of women in Congress will be the largest ever, 102 female representatives and 25 female senators, increasing female representation in Congress from 20% to 24%.

Women account for nearly half of U.S. architecture school students, compared to the AIA's 22% female membership. Women also hold 33% of legal jobs, up from 29% in 2000. The share of female physicians and surgeons is 32%, up from 27% in 2000.

Kylie Jenner's Instagram post of her newborn baby girl Stormi Webster draws more than 14 million likes.

Timeline axis: 2000 · 2010 · 2018

Bottom timeline

991

The Family and Medical Leave Act goes into effect.

Appointed by President Bill Clinton in 1993, Ruth Bader Ginsburg is the second female Supreme Court justice.

1993

The televised testimony of Anita Hill to an all-male, all-white Senate Judiciary Committee that Clarence Thomas, nominated for the Supreme Court of the United States, had sexually harassed her, marks the beginning of the third wave of feminism.

The term "Cougar" surfaces, referring to older women who actively pursue casual, and usually sexual, relationships with younger men. In 2001, Valerie Gibson authors *Cougar: A Guide for Older Women Dating Younger Men.*

1999

Valerie Gibson
COUGAR
A GUIDE FOR OLDER WOMEN DATING YOUNGER MEN

The Supreme Court rules in Nevada Department of Human Resources v. Hibbs that states can be sued in federal court for violations of the Family Leave Medical Act.

2003

Women-owned businesses are fastest-growing segment of small business sector.

WOMEN OWNED

Hillary Clinton becomes the first First Lady to be elected to public office as U.S. Senator from New York. Condoleezza Rice becomes the first black female Secretary of State.

2005

A drunk, 11-year-old girl leads police on a car chase at speeds of up to 100 mph through Orange Beach, Alabama.

2007

For the first time, women surpass men in obtaining advanced college degrees.

Laura Dekker, a 16-year-old Dutch girl, is the youngest person ever to sail solo around the world.

Mothers spend 10 hours more a week multitasking than fathers.

Women, even those who are managers themselves, are more likely to want a male boss than a female one.

2011

Appointed by President Barack Obama, Sonia Sotomayor is the first Latina Supreme Court justice.

2009

U.K. study reports women outperform men in two multitasking experiments involving computer-based task-switching and paper-and-pencil multitasking.

2013

Christine Mau is the U.S. Air Force's first female F-35 pilot and a mother of two daughters.

Women make up 20% of Congress, including 20 in the Senate and 88 members of the House of Representatives.

2015

Women social media influencers post 84% of posts hashtagged with #ad in 2017.

84
PERCENT

Women comprise 56% of students on campuses nationwide and for the first time outnumber Oxford University men.

2017

#metoo movement grips nation. More than 400 men stand accused.

#METOO

Wonder Woman, starring Gal Gadot, breaks domestic box office records for a movie directed by a woman, Patty Jenkins.

Of the 123 million U.S. women age 16+, 72 million, or 59%, are labor force participants, either working or looking for work. Women comprise 47% of the total U.S. labor force.

The pussyhat, designed by Krista Suh, is a popular symbol of female empowerment at the January 2017 Women's March.

Innovation is part of a ceaseless Darwinian struggle for existence. Of the original 12 Dow Jones companies only one still survives. And that company was just removed from the Dow Jones Industrials index. To ensure success, practice relentless innovation.

9

Innovation

Reinventing Business and Life

In this get-it-done-yesterday world, everything, it seems, is accelerating, including innovation. Time Compression has condensed business lifecycles, and it's about to do the same thing for research and development. Propelled by an influx of technology that will quadruple the speed of bringing innovations to market, innovators have to move at lightning speed. Change, however, is not easy. It requires adopting a guerilla-warfare-ready startup mentality while fielding a lean-and-mean innovation team. The payoff is well-established. Innovation case studies show that when practiced relentlessly, and paying attention to detail, innovation virtually guarantees financial success. The key is actually putting innovative ideas into practice. Talking about being innovative is simply not enough.

An Upward Trajectory

Innovation is at the top of everyone's agenda these days. Yet despite its modern-age popularity, the term "innovate" dates back to 1548 when it first appeared in print. [1] It is derived from the Latin noun *innovatus*, meaning renewal or change, which is the past participle of *innovare* — "to renew, restore."

Merriam-Webster defines innovation as 1. a new idea, device, or method 2. the act or process of introducing new ideas, devices, or methods. The crucial part of Merriam-Webster's definition is the word "new."

History tells us that the concept of innovation is age-old. Stone-age inventions, such as the club, controlled fire, bow and arrow, plus the development of language transformed the evolution of early humans. The bronze age brought the wheel, the plow, soap and rope.

The industrial age ushered in the steam engine, light bulb and loom, all disruptive innovations in their time. Each of these inventions impacted society in material ways and changed the competitive landscape. In 1939, Austrian economist, Joseph Schumpeter offered a new twist on innovation. [2] Schumpeter defined invention as an expression of intellectual creativity that was undertaken without any consideration to its possible economic impact. Innovation, on the other hand, were inventions designed to bring positive changes to a business model or target market.

Until the early 1970s, written use of the word "invention" was more popular than "innovation." Google Books Ngram Viewer, a database of text scans

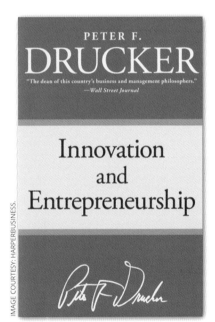

IMAGE COURTESY: HARPERBUSINESS.

Innovation and Entrepreneurship Broke Ground on a New Era

Considered one of the most influential management thinkers ever, Peter Drucker's 1985 *Innovation and Entrepreneurship* explored entrepreneurship and the constant search for innovative ideas.

---

1. "innovate," *Merriam-Webster*, ret. 19-Dec-18.
2. Emma Green, "Innovation: The History of a Buzzword," *The Atlantic*, 20-Jun-13.

of books written between 1800 and 2000, shows that use of the word innovation passed invention in 1973. [3]

The first book to register on everyone's innovation Richter scale was *Innovation and Entrepreneurship*, written by Peter Drucker in 1985, which formalized the constant search for innovative product ideas and building a business around it. Another is Eric von Hippel's 1988 *The Sources of Innovation*, which describes the process of end-user innovation — creating innovative solutions because existing products do not meet your needs. A timely example of end-user innovation is the GoPro camera, developed by Nick Woodman for his personal use (page 250).

The 1990s saw another sea-change shift in executive attitudes toward innovation. Increased global competition, read China, the internet, and the 95% failure rate of the more than 30,000 consumer product launched each year, helped change many minds about the importance of innovation.[4]

A McKinsey survey shows just how much the "C" suite pivoted on the challenge of becoming a "category innovation leader." In 1993, 37% of executives surveyed reported wanting to become an innovation leader, while 26% were content to remain a "follower" (chart). By 1999 no one wanted to be a follower, and 95% wanted to lead the innovation pack. [5]

Transformative conversations about modern innovation arose from bestselling books published during that period, including the 1996 release of James Utterback's *Mastering the Dynamics of Innovation* and Harvard professor Clayton Christensen's 1997 *The Innovator's Dilemma*, which helped popularize the concept of "disruptive innovation.'

Christensen's book challenged companies to predict consumer needs and adopt new technologies and business models to address emerging market requirements. It was widely read and changed the way managers and industry leaders thought about innovation.

The last year McKinsey studied innovation intentions, 1999, was the zenith of dotcom mania, a period that saw dizzying valuations ascribed to technology innovators. The bubble may have burst, but as the table below convincingly illustrates, the impact of innovation is unassailable:

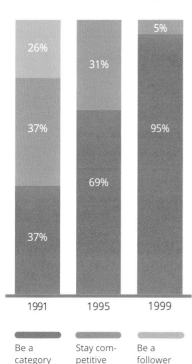

Top Management Strategy

Be a category innovation leader

Stay competitive

Be a follower

Source: 2004 McKinsey & Company I&TM Survey

2006-2019 Comparison of Five Largest U.S. Companies by Market Cap				
2006 Rank	**Company**	**2018 Rank**	**Company**	**Valuation**
1.	ExxonMobil	1.	Amazon.com Inc.	$803 billion
2.	General Electric Co.	2.	Microsoft Corp.	$792 billion
3.	Microsoft Corp.	3.	Alphabet Inc.	$736 billion
4.	Citigroup Inc.	4.	Apple Inc.	$720 billion
5.	Bank of America Corp.	5.	Facebook Inc.	$413 billion
Source: 02-Aug-16 *The Wall Street Journal*; 11-Jan-19 Yahoo Finance				

If the value of innovation remained fuzzy in the 1990s, despite the launch of Amazon and Google during that era, a compelling lesson was yet to come.

3. "Invention vs. Innovation," *Google Ngram Viewer*, ret. 19-Dec-18.
4. Lonny Kocina, "What percentage of new products fail and why?," *Media Relations Agency*, 03-May-17.
5. Michael Tchong, "The Culture of Innovation," *FAST Company*, 18-Oct-04.

A Pocketful of Innovation

The year 1996 was an auspicious one. In the midst of the dotcom boom, a figure who had been synonymous with the personal computer revolution of the 1980s, Steven P. Jobs, returned to the company he co-founded. But all was not well in Cupertino, Calif.

A succession of CEOs, John Sculley, Michael Spindler and Gil Amelio, had left Apple Computer in shambles. Cupertino's most famous progeny was almost bankrupt but thanks to a $150 million loan from none other than Bill Gates and Microsoft, Apple was rescued from the brink of bankruptcy.

In what became a master class in innovation, Jobs launched a "Think Different" advertising campaign in 1997. Thinking differently, or orthogonal thinking, is what organizations need to get good at in order to foster innovation. Despite a briskly selling line of colorful iMac computers, the road back to profitability for Apple was a long and arduous one.

Five years after Jobs' return, Apple was back on the ropes. In fiscal 2001, Apple's revenues were down $2.6 billion, or 34%, compared to the $8 billion in fiscal year 2000 revenues (chart). [6] That $5.4 billion was even less than the $6.1 billion the company reported in *1999*. This setback was the double whammy of the dotcom bust and 9/11.

> "Innovation distinguishes between a leader and a follower."
>
> **Steven P. Jobs**
> Co-Founder Apple Inc.

However, 2001 was also a pivotal period for Apple. On May 15 of that year, Jobs gave journalists, including *The Wall Street Journal*'s Walt Mossberg, a personal tour of Apple's first retail store, located at the Tysons Corner Center shopping mall in McLean, Virginia. [7] When that store opened on May 19, 2001, together with another one at the Glendale Galleria in Glendale, Calif., a crowd of 500 people had formed a line to enter the store, a preview of lines to come. [8] It was a risky proposition said *The New York Times*, calling it "an aggressive move during an economic slowdown." [9]

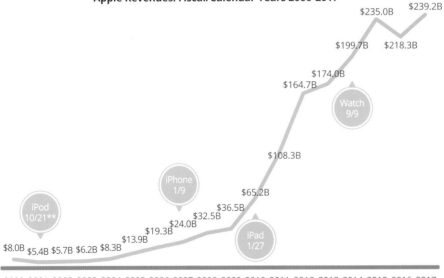

Apple Revenues: Fiscal/Calendar Years 2000-2017*

$239.2B
$235.0B
$218.3B
$199.7B
$174.0B
$164.7B
Watch 9/9
$108.3B
iPhone 1/9
$65.2B
$36.5B
$32.5B
iPad 1/27
iPod 10/21**
$24.0B
$19.3B
$13.9B
$8.0B $5.4B $5.7B $6.2B $8.3B

2000 2001 2002 2003 2004 2005 2006 2007 2008 2009 2010 2011 2012 2013 2014 2015 2016 2017

Source: 21-Oct-18 Apple Press Releases. * Fiscal years: 2000-2011. Calendar years: 2012-2017. ** Dates shown for each device are product introduction dates. The iPod was shipped two days later on October 23, 2001. The iPhone was released on June 29, 2007, iPad on April 3, 2010, and Apple Watch was not shipped until April 10, 2015.

That same *New York Times* article quoted Channel Marketing Corp. President David Goldstein commenting, "No computer manufacturer has successfully branched into retail stores. It's completely flawed. They'll shut it down

6. Michael Kanellos, "Jobs earns $1; Apple stores forecast loss," *CNET*, 02-Jan-02.
7. Joe Wilcox, "What was the first Apple Store like?," *BetaNews*, 15-May-11.
8. Nicole Martinelli, "May 2001: The First Apple Store Opens," *Cult of Mac*, 16-May-11.
9. Jennifer Lee, "To Cash In on a Lifestyle, Apple Hits the Mall," *The New York Times*, 12-Jul-01.

Think different.

Think Different

Conceived by Art Director Craig Tanimoto who worked in the L.A. office of TBWA Chiat/Day, the "Think Different" ad campaign was inspired by Rene Magritte's surrealist work, *Ceci n'est pas une pipe*. [1] These bold yet straightforward ads featured a host of famous thinkers and individualists, including Albert Einstein, Mahatma Gandhi, Martin Luther King, Jr., Muhammad Ali, Pablo Picasso and Amelia Earhart, pictured here, among others. Thinking different is a core tenet of practicing innovation.

1. Jonathan Littman, "Think Different," *SmartUp*, 15-Jun-15.

and write off the huge losses in two years." That comment has come back to haunt Goldstein. Today, Apple operates 506 stores in 24 countries, including 272 U.S. stores. [10] With an average revenue of $48.5 million per store, Apple generates nearly $25 billion in sales from its stores or about 10% of its total annual revenues.

According to retail analysts, Apple stores produce the highest retail sales, with sales estimated at $5,546 per square foot. [11] That means that, based on its current 32,000-square-feet size, Apple's New York flagship store generates as much as $177 million per year. [12]

Later that same year, on October 23, 2001, Apple introduced the iPod. Then came the iPhone, iPad and Apple Watch — each device setting a new standard in its particular product category. Today, Apple is worth more than $720 billion, after becoming the first company ever to be valued at $1 trillion. In a little over two decades, Apple went from teetering on the precipice of bankruptcy to the world's most valuable corporation. [13]

Apple unquestionably is the most stellar example of what innovation can contribute to the bottom line. The company personifies one of Jobs' tenets: "Innovation distinguishes between a leader and a follower." An uncanny assessment, particularly given those 1990s McKinsey studies that heralded an innovation paradigm shift among executives.

The lesson was not lost on the executive suite. By July 2011, just four years after the iPhone shipped, a global survey by *Forbes* and Wipro of 300 CEOs and other C-level executives at global enterprises found that two-thirds believed that innovation was more critical than ever, especially in light of the economic downturn of 2008-09. [14] The study also reported that studying best practices was the primary innovation assimilation tool for 80% of survey respondents.

The resounding success of Apple's innovation strategy lit a fire under business executives everywhere. *The Wall Street Journal* confirmed innovation's big buzz status with a search of SEC reports that found that the use of some form of the word "innovation" occurred 33,528 times in 2011, up 64% from five years earlier. [15]

What did five years earlier look like? It was 2006, the year Apple's revenues were three times higher than before the iPod launch. It was the year Google's advertising revenues exceeded $10 billion for the first time. [16]

Also, it was the year when Facebook reached 12 million active users and began adding feeds. [17] A period that also saw anticipation building for the imminent arrival of Apple's iPhone.

And what companies used the "I" word most in the *Journal*'s search? Apple and Google, naturally. But among the top five users of the word innovation was also Procter & Gamble, Scott's Miracle-Gro and Campbell Soup (chart).

Top Users of the Word "Innovation"

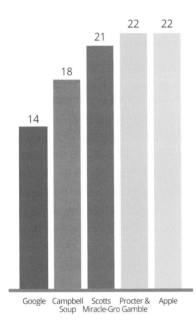

Source: 23-May-12 The Wall Street Journal

10. Apple Stores, *MacRumors*, ret. 19-Dec-18.

11. "Retail's Most Profitable Square Footage," *CoStar/Cision*, 27-Jul-17.

12. Christian de Looper, "Apple is looking to double the size of its famous flagship retail store in NYC," *Digital Trends*, 01-Feb-17.

13. Jack Nicas, "Apple Is Worth $1,000,000,000,000. Two Decades Ago, It Was Almost Bankrupt.," *The New York Times*, 02-Aug-18.

14. "Wipro-Forbes Insights Global CXO Outlook Reveals Strategic Innovation Key Driver for Future Growth," *Forbes Insights/Wipro*, 29-Jul-11.

15. Leslie Kwoh, "You Call That Innovation?," *The Wall Street Journal*, 23-May-12.

16. "Google's ad revenue from 2001 to 2017," *Statista*, ret. 19-Dec-18.

17. "Mapping Facebook's Growth Over Time," *Adweek*, 19-Aug-08.

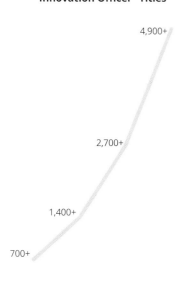

LinkedIn Members with "Chief Innovation Officer" Titles

4,900+

2,700+

1,400+

700+

2010   2013   2015   2018

Source: 21-Oct-18 LinkedIn Title Search

Why had innovation become mission critical? As Microsoft Co-Founder Bill Gates puts it, "innovation fundamentally shifts the trajectory of development." [18] Two confluent examples of how innovation changes market trajectories are Apple and Google, frequent users of the word innovation in their financial reports. Both companies introduced disruptive technologies that significantly changed the destinies of their respective markets, smartphones and search, each shifting Microsoft's trajectory.

Bill Gates knows this first hand. In August 1997, Gates and Jobs announced that in exchange for Apple bundling Internet Explorer with each Mac sold, and Microsoft supporting the Mac with Microsoft Office, Microsoft would lend Apple $150 million. [19] Since the company was mired in an anti-trust investigation by the Department of Justice, the deal kept a weakened Apple alive while alleviating concerns about Microsoft's monopolistic behavior.

That $150 million investment netted Microsoft 150,000 preferred shares, convertible to Apple common shares at a price of $8.25 with a three-year lockup. By 2001, Microsoft had converted all of its shares into common stock, netting the company approximately 18.1 million shares. It sold all of its Apple holdings by 2003. Since then, Apple's stock has split three times, including a 2-for-1 split on June 21, 2000 and February 28, 2005, plus a 7-for-1 basis on June 9, 2014, which would have resulted in Microsoft owning 506.8 million Apple shares. Had Microsoft held on to its Apple stock until 2018, it would have been able to unload it for about $109 billion at current stock prices, a very tidy profit on a $150 million investment.

As Gates said, innovation fundamentally shifts the trajectory of development, and it frequently changes history in the process too.

More evidence of the fervor for innovation came courtesy of *The New York Times*, which reported in August 2010 that a search of LinkedIn revealed that more than 700 people listed their current job title as "Chief Innovation Officer." [20] Today, there are more than 4,900 people on LinkedIn with Chief Innovation Officer in their title, a 600% increase in just eight years (chart).

Part of that growth is due to the hybridization of some titles, i.e., "Chief Strategy and Innovation Officer," but this title explosion demonstrates just how enamored corporations have become of innovation. Yet, it's quite evident that while nearly 5,000 organizations worldwide boast a Chief Innovation Officer, the practical applications of innovation are few and far between, a subject to be explored later in this chapter.

This lack of evidence is an increasingly structural shortcoming because as London Business School Dean Sir Andrew Likierman notes, "innovation is one of the key drivers of everything that goes on in business." [21]

As more organizations realize the importance of innovation and its role in the workplace of keeping products, people and profits on the cutting edge of emerging business strategies, hopefully, more will actually put innovation into practice and help boost their financial success.

Mirroring what activists are apt to exclaim under these circumstances, "What do we want? Innovation! When do we want it? Now!"

18. Bill Gates, "Innovation with Impact: Financing 21st Century Development," *The Gates Notes*, 03-Nov-11.
19. Yoni Heisler, "What ever became of Microsoft's $150 million investment in Apple?," *Engadget*, 20-May-14.
20. Steve Lohr, "Innovate, Yes, but Make It Practical," *The New York Times*, 14-Aug-10.
21. Melissa Korn, "Dean in London Champions Innovation," *The Wall Street Journal*, 04-May-11.

Innovation Typology

We are in the midst of an era of sweeping change, with major challenges to address, including global warming, hunger, poverty, and the decline of the American middle class. Some entrepreneurs believe that colonizing distant planets, like Mars, will help the lucky, and rich, few escape a dying earth. [22] The urgent need for common sense change and reinvention points to a future in which innovation accelerates.

Disney CEO Bob Iger famously said that the heart and soul of a company are creativity and innovation. But what exactly is innovation? The past millennium has produced a host of transformational inventions, including the printing press, photography, microscope, telescope, engine, automobile and light bulb. However, there have many less obvious disruptive innovations too, like the paper milk bottle, which received a U.S. patent on October 19, 1915. To this day, the Pure-Pak "gable-top" carton, as it came to be known, is one of the world's most instantly recognizable innovations. [23]

After John Van Wormer received a patent in 1915 for his paper container, he struggled to perfect its mass production. Unable to make milk cartons in quantity, he ended up selling his patents and trademark in 1928 to American Paper Bottle Company. That company also struggled for the next few years and sold its rights to Detroit-based Ex-Cell-O, which succeeded in getting the Borden Company to use its containers.

The Pure-Pak milk carton met with much resistance from dairies because they were heavily invested in glass bottles. Dairy producers were so hostile to carton containers that they got local health authorities to ban them.

The Pure-Pak story illustrates just how difficult innovation can be, both from an idea development and marketing perspective, particularly if it's disruptive and upsets the income streams of established players. The term "disruptive innovation" applies to inventions that disturb the existing world order. In other words, they upset the proverbial applecart.

Airbnb and Uber are case-study examples of disruptive innovations. Both have been met with fervent opposition from government, local labor unions, industry lobbying groups and concerned citizens. When a dust-up produces a lot of dust, some parties are bound to get coated with dirt.

The smartphone, and in particular the iPhone, is considered a disruptive, or groundbreaking, innovation — one of the most important inventions of the 21st century. The milk carton was equally disturbing, to some.

Whether it's a simple, paper milk container or a complicated communications device, it's innovative as long as it's something that hasn't been created before or functionally works like nothing else before. From there, the concept of innovation can be broken down into several types, based on what kind of problem needs to be solved, and the approach chosen to solve it. The following classifications are good starting points for organizations looking to create or expand innovation strategies. No innovation strategy

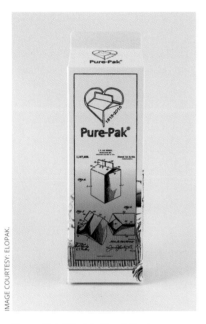

Pure-Pak "Gable Top" Carton

The gable top milk carton was patented in 1915 and is one of the most widely adopted product innovations. The original container features a fold-out spout, which has been enhanced with a screw cap in newer packaging. The first practical examples were sold on the streets of San Francisco and Los Angeles as early as 1906.

22. Olivia Solon, "Elon Musk: we must colonise Mars to preserve our species in a third world war," *The Guardian*, 11-Mar-18.
23. "Elopak Celebrates 100 Years Of The Pure-Pak Patent," *Elopak*, ret. 22-Oct-18.

should rely on a single form of inventiveness; it may make sense to pursue a combination of the following strategies:

Efficiency or Incremental Innovation

Efficiency innovations seek to produce the same product more cheaply or efficiently and are the most popular type of innovation. It involves small upgrades or enhancements to existing products, services, processes or methods over time order to maintain or improve a competitive position, think automated credit checks. Incremental innovation means advancing a product by manufacturing it with materials of a higher quality, by making partial changes to a complex product made up of many integrated technical subsystems, or by using industrial robots, an innovation on to itself, to make automobiles more efficiently consistently and cost-effectively.

Sustaining or Orthogonal Innovation

Sustaining, or orthogonal, innovation turns good products into better ones. Coined by Judy Estrin, orthogonal refers to inventions that don't create new technology but use existing tools, products, and services to create something distinctly new. The iPod is an orthogonal innovation because Apple didn't invent the portable MP3 player, it was beaten to the market in 1997 by South Korea-based Saehan Information Systems. The iPod quickly dominated the market despite being a latecomer because it introduced an innovative click-wheel interface; an easy way to buy music from the iTunes store; plus an amazing, at the time, 5-GB capacity. The Toyota Prius' hybrid engine design is another example.

Disruptive or Breakthrough Innovation

Disruptive innovations are those rare inventions that change the way the world works, including the automobile, television, the personal computer, VCR, compact disc, cellular telephone, desktop publishing, digital photography, e-commerce, TiVo, OpenTable, Netflix, iPhone, Airbnb and Uber. These innovations roiled industries and competitors in their respective spaces, rendering a host of tools, formats, services and media, ranging from horse and buggies to records to typesetters to BlackBerries obsolete. Disruptive innovations distinguish themselves as much for the market impact created by a new product or service as well as for the originality of the entry itself.

Modes of innovation and rates of technological change vary from sector to sector, and factors such as market appeal, growth potential, industry restructuring capability and competitor reactivity should be considered before executing a new strategy.

Service and low- to medium-technology sectors tend to favor lower-risk forms of incremental innovation, relying on existing methods and technologies to drive sales. Companies that employ incremental innovation strategies focus on efficiency in manufacturing, marketing and product differentiation. Tech companies tend to place greater resources in research and development and are more likely to go for the riskier disruptive or breakthrough forms of innovation.

Inspiring Transformation

Innovation

Innovation is like teenage sex, everyone is talking about it, but few are doing it. Many organizations, particularly larger enterprises, suffer from hardened arteries. They need a giant enema to allow innovation to flow out freely.

> 66 Businesses throw around the term to show they're on the cutting edge of everything from technology and medicine to snacks and cosmetics. Companies are touting chief innovation officers, innovation teams, innovation strategies and even innovation days. But that doesn't mean the companies are actually doing any innovating."
>
> **The Wall Street Journal**
> 23-May-12

In a seminal 2012 article, entitled "You Call That Innovation?," *The Wall Street Journal* called out what it saw as a recurring theme: "Businesses throw around the term to show they're on the cutting edge of everything from technology and medicine to snacks and cosmetics. Companies are touting chief innovation officers, innovation teams, innovation strategies and even innovation days. But that doesn't mean the companies are actually doing any innovating." [24]

One of the biggest challenges facing our world today is chief executives, top educators and government officials giving lip service to innovation without actually pursuing it. As noted earlier, there are now nearly 5,000 organizations worldwide with a Chief Innovation Officer (CINO) in place, up from just 800 eight years earlier, yet concrete evidence of this massive injection of innovation remains noticeably scant.

In some industries, such as automotive, it's not the innovation team that drives renewal but rather the specter of a new rival, Tesla. This Silicon Valley upstart tackled two major industry challenges: "Why can't we build a great electric car and why can't we sell direct to consumers?" Just 10 years after delivering its very first car, the Roadster, Tesla surpassed Mercedes-Benz in terms of vehicles sold in the third quarter of 2018. [25]

Tesla's Model S was officially launched on June 22, 2012, when the first 10

---

24. Leslie Kwoh, "You Call That Innovation?," *The Wall Street Journal*, 23-May-12.
25. Jean Baptiste Su, "Tesla Outsells Mercedes-Benz In America And BMW Is Next To Be Toppled," *Forbes*, 09-Oct-18.

Shocking Proof: Tesla Model S

When an automotive writer concludes than an American-built car can be as good, shockingly, as expensive imports, you know Tesla broke the mold and dispelled all preconceived notions about U.S. cars. Tesla is *prima facie* evidence of how innovation transforms the landscape.

customers received their car.[26] That same year, *Motor Trend* named the Model S "2013 Motor Trend Car of the Year." [27] The article was tellingly subtitled: "Shocking Winner: Proof Positive that America Can Still Make (Great) Things." In February 2015, *Consumer Reports* named the Model S "The Best Overall Vehicle" for the second year in a row. [28] In July 2018, collector-car insurer Hagerty Insurance said the Tesla Model S was "the greatest car of the decade." [29]

If anything, Tesla has disturbed the business-as-usual attitude of the luxury automotive sector. Shortly after *Consumer Reports* named the Model S the best overall vehicle for the first time in 2014, German luxury car manufacturers accelerated their electric vehicle R&D program, to respond "to the success of the California newcomer Tesla with its Model S." [30]

Paying respect to the new hub of automotive innovation, Audi introduced its first EV, the e-tron, in San Francisco in September 2018. The launch even used the latest visual trickery in the grab bag of new-age marketing — a drone light show co-produced with Intel. [31] Had Tesla not intervened, Audi would never have launched an electronic vehicle at such a breakneck pace.

Unfortunately, having a creative visionary run amok exerting competitive pressure is usually missing from most market segments. That explains why many enterprises rely on a process resembling osmosis — the transfer of innovation molecules through a semipermeable membrane — to acquire the mindset required to nurture innovation.

26. "Tesla Model S," *Wikipedia*, ret. 05-Jan-19.
27. Angus MacKenzie, "2013 Motor Trend Car Of The Year: Tesla Model S," *Motor Trend*, 10-Dec-12.
28. Victor Luckerson, "Tesla Model S Named Best Car for 2nd Year in a Row," *Time*, 24-Feb-15.
29. Andrew Newton, "Tesla Model S: Greatest car of the 2010s," *Hagerty*, 12-Jul-18.
30. Megan Geuss, "Porsche, Mercedes building electric cars to challenge Tesla," *Ars Technica*, 25-Oct-14.
31. Matt Burns, "An Intel drone fell on my head during a light show," *TechCrunch*, 18-Sep-18.

The Ultimate Incubator

In 1980, IBM was absent from the most dynamic sector of the tech industry, personal computing. That year, IBM established the Personal Systems Division in Boca Raton, Fla. tasked with developing a new computer, code-named "Acorn." A small engineering team, led by Bill Lowe and later by Philip "Don" Estridge, received an unprecedented level of autonomy from IBM's top brass in far-away Armonk, N.Y. In August 1981, IBM debuted the 5150 Personal Computer, a product that launched an entire industry. Under pressure to meet an incredibly tight one-year deadline, IBM made a breakthrough decision to rely on an open architecture, consisting of Microsoft MS-DOS, Intel 8088 microprocessors, Tandon disk drives and SCI Systems circuit boards. That open design created a huge aftermarket of add-ons that could be used to expand the system, a move that instantly solidified IBM's lead in an embryonic personal computer market. In another break with tradition, IBM sold its PC via outside retailers, including Macy's (where I purchased my PC AT), Sears and Computerland. In 1983, *Time* named the IBM PC, "Machine of the Year," the first time the honor was bestowed on an inanimate object. This remarkable success story of incubating ideas independently and remotely makes one wonder why this innovation model hasn't been used more often since.

Innovation Osmosis

As *Forbes* and Wipro discovered, studying best practices is the primary way executives today introduce innovation into their organizations. That has resulted in thousands of books, hundreds of conferences and countless innovation consultants whose job it is to try to make readers, attendees and clients take action.

Unfortunately, spurring action is the biggest challenge facing organizations when trying to instill more innovation. This issue looms large in companies that want to balance pleasing short-term-profits-focused Wall Street while also driving innovation forward.

Subterfuge revolving around how well an organization is handling innovation can reach the highest levels. One perfect example is a speaking engagement I had for one of Mexico's top luxury real estate firms. The firm's principal warned me not to include content in my presentation that mentioned digital tools for fear of unleashing a storm of "why don't we have that?" questions from the sales team. It's a telltale sign that an organization is not as cutting edge as it says it is.

While it's not easy to bring about a culture of innovation, follow these four core principles to help bring about change:

- **Challenge orthodoxies** – Clogged arteries keep blood from flowing to the heart and brains. So does an "If it ain't broke why fix it?" mentality. To create innovative products or services requires an unfettered flow of ideas, free from old, calcified thinking.

- **Identify unmet needs** – When creating innovative products, there are several essential questions one should ask. How do customers interact with current market solutions? What challenges do they encounter with current offerings? This so-called "pain point" analysis is one of the quickest ways to bring about innovation. Imagine what Steve Jobs was thinking around 1999: "Why is it so hard to buy music to download to an MP3 player and why is it so difficult to navigate a music library?" Nest Labs Founder Tony Fadell had a similar question, "Why are thermostats so unresponsive to user needs?" A bit of due diligence in researching target audiences can shed light on issues consumers may not know they have. Remember not to put the what before the why and pay attention to how other companies approach innovation.

- **Leverage resources** – Large organizations can easily leverage existing resources, including corporate libraries and customer research, to help the process of generating innovations. Employees brainstormed the Disney MagicBand RFID bracelet at an offsite meeting. Smaller organizations should look to Silicon Valley and copy some of their ideas, from open offices, where employees can more easily share information, to incubators and hackathons — all concepts that propel creative thought. Keep in mind that hackathons are not just for techie nerds, the concept can be adapted to brainstorm any type of idea.

Disney MagicBand: Leveraging Employee Resources

Disney's MagicBand, which is only available at Disney World in Orlando, Fla., offers theme park visitors the ability to enter the park and use priority FastPass+ entrances. Disney Hotel guests can also unlock their room with MagicBand. Disney employees brainstormed the RFID bracelet at an offsite meeting.

IMAGE COURTESY: THE WALT DISNEY COMPANY.

> 66 I have no special talents. I'm only passionately curious." (*Ich habe keine besondere Begabung, sondern bin nur leidenschaftlich neugierig.*)
>
> Albert Einstein
> 11-Mar-52

• **Ride trend waves** – Trends are undoubtedly the best platforms for innovation because change equals disruption. There's no greater colliding force with the future than the Ubertrend, so try to adapt your innovative solution to addressing pain points raised by the Unwired and Time Compression Ubertrends, for example, with products and services that are connected and save time. Ubertrends change consumer values, and it's these value changes that open up markets to new opportunities. The iPod saved music lovers time by allowing them to find, buy and store music quickly. The Nest Smart Thermostat conveniently learns from your behavior to create a comfortable home environment.

Not everyone can be a Steve Jobs or Tony Fadell, of course, but with some proper motivation and training, one can acquire many of the attributes necessary to become an innovation leader. Some may not believe that they possess visionary traits, but the reality is that both Jobs and Fadell merely observed human behavior and saw something was missing.

This requires constantly broadening one's perspective by staying on top of trends, technology and human culture. Remember what Albert Einstein once wrote to Carl Seelig, "I have no special talents. I'm only passionately curious." Innovators know that curiosity does not kill the cool cat. 😸

To accomplish results, innovation leaders must be resilient and not easily impeded by structural, procedural, cultural or political barriers. Remember that there are all too many assclowns all over the world today. Being an innovator requires having compassion for others and continuously looking for ways to improve results, a philosophy dubbed *kaizen* in Japan, or the practice of "continuous innovation." [32]

Steve Jobs was not a nice person, but his early market success meant that he could dispense with niceties and demand only the best from his team.

32. "Kaizen," *Wikipedia*, ret. 28-Nov-18.

Becoming an innovator requires being savvy enough to be able to deftly navigate an organization's morass of culture and politics — not a trivial task by any stretch of the imagination. A big dose of self-awareness is required.

They must also be resourceful, able and willing to leverage networks and relationships while using their influencing skills to cross company boundaries and divisions. When IBM gave Bill Lowe the go-ahead to quickly and independently develop the IBM Personal Computer in Boca Raton, it undoubtedly irked many members of the rank and file (sidebar, pg. 298). [33]

Yet, by 1985 some 10,000 IBMers were enjoying Boca's balmy weather. Then the corporate winds changed and employees were shipped out to Raleigh, N.C. and Austin, Tex., leaving just 1,500 employees in Boca Raton. [34] The moves were clearly related to the untimely death of IBM Vice President Don Estridge, who, along with his wife, Mary Ann, perished in an August 2, 1985 Delta plane crash, while on approach to Dallas/Ft. Worth airport. [35]

In 1985, Apple Computer had just completed its second year of selling its innovative Macintosh computer with total revenues just shy of $1.9 billion. [36] IBM, by comparison, was a $50 billion behemoth. [37] In 2017, IBM revenues reached $79 billion. [38] That's less than one third the $266 billion in revenues Apple generated in its latest fiscal year. [39]

In 2004, IBM sold its PC division to Lenovo for $1.75 billion. [40] When IBM entered the PC market in 1981, Apple ran an ad in the *The Wall Street Journal* headlined, "Welcome, IBM. Seriously." [41] After crushing the computer market with a global standard for PC innovation, IBM seriously failed to evolve its innovation model and slowly ebbed away, taking the company along with it. Could Estridge have reversed IBM's slow, death march? We'll never know. In the next section, you will see plenty of evidence that relentless innovation offers the best avenue to financial success.

Innovation leaders must be prepared for the long haul. They cannot afford to slack off because in this connected world, with its nearly 1.1 million startups raking in more than $300 billion each year in venture capital, virtually every pain point will eventually be addressed. [42] Thwarting lurking competition requires building a strong and diverse team with a clear sense of purpose while fostering a climate that facilitates innovation and develops worker skills. If your team thrives, your organization will thrive too.

Many other elements come into play, of course, including a sound, and aspirational, financial plan. A well-crafted discovery process that searches for pain points to solve is also critical. Once everyone agrees on a viable solution, the key is to move with high speed to get innovations to market quickly. Mobilize your workforce by making innovation part of your company's core values. Respect any move the competition makes to help you improve your innovation. It's a life and death struggle.

> " Innovation leaders must be prepared for the long haul. They cannot afford to slack off because this connected world with its more than 1 million startups, which are raking in hundreds of billions of dollars each year in venture capital, virtually every pain point will eventually be addressed."
>
> **Michael Tchong**
> Ubertrends

33. "The birth of the IBM PC," *IBM Corp.*, ret. 10-Nov-18.
34. "IBM: Boca Raton," *Boca Raton Historical Society & Museum*, ret. 10-Nov-18.
35. "Philip D. Estridge," *IBM Corp.*, ret. 10-Nov-18.
36. "History of Apple Inc." *Wikipedia*, ret. 10-Nov-18.
37. "1985," *IBM Corp.*, ret. 10-Nov-18.
38. "About IBM," *IBM Corp.*, ret. 10-Nov-18.
39. "Global revenue of Apple from 2004 to 2018," *Statista*, ret. 10-Nov-18.
40. John Spooner, "IBM sells PC group to Lenovo," *CNET*, 08-Dec-04.
41. Bill Murphy, "37 Years Ago, Steve Jobs Ran Apple's Most Amazing Ad. Here's the Story," *Inc.*, 23-Aug-18.
42. "Startup Dashboard," *F6S*, ret. 05-Jan-19.

> "The successful companies of tomorrow will address the changing customer values of today."

Michael Tchong
Ubertrends

OR ELSE...

BlackBerry®

BORDERS®

EASTERN

ENRON
Endless possibilities.™

[Friendster]

good guys

GYMBOREE®
GROWING YOUNG MINDS

circuit city
We're with you™

InfoSpace®

myspace

NOKIA

KODAK

LEHMAN BROTHERS
150 1850-2000
years
A TRADITION OF INNOVATION

[Napster]

® RadioShack®

N

PAN AM

Payless Shoe Source®

SPORTS AUTHORITY®

THE LIMITED

TRUE RELIGION
BRAND JEANS®

The Learning Company®

TOWER RECORDS®
www.towerrecords.com

TOYS Я US

Wet seal

TWA

WOOLWORTHS

Case Study Techniques

Innovation

PillPack: Simple Innovation

Innovations do not have to involve complex solutions. Some of the best ones are based on simple ideas. Since 2014, I've been singing the praises of PillPack, which addresses the convergence of the Time Compression and Fountain of Youth Ubertrends. Every two weeks, PillPack sends customers their medication in a container that dispenses tearable packets, organized by date and time. PillPack eliminates confusion while offering consumers convenience, key benefits for an aging and demanding population. *Time* named it one of "The 25 Best Inventions of 2014." [1] In June 2018, Amazon.com acquired PillPack for a reported $1 billion. [2] Take two of these and call me in the morning.

1. "The 25 Best Inventions of 2014," *Time*, 20-Nov-14.
2. Ingrid Lunden, "Amazon buys PillPack, an online pharmacy, for just under $1B," *TechCrunch*, 28-Jun-18.

In 1964, U.S. Supreme Court Justice Potter Stewart used the expression "I know it when I see it" to describe his test for obscenity in the case of Jacobellis v. Ohio. [43] Much like obscenity, successful innovators are obscenely easy to spot.

In my presentations, I frequently use a simple quiz, "How many innovative companies can you name?" The responses include all the usual suspects, Amazon, Apple, Facebook, Google, Tesla...but the audience usually runs out of ideas before even reaching 10. An even tougher question is, "Can you name three innovative organizations in *your* sector?" These quizzes demonstrate how few and far between true innovations really are.

That's disappointing considering that the Dun & Bradstreet global database contains more than 300 million businesses. [44] Narrowing the list to the number of publicly traded companies, of which there are 63,000 around the globe and 15,000 in the U.S., does not materially improve results. [45]

Many media, including *Fast Company, Forbes* and *USA Today* all publish lists of "the most innovative companies," which are often based on some debatable ranking methodology. *USA Today* and 24/7 Wall St. rank companies based on the number of patents issued, a list topped by Samsung and IBM. [46] In 2011, *Forbes* named Salesforce.com "the world's most innovative company" — an accolade even *Forbes'* own contributor Haydn Shaughnessy took issue with. [47] That could be because Salesforce.com is not necessarily well regarded when it comes to innovative user experiences. What follows is a series of case studies of real innovation.

43. "I know it when I see it," *Wikipedia*, ret. 19-Dec-18.
44. "Our History," *Dun & Bradstreet*, ret. 19-Dec-18.
45. "How many publicly traded companies are in the US and the world?," *Answers.com*, ret. 19-Dec-18.
46. Michael Sauter and Samuel Weigley, "24/7: 10 most innovative companies in the world," *USA Today*, 20-Jan-13.
47. Haydn Shaughnessy, "The World's Most Innovative Company? I Doubt It," *Forbes*, 15-Oct-12.

Airbnb Inc.

SAN FRANCISCO, CALIFORNIA

» **Innovation: Peer-to-peer space sharing**

» **First innovation: 2009**

For decades, airlines have enjoyed a technology dubbed "seat optimization," which lets them manage inventory, prioritizing higher paying, loyal customers while moving less desirable fares to middle seats or the rear. Airbnb ushered in the concept of "home optimization," offering homeowners the same opportunity to boost cash flow the major airlines have enjoyed for years. Its space-sharing platform is a disruptive innovation.

The option of staying in someone's private dwelling as an alternative to hotels can be truly liberating. Many times, it's cheaper too. Airbnb already claims an inventory of 5 million rooms. [48] That makes it larger than the three largest hotel chains, Hilton, InterContinental and Marriott, which offer 2.6 million rooms, combined.

No wonder Airbnb is sending shock waves throughout the $570 billion global hotel industry. [49] Airbnb is roiling hospitality, which is quite evident at travel conferences where it is frequently the topic of heated discussion. It has also radically transformed the rental landscape in many cities, another measure of its power to disrupt.

Airbnb has become the darling of many travelers. On New Year's Eve 2017, the company hosted 3 million guests, a startling jump over 1,400 in 2009. [50] Airbnb now draws more traffic than any other hotel brand or metasearch site, 107 million visits in first quarter 2017. [51]

Airbnb, incubator Y Combinator's #1 alumni, has a current valuation of $31 billion. [52] It will be fascinating to see what happens when more people catch on that they can use their real estate inventory to generate cash while meeting some charming people.

Amazon.com Inc.

SEATTLE, WASHINGTON

» **Innovations: Alexa, AWS, Online retailing**

» **First innovation: 2006**

More than 22,000 U.S. stores have shuttered since the Great Recession of 2007. While many closed due to other circumstances, there's no denying that Amazon has changed the way America shops.

While Amazon's e-commerce business model in 1995 was not unique, it has slowly transformed itself into the innovator it is today. To solidify its e-commerce lead, Amazon leveraged free shipping to sign up 100 million members for its Amazon Prime program, the largest list of volume buyers in the world. [53]

Amazon's first business model transformation came in 2006 with the launch of Amazon Web Services. It was orthogonal thinking at its best. Why not offer cloud-based services using a well-tested platform? In its latest fiscal quarter, AWS contributed 56% of Amazon's total operating income. [54] One analyst believes AWS could reach $50 billion in revenue by 2020.

The acquisition of industrial robot manufacturer Kiva Systems in 2012 for $775 million effectively shut out the competition from the warehouse robot market and reduced Amazon's operating expenses by about 20%. [55]

But it's Amazon's Echo smart speaker featuring intelligent voice assistant Alexa that established the company as a true innovator. Canalys predicts that some 56 million smart speakers will be sold worldwide in 2018, thanks mainly to Amazon. [56] Alexa has established order in the connected home market's cacophony of smart devices by attracting some 56,750 "skills" or apps. [57] Someday, you'll be able to ask, "Alexa, tell me an innovation joke."

48. Dennis Schaal, "Booking Claims It Beats Airbnb With 5 Million Alternative Accommodations Listings," *Skift*, 10-Apr-18.
49. "Statistics & Facts on the Hotel and Lodging Industry," *Statista*, ret. 19-Dec-18.
50. Theodore Schleifer, "Three million people are staying in Airbnbs over New Year's. Eight years ago, only 1,400 were," *Recode*, 30-Dec-17.
51. "Airbnb Traffic Surges, Surpassing Older Brands," *eMarketer*, 30-May-17.
52. Jonathan Shieber, "How Airbnb went from renting air beds for $10 to a $30 billion hospitality behemoth," *TechCrunch*, 12-Aug-18.

53. Jeremy Owens, "Bezos discloses Amazon Prime membership total for first time," *MarketWatch*, 18-Apr-18.
54. Jordan Novet, "Amazon says AWS revenue jumped 46 percent in third quarter," *CNBC*, 25-Oct-18.
55. Kim Bashin, "How Amazon Triggered a Robot Arms Race," *Bloomberg*, 29-Jun-16.
56. Sarah Perez, "Smart speakers top AR, VR and wearables to become fastest-growing consumer tech," *TechCrunch*, 04-Jan-18.
57. Sarah Perez, "The number of Alexa skills in the U.S. more than doubled in 2018," *TechCrunch*, 02-Jan-19.

Apple Inc.
CUPERTINO, CALIFORNIA

» **Innovations: Apple II; Apple Watch; AirPods; iPod; iPhone; iPad; Graphical user interface; HyperCard; iMac; MacBook Air; Newton**

» **First innovation: 1977**

Apple has transformed the way we live our lives today. The company has sold more than 1.5 billion iPhones, the most successful consumer product in history.

By vaulting from near bankruptcy to the world's most valuable corporation, Apple proved that relentless innovation is financially rewarding. Never resting on its laurels, it improved the iPhone year after year, introducing such innovations as Retina screens (2010), Touch ID (2013), AirPods (2016) and Face ID (2017).

In virtually every market it has entered since 2001, Apple has set the pace for product innovation *and* profits. In May 2006, Apple's share of the digital audio player market was 77%, according to NPD Group. [58] According to Counterpoint Research, the iPhone harnesses 86% of the smartphone industry's total profits. [59] The iPad is the top tablet brand with a 29% market share. [60]

When Apple Chief Design Officer Jony Ive told *The New York Times* in 2014 that Switzerland's traditional watchmaking industry was in trouble, while using a much "bolder term for trouble," many pundits dismissed the boast as pure hubris. [61] In 2017, Apple's 18 million shipments topped the entire Swiss watch industry. [62]

Apple reached those lofty milestones with breakthrough retail innovations, including stores devoid of cash registers but backed by roving "cashiers" and a Genius Bar service that, 17 years after launch, still has no equal.

How's that for hubris?

Domino's Pizza Inc.
FLINT, MICHIGAN

» **Innovations: Pizza tracking; Amazon Echo, Twitter emoji or smartwatch ordering; "Pizza tasted like cardboard" ad campaign**

» **First innovation: 2008**

When discussing innovation, pizza is not the first thing that comes to mind but Domino's has revolutionized the industry starting with its pizza tracker, launched in 2008.

In 2010, Domino's launched an advertising campaign that admitted that its pizzas used to taste like cardboard. [63] Know of any other company that has publicly admitted that its product used to suck? That was a truly remarkable reinvention strategy, and it worked.

Domino's has continued to innovate relentlessly with a host of novel ways to order pizza. In November 2011, Domino's launched the Hero iPad app that gamified pizza ordering. In March 2015, it introduced the ability to order via smartwatch. [64] In May, Domino's creatively leveraged Twitter's API to let users order by tweeting the pizza emoji. [65] Ordering via Amazon Echo's Alexa followed in February 2016. [66]

Then came self-driving delivery vehicle testing with Ford in August 2017. [67] Not surprisingly, Domino's revenue growth has consistently outpaced the 3% industry average in the past five years, quadrupling it at 12.8% in 2017. In its latest fiscal year, Domino's domestic same-store sales grew 7.7% for the full year. [68]

In April 2017, The Motley Fool observed: "Since 2010, Domino's stock has outperformed some of the most well-known tech companies out there, including Alphabet, Amazon, Apple and Netflix. In that time frame, Domino's has appreciated more than 2,000%."

58. Rachel Rosmarin, "Apple's Profit Soars On iPod Sales," *Forbes*, 19-Jul-06.
59. Mike Wuerthele, "Apple grabs 86% of global smartphone profits, iPhone X alone seizes 35%," *AppleInsider*, 17-Apr-18.
60. Stephen Silver, "Apple iPad expands to 28.8% market share, growing in contracting tablet market," *AppleInsider*, 03-May-18
61. Nick Bilton, "Tech, Meet Fashion," *The New York Times*, 03-Sep-14.
62. Joe Rossignol, "Apple Watch Had Record Year With Estimated 18M Shipments in 2017, Topped Entire Swiss Watch Industry Last Quarter," *MacRumors*, 06-Feb-18.

63. Cynthia Than, "Domino's Admitted Their Pizza Tastes Like Cardboard And Won Back Our Trust," *Inc.*, 31-Mar-17.
64. Natalie Broda, "Domino's Pizza launches smartwatch ordering app," *Crain's Detroit Business*, 02-Mar-15.
65. Rich McCormick, "Now you can use emoji to order pizza," *The Verge*, 13-May-15.
66. Sarah Perez, "Amazon Echo Can Now Order Your Pizza," *TechCrunch*, 03-Feb-16.
67. Darrell Etherington, "Ford and Domino's to deliver pizza using self-driving cars in new test," *TechCrunch*, 29-Aug-17.
68. "Domino's Pizza Announces Fourth Quarter and Fiscal 2017 Financial Results," *Cision PR Newswire*, 20-Feb-18.

Ingenious Designs LLC

ST. PETERSBURG, FLORIDA

» **Innovations: Miracle Mop, Huggable Hangers**

» **First Innovation: 1990**

You know that something is unique about you when a movie is made about your life. That's what happened to Joy Mangano, who was played by Jennifer Lawrence in the film, *Joy*, which was the third highest grossing movie of the 2015 holiday season.

Mangano had a hard-scrabble life, having survived a divorce while taking care of three children. Then a thought occurred to her, "Why isn't there an easier-to-use mop that doesn't get your hands wet and dirty?"

In 1990, she invented and patented the self-wringing Miracle Mop, which requires no direct manipulation of the dirtiest part of this age-old cleaning device. In 1992, Mangano approached Home Shopping Network and the first time she pitched the mop herself, HSN sold 18,000 mops in 20 minutes. [69]

Today, her company, Ingenious Designs, generates more than $150 million in annual revenues. [70] With success comes stature: Mangano now lives in a 14-bedroom, 42,000-square-foot mansion in St. James, N.Y.

One pain point solution was not enough for Mangano. Her next invention directly tackled an even more widespread challenge, how to keep clothes from falling off those slippery, bulky clothes hangers? So, Mangano invented the JOY Huggable Hanger, which is covered in a non-slip, velvet fabric and is relatively thin, so it doesn't take up too much closet space.

From her tough slough, demonstrating her mop in Long Island store parking lots in the pouring rain to a net worth estimated at $50 million, Mangano is living proof that, as another woman, author Iveta Cherneva, puts it, "Only those who risk win. History favors risk-takers. Forgets the timid. Everything else is commentary." [71]

lululemon athletica inc.

VANCOUVER, CANADA

» **Innovations: Yoga streetwear**

» **First Innovation: 2000**

Vancouver, B.C. is the unlikely setting of the world's largest yoga brand, lululemon, founded by Chip Wilson, a recognized eccentric. [72] The company has inspired a yoga cult both inside and outside lululemon. It began in 1998 as a daytime design and nighttime yoga studio in Vancouver's Kitsilano neighborhood on West 4th Avenue. By November 2000, it was a standalone store.

lululemon rode the crest of the athleisure wave into the hearts and minds of North American "luluheads," singlehandedly spawning the yoga streetwear trend.

Wilson's kinetic energy helped create an aura around the lululemon brand, which was further fueled by its luxurious fabrics, the rear-body placement of its Omega-like logo, plus artificially high pricing. Wilson chose the company's name because brands in Japan with an "L" are considered authentically Western, due to the L letter's absence in the Japanese alphabet.

lululemon went public in 2007, and in its first post-IPO year, it sold $350 million worth of apparel in 113 stores.[73] Buoyed by the Time Compression and Fountain of Youth Ubertrends, lululemon has reached a market cap of $17 billion and more than $3 billion in annual revenues. [74]

While that success is chiefly due to riding trend waves with innovative products, a big dash of marketing didn't hurt. lululemon recruits popular yoga teachers and athletes as lululemon "ambassadors," who are invited to store openings. This unpaid viral army helps spread the gospel to Instagram and Twitter followers and are prominently featured on in-store bulletin boards, lending the company "street cred" in local communities.

Another brilliant move was featuring live yogi precariously balancing each other in store windows, a retail experience guaranteed to draw a crowd.

69. Susan Konig, "Cleaning Up in Business, With a Mop," *The New York Times*, 11-Feb-01.
70. Zoë Henry, "The Real Joy Mangano on the Biggest Challenges of Building a $3 Billion Empire," *Inc.*, 09-Jan-16.
71. Amy Freeman, "Joy Mangano's net worth is $50 million," *Bankrate*, 09-May-17.

72. Becki Ledford, "Secrets Lululemon doesn't want you to know," *The List*, ret. 24-Nov-18.
73. Bryant Urstadt, "Lust for Lulu," *New York*, 26-Jul-09.
74. "Lululemon Athletica Inc. (LULU)," *Yahoo! Finance*, ret. 11-Jan-19.

Nest Labs

PALO ALTO, CALIFORNIA

» **Innovations: Nest Smart Learning Thermostat**

» **First Innovation: 2011**

Google is a company that defies description. It has generated vast sums of money from an amazingly unattractive and user-unfriendly product, AdWords. Yet it lumbers into markets like a classic 800-pound gorilla with some remarkably elegant and innovative solutions, including Google Maps, Inbox and Cardboard.

In 2014, Google paid $3.2 billion for Nest Labs, a company Tony Fadell founded to develop a truly innovative, smart thermostat. [75] Fadell did what anybody can also do, and that is determine that something is difficult to accomplish, in this instance maintaining the right temperature in one's home, a so-called "pain point."

So, Fadell set out to create the ultimate thermostat, one that was connected to the internet and could learn from user behavior to optimize temperature settings while saving energy. Having served as an Apple Senior Vice President of the iPod division, Fadell was acutely aware of the importance of ease of use. [76] Since the iPod made the click wheel famous, the Nest Smart Thermostat was blessed with one. Nest understands the role premium packaging plays in consumer perception, and like Apple, elegantly packages each product, down to including one of the most beautiful screwdrivers ever in a home product. Its smartphone app was also without equal in the early connected home days.

Premium pricing was a logical decision, given the Apple-inspired strategy but Nest's innovative solution featuring a well-designed, intuitive interface, all luxuriously boxed, easily overcame its relatively steep pricing.

On Amazon, Nest is the top-rated smart thermostat with a 4.3 rating and more than 13,000 reviews. Let's hope that others will see the light and follow Nest because consumers need more innovative solutions in their life.

75. Aaron Tilley, "Google Acquires Smart Thermostat Maker Nest For $3.2 Billion," *Forbes*, 13-Jan-14.

76. "Tony Fadell," *Wikipedia*, ret. 19-Dec-18.

Spanx Inc.

ATLANTA, GEORGIA

» **Innovations: Spanx Shapewear**

» **First Innovation: 2000**

In 2012, *Forbes* named Spanx Founder Sara Blakely the world's youngest self-made female billionaire at age 41. [77] In June 2016, *Forbes* pegged Spanx' annual sales at $400 million. [78] The magazine had estimated earlier that Spanx nets an estimated 20% on revenue and was valued at $1 billion. Blakely owns 100% of the private company, has zero debt, has never taken any outside investments, although she is currently considering it, and hasn't spent a dime on advertising.

How did Spanx achieve such exceptional results? As Blakely tells it, "People gotta understand why you're different really quickly." [79] Helping her pitch this unique concept was Blakely's seven-year experience selling fax machines and hearing the word "no" frequently.

After landing a 10-minute meeting with a Neiman Marcus department store executive, she quickly sensed that her spiel was falling on deaf ears. So, Blakely persuaded the executive to join her in the bathroom to demonstrate her white pants with and without Spanx. [80] Neiman Marcus trialed the product in seven stores.

Spanx reinvented the category our grandparents used to call girdles. Craftily christened "Shapewear" by Blakely, Spanx is to girdles what iPhones are to landlines: ingenious, sleek, ultra-modern and hard to live without.

Unlike pantyhose, Spanx does away with thigh leg bands, which eliminates unsightly bulges, particularly cellulite. Because Spanx waistbands are sized, there is no need for rubber cords, which helps reduce panty lines. Blakely says she chose "Spanx" because it was fun and no one would forget it. Millions of women won't.

77. Clare O'Connor, "Undercover Billionaire: Sara Blakely Joins The Rich List Thanks To Spanx," *Forbes*, 07-Mar-12.

78. Clare O'Connor, "Inside Forbes' Historic $10 Billion Richest Self-Made Women Cover," *Forbes*, 01-Jun-16.

79. "Differentiating Her Business Idea," *Inc.*, 20-Jan-12.

80. Julia La Roche, "How billionaire Sara Blakely pitched SPANX to Neiman Marcus in a bathroom," *Yahoo! Finance*, 13-Feb-18.

Square Inc.
SAN FRANCISCO, CALIFORNIA

» **Innovations: Square Reader credit-card processing platform; Square Register, Terminal**

» **First Innovation: 2010**

In 2008, a St. Louis seller of glass faucets was unable to make a sale because he could not accept credit cards. So, an idea was born. In 2009, Square was founded to develop an innovative reader that connects to the iPhone's audio port and converts a credit card's magnetic stripe into sound pulses. This truly innovative approach led Square to generate $3 billion in 2018 revenues. [81]

When I signed up for a Square account on Oct. 14, 2010, I became a credit-card accepting merchant within minutes with the purchase of a $5 Square reader. Contrast that to a 2003 experience involving the purchase of a $900 Nurit 8000 Wireless Credit Card Terminal, which required a separate $20-per-month subscription to the RIM wireless network.

To make the Nurit work, one needed to apply for a bank merchant account, which required filling out a lengthy account application, undergo a credit check, pay activation fees, plus separate per-transaction and monthly minimum charges. It was an insufferable series of pain points.

Square eliminates all these annoyances and charges a low transaction fee, a benefit usually reserved for merchant accounts that process high volumes of transactions. Square removes this source of stress and inconvenience for merchants and lets millions of entrepreneurs ring up sales anywhere, anytime, what innovators like to call "disruptive innovation."

What makes an innovation disruptive? Inventions that help create or grow new markets and value networks, while disrupting existing ones over a few years or decades, by displacing an earlier technology or process, are disruptive. Square's ability to convert a credit card's magnetic stripe into audio pulses falls into that category.

81. "Square Updates Second Quarter and Full Year 2018 Guidance," *Square*, 31-May-18.

Starbucks Corp.
SEATTLE, WASHINGTON

» **Innovations: Coffee retail stores; Electronic payment system; Free Wi-Fi, Mobile app**

» **First Innovation: 1987**

In March 2015, Starbucks passed Subway to become the No. 2 restaurant chain in U.S. sales — second only to McDonald's. [82] Today it boasts 29,324 retail locations and is the world's largest coffee retailer with nearly $25 billion in annual revenues. [83]

The success of Starbucks is driven in part by the Time Compression Ubertrend, but the company also has an enviable record of driving relentless innovation, all while paying attention to details.

In Spring 2009, Starbucks launched an iPhone app that was enhanced in January 2011 by a Starbucks-developed electronic payment system.[84] The app later featured a gamified loyalty program that offers rewards for using the system. Another trendsetting Starbucks first was free Wi-Fi introduced at stores on July 1, 2010, without requiring either registration or setting time limits. [85]

These innovations are crucial to Starbucks' success. Its "Mobile Order & Pay" initiative now represents 14% of U.S. company-operated transactions. [86]

Starbucks also treats its employees right. It's one of the rare restaurants to provide comprehensive health benefits and stock to part-timers. Employees have realized more than $1 billion worth of financial gains in the form of stock options, according to *Fortune*. [87]

Starbucks once again proves that relentless innovation drives financial success. In fiscal 2018, consolidated net revenues rose 11% to a record $6.3 billion while its U.S. Starbucks Rewards membership reached 15.3 million.

82. Bruce Horovitz, "Starbucks passes Subway in U.S. sales," *USA Today*, 20-Mar-15.
83. "Starbucks - Statistics & Facts," *Statista*, ret. 29-Dec-18.
84. Olga Kharif and Leslie Patton, "Starbucks Takes Its Pioneering Mobile-Phone App to Grande Level," *Bloomberg*, 30-Mar-16.
85. Christina Warren, "Starbucks to Offer Free Wi-Fi at All Stores Nationwide," *Mashable*, 14-Jun-10.
86. "Starbucks Reports Q4 and Full Year Fiscal 2018 Results," *Starbucks*, 01-Nov-18.
87. Laura Lorenzetti, "Fortune's World's Most Admired Companies: Starbucks, where innovation is always brewing," *Fortune*, 30-Oct-14.

The Procter & Gamble Co.
CINCINNATI, OHIO

» **Innovations: Swiffer Sweeper**

» **Launch Year: 1999.**

Sometimes pain-point analysis lies beyond the capabilities of large organizations. When Proctor & Gamble decided in 1994 it needed to generate $5 billion in revenue from new product lines, the company turned to innovation consultancy Continuum for help. [88]

Innovation consultancies bill their clients anywhere from $300,000 to $1 million per project. [89] They all claim to have gee-whiz innovation processes and methods. Defending their methodologies can often lead to vociferous disagreements, like the one between Alan Klement and Tony Ulwick. [90] Continuum's pain-point detection process is dubbed "Phase Zero."

After researching the market, Continuum "realized that people were cleaning their mops as much as they were cleaning their floors." [91] Conclusion: P&G customers needed a faster way to clean floors. It was the same inference Joy Mangano drew in 1990 for a lot less money. So, P&G set out to create something that worked like a mop, but better. *Voilà*, the Swiffer Sweeper.

Launched globally in July 1999, Swiffer generated $100 million in sales in the final four months of that year. According to *Cincinnati Enquirer*, as of July 2014, the Swiffer Sweeper was vying to join the P&G $1 billion club, which already encompasses some 25 brands. [92]

As this case study illustrates, innovation consultants can be helpful for organizations that need to outsource the brainstorming of solutions. The key message is that brands need to reinvent themselves continuously. Remember this chapter's opening stat: Only one of the original Dow 12 industrials is still in business today.

T-Mobile US Inc.
SEATTLE, WASHINGTON

» **Innovations: Un-carrier marketing strategy**

» **First Innovation: 2013**

Need more evidence of how innovation can help a company rise above the rest? Look no further than T-Mobile. Here's an outfit that operates in a much-disliked industry sector. In the 2017 American Customer Satisfaction Index, the wireless industry was ranked near the bottom, in 38th place among 43 industries, just below the U.S. Postal System. [93]

In early 2013, T-Mobile was consistently losing market share. Enter T-Mobile CEO John Legere with his Un-carrier repositioning strategy. In March 2013, T-Mobile launched the Simple Choice Plan, which broke with long-standing industry practices. Contracts were replaced with monthly plans with no long-term commitment. By eliminating phone subsidies, T-Mobile was able to cut prices significantly

In summer 2013, Un-carrier 2.0 introduced family plans without credit checks, a great deal for users who were routinely charged $200 deposits. In October 2013, T-Mobile upped the ante with Un-carrier 3.0, which offered users unlimited global data at no extra charge in 100+ countries. A month earlier, Verizon CEO Lowell McAdam had famously claimed that unlimited plans were not sustainable. [94] In 2014, the FTC sued AT&T for limiting "unlimited data." [95]

In August 2016, T-Mobile introduced T-Mobile One, an unlimited $70 data plan. [96] In August 2018, it completely overhauled customer service with its "Team of Experts" initiative. Next up, a 2019 launch of a streaming service.

Legere's tireless quest to upset the establishment brought an entire industry to its knees. In 2018, T-Mobile grew sales twice as fast as industry leader Verizon, 8% compared to 4% [97] Score: Un-carrier: 5, Carriers: 0.

88. "Procter & Gamble: Swiffer," *Continuum*, ret. 25-Nov-18.
89. Leslie Kwoh, "You Call That Innovation?," *The Wall Street Journal*, 23-May-12.
90. Tony Ulwick, "Klement's Fallacy Misleads The Jobs-to-be-Done Community," *Medium*, 10-Aug-17.
91. Drake Baer, "The Innovation Method Behind Swiffer Madness," *Fast Company*, 11-Mar-13.
92. Alexander Coolidge, "Which will be P&G's next billion-dollar brand?," *Cincinatti Enquirer*, 19-Jul-14.

93. Aaron Pressman, "The Cable TV Industry Is Getting Even Less Popular," *Fortune*, 25-May-17.
94. Roger Cheng, "Verizon CEO: Unlimited data plans just aren't sustainable," *CNET*, 24-Sep-13.
95. Lisa Weintraub Schifferle, "FTC sues AT&T for limiting 'unlimited data'," *FTC*, 28-Oct-14.
96. Brian Barrett, "Unlimited Data Plans Are Back—With Some Big Catches," *Wired*, 18-Aug-16.
97. Philip van Doorn, "Fast-growing T-Mobile picked a real laggard," *MarketWatch*, 01-May-18.

Tesla Inc.

PALO ALTO, CALIFORNIA

» **Innovations: Electric vehicles, autopilot, Semi**

» **First Innovation: 2008**

One has to wonder why more multi-million-dollar-compensated CEOs can't think the way Tesla CEO Elon Musk does. He asked two simple questions: "Why can't we build a great electric car?" Moreover, "Do I have to sell through car dealers?"

The resounding answers were "Yes, we can" and "No." Tesla has clearly disrupted the automotive industry. Headlines are telling: "Porsche, Mercedes building electric cars to challenge Tesla." [98] And: "Stunning Rivian electric pickup truck being unveiled as rival to Tesla." [99] As these headlines suggest, Tesla has become the gold standard of electric vehicles.

Despite *USA Today*'s sensational headline, Rivian's pickup truck presents no direct competition to Tesla. What the writer is suggesting is that Rivian is competing indirectly with Tesla's line of electric sedans and SUVs.

The company did launch a Tesla Semi truck in November 2017, which presents it with a superb opportunity to disrupt the $700 billion trucking industry. Signaling that the Tesla Semi could have a bigger impact than some might suspect, Walmart promptly announced that it would be pilot testing the Semi. [100] Three weeks later, Anheuser-Busch put down an $800,000 deposit for 40 Semi trucks. [101] One month later, UPS chimed in with an order for 125 verhicles. [102]

A fully loaded Semi will be three times faster than a diesel model and cheaper to operate. It's yet another Musk disruption, which already includes EVs, autopilot, battery factories, solar roof tiles and The Boring Co.

Uber Technologies Inc.

SAN FRANCISCO, CALIFORNIA

» **Innovations: Peer-to-peer ridesharing**

» **First Innovation: 2011**

After Garrett Camp and his friends spent $800 on a private driver one New Year's Eve, Camp, a computer programmer and co-founder of StumbleUpon, wanted to find a way to reduce the cost of transportation. Uber was founded in 2009 as UberCab with Travis Kalanick as a company "mega advisor." [103]

Following a May 2010 "beta" launch, Uber and its mobile app officially debuted in San Francisco in 2011. In 2014, Uber landed $1.2 billion at a $41 billion valuation, indicating just how valuable venture capitalists considered the company. [104] By 2014, entrepreneurs were describing their startups as "the Uber of X." [105] One year later, *Fast Company* observed that Uber had become a verb, as in to "Uber over." [106]

In June 2016, Uber raised a staggering $12.5 billion at a $66 billion valuation. [107] Uber's massive financial momentum was fueled in part by the September 2014 news that Nashville had become the first U.S. airport to approve Uber and Lyft. [108] Reports were also starting to trickle in that more business travelers were ditching rental cars and using ridesharing services like Uber. [109]

As with many disruptive startups, Uber had its issues. One was belligerent Co-Founder Kalanick who had instilled and encouraged a dubious company culture. [110] However. now that those issues are resolved, Morgan Stanley is reportedly prepping Uber for an IPO that values the company at $120 billion. [111]

Uber will need those funds to build its flying car service.

98. Megan Geuss, "Porsche, Mercedes building electric cars to challenge Tesla," *Ars Technica*, 25-Oct-14.
99. Eric Lawrence, "Stunning Rivian electric pickup truck being unveiled as rival to Tesla," *USA Today*, 26-Nov-18.
100. Darrell Etherington, "Walmart plans to pilot test the new Tesla Semi," *TechCrunch*, 17-Nov-17.
101. Andrew Hawkins, "Tesla just received its largest preorder of Semi trucks yet," *The Verge*, 07-Dec-17.
102. Darrell Etherington, "UPS reserves 125 Tesla Semi fully electric heavy-duty trucks," *TechCrunch*, 19-Dec-17.

103. "Uber," *Wikipedia*, ret. 19-Dec-18.
104. Douglas MacMillan et al., "Uber Snags $41 Billion Valuation," *The Wall Street Journal*, 05-Dec-14.
105. Laura Entis, "We're the Uber of X!," *Entrepreneur*, 12-Aug-14.
106. Evie Nagy, "Uber Is A Verb," *Fast Company*, 09-Sep-15.
107. David Spiegel, "Uber's books still top secret, but its biggest weakness isn't," *CNBC*, 08-Jun-16.
108. Jamie McGee, "Nashville airport first in U.S. to OK Uber, Lyft," *USA Today*, 25-Sep-14.
109. Charisse Jones, "More business travelers are ditching rental cars and turning to Uber and Lyft," *USA Today*, 21-Apr-16.
110. Joe Kukura, "Top 10 Reasons Uber Fired CEO Travis Kalanick," *SF Weekly*, 21-Jun-17.
111. Chris Morris, "An Uber IPO in 2019 Could Make It More Valuable Than Ford, Chrysler, and GM—Combined," *Fortune*, 16-Oct-18.

Success Tools

Innovation

The success of a global startup culture has transformed the way many enterprises view their path to future success. Amazon, Nest Labs, Spanx and Tesla represent impressive role models for corporate innovation. Startups, however, exert much more control over discretionary spending.

Startups can easily spend as much as 50% of their revenue on research and development (R&D). [112] While R&D spending is not a definitive measure of the innovation quotient (IQ) of a company, it does provide a rough measure of how much a company is willing to bet on creating breakthrough future products and services.

Even after transitioning from their early seed stage and financing rounds, innovative startups continue to spend approximately 12% of their revenue on R&D. As the table, left, shows, even mature companies spend far in excess of that amount. Most of the companies on this list have little choice regarding R&D spending — their industries, semiconductor equipment, software, biotech, all require R&D spending well in excess of 15% of sales.

At the other end of the spectrum lie laggards like Dell, which spends between 1% and 2% of revenue on R&D. Wall Street prefers seeing a public company investing 10% in R&D. It should be noted that Strategy&, a business unit of PriceWaterhouseCoopers, has found no statistically significant relationship between R&D spending and sustained financial performance after compiling an annual report of the top 1000 most innovative companies in the world for more than 12 years now. [113]

As shown repeatedly in the case study section, relentless innovation

Top Corporate Innovation Budgets		
Rank	Company	R&D Spending/ Total Revenue
1.	Synopsys	35.5%
2.	Electronic Arts	32.1%
3.	Celgene	31.3%
4.	Broadcom	26.4%
5.	LSI	26.2%
6.	Marvell Technology	25.8%
7.	VMware	25.7%
8.	Biogen Idec	25.7%
9.	Autodesk	25.2%
10.	NVIDIA	24.6%

Ret. 27-Nov-18 Forbes. Data is for 12 months through first quarter of 2011.

112. Roman Stanek, "The Real Battle At Dell," *TechCrunch*, 16-Feb-13.
113. Tendayi Viki, "Why R&D Spending Is Not A Measure Of Innovation," *Forbes*, 21-Aug-16.

drives financial success. However, even when innovation is only practiced sporadically, a Steve Jobs-like level of attention to detail is necessary to maximize return on investment (ROI). Sometimes it pays to be a "control enthusiast" (page 218).

The other measure of innovation activity sourced from publicly available data is patent counts. Each of these innovation measures has advantages and disadvantages. Both are largely barometers of technology innovations and may be more useful for measuring manufacturing innovation. However, as more industries weave technology into their business models, think Domino's and its pizza tracker, firms in allied industries, such as services, may also find this measure more applicable in the future.

The main advantages of tracking R&D spending are comparability and the ability to provide insight into a firm's commitment to innovation. However, as an innovation input, it says little about innovation output or success.

Patent counts are a measure of invention activity, and partially reflect innovation output, but they can also be deceptive. A few may represent valuable inventions, but many describe inventions of lesser value. Moreover, some industries, such as pharmaceuticals and technology, make heavy use of patents, while other sectors use them sporadically.

The startup's chief ROI measure is valuation. The spectacular valuations of some startups, such as Airbnb, which is valued at $30 billion, and Uber, which Morgan Stanley reportedly values at as much as $120 billion pre-IPO, higher than the valuations of Ford, General Motors and Fiat Chrysler combined, have drawn attention in all quarters. [114]

Businesses and other organizations face a much different question: How to quantify ROI when a myriad of environmental factors are involved? The International Association of Innovation Professionals (IAOIP) "Innovation Measurement Standard Challenge" utilizing the Spigit Idea Management platform has already uncovered 71 distinct approaches, ranging from "Intelligent Failure Rate" to "Innovation Social Capital." [115]

The first step in creating a practical innovation plan is having a clear understanding of what constitutes innovation, then analyzing comparable innovation success metrics. The preceding case study section is one way to accomplish the latter.

Thanks to work by the OECD and others, there is a definition of innovation practiced by organizations that is fairly standard across a wide range of survey methodologies, industries and countries. [116] From its Oslo Manual:

> *"An innovation is a new or improved product or process (or a combination thereof) that differs significantly from the unit's previous products or processes and that has been made available to potential users (product) or brought into use by the unit (process)."*

To account for differing entities, be they businesses, government organizations, universities and non-profits in any sector of the economy, this definition uses the generic term "unit" to describe the entity responsible

Non-Profit Innovation

Asako Shimazaki, 'Dancing Girls, Tenderloin, San Francisco', 1989

Innovation is not limited to business. That's why this book uses the term "organization" as much as possible — governments and non-profits should also actively pursue innovation. One example of non-profit innovation comes from San Francisco's Museum of Modern Art, which launched an "art on demand" feature in 2017 that sends an image of art from its collection after you message 57251. [1] Not only does this teach art appreciation, but it's also a creative use of text messaging. Currently, the text concierge wants you to text "send me cats" which results in you receiving Robert Gober's 1989 "Untitled" work. Try it.

1. Fitz Tepper, "You can text SFMOMA and it will respond with art on demand," *TechCrunch*, 10-Jul-17.

114. Chris Morris, "An Uber IPO in 2019 Could Make It More Valuable Than Ford, Chrysler, and GM—Combined," *Fortune*, 16-Oct-18.
115. "Innovation Measurement Standard Challenge," *IAOIP*, ret. 03-Dec-18.
116. "Oslo Manual 2018," *OECD/European Union*, 22-Oct-18.

for innovation. It refers to any institutional unit in any sector, including households and their individual members, in order to uncover any potential Leonardo da Vinci's.

The OECD's Oslo Manual 2018, the fourth published edition, offers additional perspective on incorporated changes and enhancements.

A significant change in this edition is the innovation definition, which has been simplified by substituting "product" and "process" innovations for the four categories used earlier: product, process, organizational and marketing. The OECD's survey framework also reduces the "significant change" ambiguity by comparing both new and improved innovations to the firm's existing products or business processes.

In contrast to the three Clayton Christensen/Judy Estrin innovation typologies, i.e., Efficiency/Incremental, Sustaining/Orthogonal and Disruptive/Breakthrough, innovation metrics and ROI studies typically focus on organizational level business processes. The table below illustrates the differences between the two:

Examples of Product and Business Process Innovations and Innovation Typologies			
Category	Efficiency/Incremental	Sustaining/Orthogonal	Disruptive/ Breakthrough
Product Innovation	Credit Karma	Toyota Prius	iPhone
Process Innovation	Kiva Robots (employed by Amazon.com)	Zara "Fast Fashion"	Henry Ford's Moving Assembly Line
Supply Chain Innovation	Toyota Production System (TPS)	IBM/Maersk TradeLens Blockchain Shipping Solution	Ocean Shipping Containers
Marketing Innovation	Programmatic Advertising	Domino's "Pizza Tracker"	American Advantage Frequent Flyer Program
04-Dec-18 Michael Tchong/Ubertrends			

While it's tempting to pursue disruptive or breakthrough innovations, sometimes also referred to as "radical innovation," a more practical approach involves identifying what business process is most in need of reinvention and apply available success metrics to the chosen area of activity. The reason is simple: 85% of innovations are modest improvements over existing products — in other words, incremental change. Just 2% were considered the first of its kind on the market, or breakthrough innovations. [117]

Here are definitions of the most popular business process innovations and a sampling of related metrics research:

- **Product innovation** – The introduction of a product or service that's new or considerably improved. The Apple iPhone is an example of product innovation. According to the EBRD/World Bank's Business Environment and Enterprise Performance Survey (BEEPS V), product innovation is associated with a 43% increase in labor productivity. [118] In 1995, Brown and Eisenhardt found that a majority of innovation research focuses on product innovation in a manufacturing context. However, with changing business

---

117. Bronwyn Hall, Innovation and productivity," *Nordic Economic Policy Conference Paper*, 29-Apr-11.
118. "Transition Report 2014," *European Bank for Reconstruction and Development (EBRD)*, ret. 30-Nov-18.

Black & Decker AutoWrench: Success or Missing the Mark?

In January 2007, *AdAge* summed up the holiday sales success of Black & Decker's new battery-operated wrench as follows: "the wrench sold out quickly at Home Depot's 2,127 stores." Was it really a success or just a case of limited supply? The Black & Decker AAW100 listing on Amazon.com shows just a middling three stars for the wrench, which costs $30. Was eliminating the need to turn a worm screw worth reinventing a wrench for? When asked if the item is durable, one poster, Xii20Xii, sums it up nicely, "No."

dynamics, researchers are challenging this one-dimensional approach.

- **Administrative innovation** – The creation of a new organization design or structure that better supports the creation, production and delivery of services or products. Administrative innovation activities include facilitating relationships between team members to accomplish innovation goals; innovative ways to drive an effective system-wide implementation of policies and procedures; innovative leadership, communication, peer coaching; plus structural changes. Surprisingly, according to one study, administrative innovation appears to have the greatest impact on company sales. [119]

- **Marketing innovation** – New marketing methods or enhancements in design, packaging, promotion or pricing. Domino's Pizza Tracker is a perfect example of an orthogonal marketing innovation that helps sustain the pizza chain's revenue stream.

- **Process innovation** – The implementation of new or significantly enhanced production methods. Amazon.com estimates that the 100,000 warehouse robots the company employs around the globe reduce operating expenses by about 20% (page 42). [120]

- **Supply-chain innovation** – This organizational method innovation usually involves the transformation of input product sourcing or the delivery of products to customers. The best supply-chain innovation success story is the shipping container, which was invented by Malcom McLean. When McLean examined the expenses involved with the loading his first container ship, he found that it cost $0.16 per ton to load compared with $5.83 per ton for loose cargo. [121] ISO shipping containers have boosted globalization more than all trade agreements in the past 50 years put together.

- **Technological innovation** – This innovation refers to new products and processes that feature significant technology changes. Many people believe that "innovation" means technological innovation, due to the sea-change shifts introduced by various technologies. As this book's exploration of Ubertrends has shown, technology is so tightly interwoven with the fabric of business and life, it usually plays, at a minimum, a supporting role in every innovation category.

So what differentiates a corporation from a startup? More importantly, is it even possible to reinvent an age-old enterprise to create a startup culture?

As the IBM PC case study vividly demonstrates (The Ultimate Incubator, page 300), it's entirely feasible for a large corporation to incubate a fast-moving startup. So why is this not done more often? Also, how do you develop the intrapreneurial spirit necessary to help unclog the corporate drain?

This section reviews the tools you need to bring about innovation. However, the term "tools" used here also refers to human resources, as well as that highly desirable, mental state, "innovation culture."

119. Carol Yeh-Yun Lin and Mavis Yi-Ching Chen, "Does innovation lead to performance? An empirical study of SMEs in Taiwan," National Chengchi University, *Management Research News*, Vol. 30 No. 2, 2007.
120. Kim Bhasin and Patrick Clark, "How Amazon Triggered a Robot Arms Race," *Bloomberg*, 29-Jun-16.
121. "Why have containers boosted trade so much?," *The Economist*, 22-May-13.

Innovation Culture

In September 2013, Dell Founder & CEO Michael Dell tweeted: "Welcome to the world's largest startup" — a reference to a highly leveraged $25 billion buyout that let Austin, Tex.-based Dell and Silver Lake Partners take the company private.

It's finally beginning to dawn on major corporations, like Dell, what everyone else already knows — their corporate culture and lack of innovation is so old-school. Ironically enough, in an effort to keep up with innovative startup cultures, many corporate giants are doing their best to convince consumers, as well as their employees, that they, too, can be just as hip and innovative as Silicon Valley.

Dell's tweet struck many observers not only ironic but also completely unrealistic. As GoodData CEO Roman Stanek wrote in *TechCrunch*, "I can tell you with confidence that there is no way Dell has the culture or the ass-kicking visionary à la Steve Jobs that it needs to be even remotely considered a startup."

Creating an innovation culture is far more complicated than many imagine. Corporations like Dell try to present themselves as hip startups but lack a solid innovation foundation. The reason why is pretty straightforward; corporations and startups have very different approaches. Most startups are focused on one thing only: innovation. Even when a startup experiences unprecedented success, it rarely stops innovating. Conversely, corporations innovate only when they have to.

This message is highly pertinent to those who believe they're immune from competition. Small startups can challenge even the largest corporations. Two perfect examples of this scenario happened when the U.S. created the Flip video camera and GoPro action camera. Both quickly rose to prominence in the digital camera field, catching napping camera giants Canon and Nikon flatfooted. GoPro, notably, was the best-selling digital camera on Amazon.com around 2014. Had someone told you in the 1990s that two U.S. startups would successfully take on the dominant Japanese camera makers, you might have called the person crazy.

A CB Insights survey of 677 corporate strategy executives confirms the lack of entrepreneurial zeal among large organizations. While 85% said innovation is very important, most, 78%, focus on incremental changes instead of taking disruptive risks. [122]

As discussed earlier, speed is a critical aspect of a thriving innovation culture. Since IBM brought its PC to market in one year, it's a goal worth emulating. Moreover, IBM did it without being able to Google, crowdsource ideas or use AI, or machine learning, to optimize product development.

Today, AI (Artificial Intelligence) is accelerating the pace of innovation. AI and three other converging factors are set to bring innovations to market a minimum of four times faster than before (chart). Despite these upheavals, it should be noted that successful innovation does not necessarily require radical change, just speedy action.

Pure Digital Flip Video Camera

Pure Digital launched the Flip as the "Pure Digital Point & Shoot" in 2006 and renamed it one year later. The easy to connect video camera became an instant hit, that is, until the iPhone added video capability in 2009. Cisco Systems acquired Pure Digital in May 2009 for $590 million and shut the Flip division down in April 2011.

---

122. "State of Innovation 2018," *CB Insights*, 24-Apr-18

How Time Compression Accelerates the Innovation Cycle

The centrifugal force propelling the Time Compression Ubertrend is the codec, a COmpression/DECompression algorithm. As each successive generation codecs compresses more data into ever smaller packages, information moves faster thereby compressing time. Around the periphery of this central force lie four accelerants that will help bring innovations to market faster, by a factor of at least four, which is the smallest perfect square root that produces a tangible result.

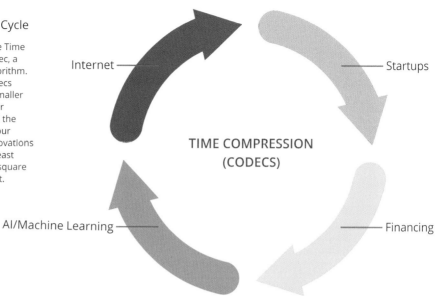

Internet

Startups

**TIME COMPRESSION
(CODECS)**

AI/Machine Learning

Financing

An earlier chapter revealed that the driving force behind the Time Compression Ubertrend is compression/decompression algorithms or codecs. As each successive generation of codec technology compresses more data into ever smaller packages, information moves faster, thereby compressing time. As the above chart illustrates, the innovation cycle is accelerating, propelled by four accelerants around its periphery, the internet, startups, venture financing and AI/machine learning.

The internet is spreading information faster. Ideas shared across social media rapidly reach their intended target audience. Information now moves at internet speed, or approximately 200,000 kilometers per second (124,000 miles per second), accounting for average connection latency. These fast-moving ideas are shared by 1,093,123 startups existing around the globe today, according to the F6S database. [123] The number of startups in the F6S database is growing by 17,000 startups each month, or about 567 new startups each day.

These startups are tapping into a vast pool of venture financing, which reached $304 billion through August 9, 2018, according to CB Insights. [124] That means that more than $40 billion is flowing into the rapidly growing startup community each month.

Some of these startups are raising vast amounts of money. In July 2018, 55 companies raised so-called "mega-rounds" — which involve funding of $100 million or more. [125] It was the highest number of mega-rounds in the past decade, and the target continues to move. Given the large number of companies landing mega-rounds, some have suggested that the threshold should be raised to $500 million.

Given this staggering inflow of entrepreneurial talent and money, it's easy to see why startups will eventually zero in on every conceivable market pain point existing today. Their quest to bring innovative products and

> **❝** I can tell you with confidence that there is no way Dell has the culture or the ass-kicking visionary à la Steve Jobs that it needs to be even remotely considered a startup."
>
> **Roman Stanek**
> TechCrunch

123. "Startup Dashboard," *F6S*, ret. 08-Jan-19.
124. "Tech Market Intelligence Platform," *CB Insights*, ret. 09-Aug-18.
125. Erin Griffith, "Peloton's New Infusion Made It a $4 Billion Company in 6 Years," *The New York Times*, 03-Aug-18.

Automated Labeling

The first step in building a machine-learning solution is creating a training data set. Creating those training sets, however, usually involves laborious manual input. Amazon's AWS division has launched Ground Truth; a training set labeling service for SageMaker, its machine learning modeling tool.[1] Ground Truth lets developers parse storage buckets of data to label, say, thousands of images automatically. Ground Truth heralds in a future of machine learning tools that will accelerate the process of building viable solutions.

1. Frederic Lardinois, "Amazon launches an automated labeling service for its SageMaker machine learning tool," *TechCrunch*, 28-Nov-18.

services to market will be significantly aided by the blossoming machine learning market, which is guaranteed to accelerate design and development.

One much-needed innovation that would help many a software-based startup is machine-learning-based coding automation to simplify the task of writing clean, well-documented code. With all elements of society now reliant on software-based solutions, code-writing robots will lead to an explosion in programming-based innovation.

So in this fast-moving world, that is in a constant state of flux, why should you build a culture of innovation? The answer should be intuitively obvious, but a growing body of evidence suggests that an organization's culture plays a major role in the speed and frequency of innovation.[126]

And what exactly is an innovation culture? The values and vision of an organization affect its ability to manage innovation, as does an organization's approach to collaboration, communication and risk. A culture of innovation introduces a work ethic that nurtures unorthodox thinking and encourages experimentation. It continuously seeks to present new ideas or ways of thinking and then translates them into action to solve specific problems or seize new opportunities. Workplaces that foster an innovation culture generally subscribe to the belief that innovative ideas can come from anyone and anywhere. Here are the principles that distinguish an innovation culture:

- **Goals** – Innovation leadership should define what innovation means for the organization and set an example. For most organizations establishing reasonable goals works well, however, sometimes it's necessary to encourage the impossible. As Big Sean sings, "I know the higher I go, the harder the climb. But after that, the bigger the muscle and smarter the mind." Don't drop everything. Remember that most innovations iterate on what already exists: 85% of innovations are modest improvements over existing products. Urge team members to think outside the box by using the creativity tips offered in the following section. Many large organizations believe they should outsource innovation to startups. That requires evaluating acquisition over invention — the classic "build vs. buy" conundrum facing many a company. Each approach has its merits, but if you want innovation to be part of your organizational DNA, there is no question as which one to choose.

- **Relationships** – As with any startup, the team makes all the difference in the world. Their relationships with each other and other organization members is mission critical. Aim for diversity and hire the best, and fast. The group should be diverse in tenure, age and seniority, with employees rotating into the group on a consistent basis. This model encourages employee ownership and takes some of the burden off management. The consensus is that small teams are best. Evan Wittenberg, former Google Head of Global Leadership Development, says; "It does tend to fall into the 5 to 12 range, and the number 6 has come up a few times."[127] A survey of companies with more than $25 billion in

> "I know the higher that I go, the harder to climb. But after that, the bigger the muscle and smarter the mind."

Big Sean
"First Chain"
27-Aug-13

126. Marisa Smith et al., "Factors Influencing an Organisations ability to Manage Innovation: a Structured Literature Review and Conceptual Model," *International Journal of Innovation Management*, Vol. 12, Issue: 4, 2008.
127. Nicolas Bry, "How Small Innovation Teams Hit the Nail," *Innovation Excellence*, 26-Feb-13.

annual revenues, revealed that teams of 1-9 were most mentioned at 36%. [128] Leverage crowdsourcing by inviting ideas from everyone and letting team members participate in idea competitions and Shark Tank-style events. These gatherings provide an opportunity for team members to discuss their ideas while also making their innovation concepts easier to understand. Accept ideas with openness. Innovation team leaders are not there to judge innovations but to encourage employees not to accept the status quo. Support all voices by openly and transparently sharing ideas

A True Innovation Culture Understands that Failure Is OK

In Silicon Valley, it's a well-accepted truth that failure means you have "done time" perfecting yourself. As this cartoon suggests, that is not always the case in the world at large. Innovation requires risk-taking and as the saying goes, "No risk, no reward." However, it should be noted that in Silicon Valley, no one fails anymore — everybody "pivots."

for improvements. A collective mindset will be needed to uncover the right problem. Collaboration also contributes to a positive organizational culture, so encourage cross-communication and get teams to work together on innovative ideas. Recite this African proverb: "If you want to go fast, go alone. If you want to go far, go together." Cultivate external relationships by hosting startup accelerators and hackathons. Because of their size, many larger organizations find it difficult to launch a new product, service, or changing their *modus operandi* quickly. Speed and agility is a strength of many startups. Getting to know startups helps innovation leaders stay on top of current trends. And if the decision is "buy," building relationships with startups is one of the easiest ways to identify and acquire strategically important startups and technologies.

- **Knowledge** – Having innovation in your DNA requires knowing who you are and what you do best. As an innovation leader, it's your honor to (re)kindle the passion for knowledge. The first step is finding out all there is to know about your products and services. Dig into your customer experience and follow their journey to uncover pain points. Amazon.com spent $13.4 billion on Whole Foods. Millions more to tie Prime promotions to local

> " If you want to go fast, go alone. If you want to go far, go together."
>
> African Proverb

128. "How big are innovation teams at the largest companies?," *Innovation Leader*, Benchmarking Innovation 2018.

stores and the Whole Foods app. But when I showed up at my Whole Foods store one evening, no one had a clue about key app promotions. Organizations spend a fortune on innovation and acquisitions but fail to do the most basic: a simple customer journey to uncover all the chinks in their armor. Encourage your team to ask: "Why is this happening?" and "What if we trained our [fill in the blank] better?" Use "Design Thinking" to help instill empathy for your customers. This iterative process seeks to understand the customer, challenges assumptions, and redefines problems to identify alternative strategies and solutions that may not have been readily apparent. At Whole Foods, it's the disconnect between Austin, Tex.-based headquarters and their local outposts. One way to avoid these issues, or identify areas for innovation, is to become a "problem seeker." Understanding your business' vision and values and gaining a deeper knowledge of your organization is an essential step in the innovation journey.

- **Resources** – Innovation can't happen without time, money and the authority to act. Create time and needed space to capture ideas. Quarterly or monthly brainwriting sessions (sidebar) can help managers leverage cross-functional viewpoints by inviting everyone to the table. A meeting that's fun, with food and drinks and maybe a quick game or non-status-quo icebreaker, will greatly improve group input. Managers may even want to consider leaving the room so employees can candidly discuss ideas among peers without oversight. Innovation leaders should create a fertile environment for innovation by letting team members know that they have the resources of authority and autonomy to act on innovative ideas, but also seek to understand why they might feel they do not. Teach team members bureaucracy breaking skills and show them how to navigate your organization. Encourage authentic engagement by moving beyond rule-conforming hierarchies. Break down silos by assisting team members in their quest to work across seniority levels, departments and functional teams. Being an innovator often means busting hierarchical structures. This action might sound like heresy in conservative corporate quarters but, to paraphrase Steve Jobs, to create insanely great customer experiences you have to sell dreams, not business as usual.

- **Rewards** – To encourage team members to appreciate the role they play, recognize and reward efforts. At the initial team organization meeting, announce a series of award celebrations that will take place at certain milestones. Team member recognition will help them appreciate contributing, while incentives will induce them to bring in more innovative ideas. Surprisingly, more than 35% of respondents to a survey by Innovation Leader, a Boston-based community for large company innovation, report that their company doesn't have any kind of innovation-related incentives. [129] By contrast, nearly 80% of the more "innovation adept" companies have an incentive program in place. Be mindful

---

Brainwriting, Not Storming

Despite the uber-popularity of "team brainstorming meetings," brainstorming doesn't work as well in real life as you might expect. The problem isn't sharing ideas; it's the "out-loud" aspect that, quite ironically, leads to groupthink instead of unique ideas. The phenomenon is dubbed "anchoring," and it tends to disproportionately favor early ideas, which, due to "conformity pressure" also lets the least creative ideas surface. To avoid this double jeopardy, use brainwriting, a term coined by University of Texas, Arlington Professor Paul Paulus. [1] The general principle, that idea generation should exist separate from a discussion, suggests writing down ideas first and discussing them last.

1. Rebecca Greenfield, "Brainstorming Doesn't Work; Try This Technique Instead," *Fast Company*, 29-Jul-14.

129. Robert Tucker, "Nine Traits Of Successful Innovation Teams," *Forbes*, 20-Jul-18.

Design Thinking: Nintendo Switch Is a Convergence Device

Nintendo brainstormed what it could do better after its Wii U stumble. The result is the Switch, which, as its name implies, functions both as a mobile gaming device and stationary videogame console. The results have been spectacular. Strategy Analytics predicts the Switch will outsell the Sony PlayStation with sales of 17.3 million units in 2019. That forecast would put Nintendo ahead of the competition for the first time in 10 years.

IMAGE COURTESY: NINTENDO OF AMERICA INC.

that competitive grand prizes create a few winners and lots of losers. Instead, reward all innovations and attempts. The online incentive program YouEarnedIt suggests prizes and bonuses for employee recognition. Even companies that don't have the resources for monetary incentives can still give kudos in creative ways to signal that innovation is a valued skill, like a free dinner or night out. Also reward team members for developing a "Maker Mindset" (Building the Maker Mindset, page 322) — which requires creativity, problem-solving, reflection, and perseverance, all in an effort to encourage ideation, experimentation and, more importantly, failing.

- **Risk-taking** – Startups take huge risks. That explains why 75% of venture-backed startups ultimately fail. [130] However, as indicated earlier, many large corporations eventually also fail, either merged into oblivion; acquired and stripped of assets; or, now more likely, disrupted by one of those 25% of startups that actually succeed, weaponized with ever larger mega-rounds. Risk taking is about establishing an organizational culture where people feel able

---

130. Faisal Hoque, "Why Most Venture-Backed Companies Fail," *Fast Company*, 10-Dec-12.

The "maker" culture is a technology-driven extension of the do-it-yourself hobby that intersects with hacker culture and enjoys creating new devices as well as tinkering with existing ones. The trend is propelled by the Maker Faire, an event produced by *Make* magazine, which debuted in San Mateo, Calif. in 2008 to "celebrate arts, crafts, engineering, science projects and the Do-It-Yourself (DIY) mindset." It also has roots in the Burning Man crowd, which revels in making large contraptions that wow attendees each year in the Black Rock, Nev. desert. Parent company Make Media claims that "the maker movement is shaping the next generation of engineers, designers and innovators." The trend has lead to "makerspaces" — media centers, industrial tech areas, and computer labs that provide students with space, technology and materials to make whatever they can think of while pursuing the Maker Mindset. [1] This creative pursuit has crossed over into innovation training, where it is used to help teams expand their intrapreneurial horizons.

1. "What is the Maker Mindset?," *Central Rivers Area Education Agencies*, 20-Nov-17.

IMAGE COURTESY: MICHEL DESCHÊNES.

to try out new ideas and, perhaps, even fail. While it's obviously key to prevent taking unnecessary risks, an astute innovation culture needs a balanced approach to avoid rejecting ideas prematurely, driven by an overly risk-averse mentality. It also requires that innovation leaders provide emotional support to those willing to try something new, regardless of whether the idea is eventually judged a failure or success. Innovation leaders need to demonstrate that they are more interested in learning from failure than trying to avoid it. An organization that only recognizes successes may stifle experimentation that leads to innovation. According to *Forbes*, "In these cultures, it is rare to find someone who has been able to rise in the ranks with a failed experiment on his or her resume, even if the failure provided valuable insights about future opportunities." [131] Try and experiment with new innovation methods *and* put them into practice. Engage in R&D, experimentation and learn from startups who develop products in "sprints" — brief bursts of intense activity. Train your team to think like intrapreneurs: no risk, no reward.

• **Tools** – A company that is still running on Office 2003 probably isn't maximizing productivity. A simple way to challenge the status quo and start getting employees to think outside the box is to send e-mail tips with links to the latest state-of-the-art tools that will make their work more efficient and better organized. For example, Airtable is a cloud-based Google Sheets on steroids. It has collaborative commenting, an audit trail for record changes, the ability to view sheets as forms, and much more, simplifying data manipulation. Workers who use the latest tools will be more inclined to innovate within their own environment. Reading helps everyone on the team gain freshest insights into the latest innovation methods. A minimum of four books should provide a foundation for further inspiration. The suggested reading list should cover lean startup methodologies such as Agile and Scrum. Use the "Business Model Canvas" to provide a map of your organization. Adopt innovative tools to manage your innovation. New ideas rarely get implemented unless they're tracked. Since everyone has their assignments, it's easy for ideas to get neglected if it's not clear who "owns" implementation. An abundant number of team collaboration tools are available for free on the web, including my current favorite, MeisterTask (page 325). Use idea management software to provide a way for every team member to review and track ideas. These tools are not to be used for "helicopter parenting" but rather to build innovation energy. Every city has events that showcase industry advancements, offer continuing education courses and seminars, and provide local association meetings. Employees should be encouraged to attend events that foster innovative thinking. Eventbrite offers an online, geographic directory of business enrichment meetings and conferences. As Alex Gammelgard of Arena Workplaces observes, "If employees regularly see innovation displayed in a positive and

131. Steve Culp, "Risk Management Can Stimulate, Rather than Deter, Innovation," *Forbes*, 07-Jan-13.

BMI●Business model canvas

<table>
<tr>
<td colspan="2">● Key partners
Who are your most important partners?
Which key resources do you acquire from partners?
Which key activities do your partners perform?</td>
<td>● Key activities
What are the activities you perform every day to create & deliver your value proposition?</td>
<td>● Value propositions
What is the value you delivery to your customer?
Which of your customer's problems are you helping to solve?
What is the customer need that your value proposition addresses?
What is your promise to your customers?
What are the products and services you create for your customers?</td>
<td>● Customer relationships
What relationship does each customer segment expect you to establish and maintain?</td>
<td>● Customer segments
For whom are you creating value?
What are the customer segments that either pay, receive or decide on your value proposition?</td>
</tr>
<tr>
<td></td>
<td>● Key resources
What are the resources you need to create & deliver your value proposition?</td>
<td></td>
<td>● Channels
How does your value proposition reach your customer? Where can your customer buy or use your products or services?</td>
<td></td>
</tr>
<tr>
<td colspan="3">● Cost structure
What are the important costs you make to create & delivery your value proposition?</td>
<td colspan="3">● Revenue streams
How do customers reward you for the value you provide to them?
What are the different revenue models?</td>
</tr>
</table>

Brought to you by Business Models Inc

www.strategyzer.com

Business Model Canvas

This template, designed for management and startups, helps entrepreneurs and innovators develop new or document existing business models. It lets users align activities by mapping potential partners, resources, value propositions, revenue streams, and other vital parameters.

IMAGE COURTESY: BUSINESS MODELS INC.

fun light, and are rewarded for their more innovative personal pursuits, they will be much more likely to mimic that behavior in the workplace." [132]

If these guidelines seem overwhelming, they are meant to be. Innovation is hard work. To paraphrase: "If innovating was easy, everyone would be doing it." Once you get into the groove, things will go much more quickly than you might expect. The "business as usual" status quo is a global addiction. To kick this ingrained habit, you have to adopt the same motto used in addiction recovery treatments, "One day at a time."

Sometimes the innovation process grinds to a halt due to a single clog in the machine. Large organizations are notorious for their bureaucracy and office politics. As Beth Comstock, a former senior executive at NBC before becoming GE's vice chair puts it, "I found I was more able to be more creative at GE than NBC." Comstock's conclusion: People in the media business are much more "territorial," which hinders innovation. [133]

That territorial ego problem is also found at the top. According to more than 1,000 "Innovator's DNA" assessments, between 10% and 15% of the world's most innovative leaders do not encourage people around them to innovate as well. [134] These kinds of leaders often believe their ideas

132. Alex Gammelgard, "Three Ideas for Encouraging Workplace Innovation," *Arena Solutions*, ret. 05-Jan-19.
133. Eric Johnson, "How to make a big company more innovative," *Recode*, 30-Nov-18.
134. Jeff Dyer and Hal Gregersen, "The Secret To Unleashing Genius," *Forbes*, 14-Aug-13.

LEGO FORMA Fish Kit

The LEGO FORMA fish kit ($88), previewed on Indiegogo, is "aimed at stressed adults and designed to add a splash of creativity to their day." Toys are one of the best ways to broaden your vistas and to begin thinking differently. If you get some additional $15 "skins," you can even roleplay — starting out as the beautiful lionfish, who meets the hapless goldfish... You get the idea.

IMAGE COURTESY: THE LEGO GROUP.

Top 15 Innovation Books		
Rnk	Book	Author
1.	The Innovator's Dilemma	Clayton Christensen
2.	The Lean Startup	Eric Ries
3.	Innovation and Entrepenurship	Peter Drucker
4.	Blue Ocean Strategy	Chan Kim/Renée Mauborgne
5.	Running Lean	Ash Maurya
6.	The Innovator's Solution	Clayton Christensen
7.	Where Good Ideas Come From	Steven Johnson
8.	Competing Against Luck	Clayton Christensen
9.	The Innovator's DNA	Clayton Christensen
10.	The Myths of Innovation	Scott Berkun
11.	Business Model Generation	Alexander Osterwalder et. al.
12.	Mastering the Dynamics of...	James Utterback
13.	The Art of Innovation	Tom Kelley
14.	Zero to One	Blake Masters/Peter Thiel
15.	The Other Side of Innovation	Trimble/Govindarajan
08-Dec-18 Google		

are so vastly superior to those of their colleagues; they see little value in building talent around them. Many also lack the patience required to give others the chance to develop and deliver their ideas, so they work solo.

Amazon.com CEO Jeff Bezos believes his leaders should not delegate the task of innovation to anyone in particular. That explains why Bezos has purposefully chosen not to appoint a chief innovation officer, unlike the nearly 5,000 organizations that have. That's an interesting point of view, but Amazon has its innovation DNA written all over it, as Bezos puts it:

> "Most large organizations embrace the idea of invention but are not willing to suffer the string of failed experiments necessary to get there. Given a 10% chance of a 100 times payoff, you should take that bet every time. But you're still going to be wrong nine times out of ten. We all know that if you swing for the fences, you're going to strike out a lot, but you're also going to hit some home runs."

Could it be that some organizations are too outdated to keep up? In a fast-moving digital world where the new arrives faster than ever, and innovation is king, only time will tell whether it's possible for some to reinvent their culture and remain relevant.

One thing is for sure, however, a culture of innovation is a reliable indicator of an organization's ability to weather the kinds of constant disruption that nearly every industry will be experiencing soon.

Practical Innovation Tools

For innovation champions, titles matter far less than breadth of knowledge and access to the latest state-of-the-art tools. Tools are central to advancing innovation as a field and a discipline, and separate true innovators from also-rans. As editor of Toolhacker.com, I've developed a strong POV on what I consider to be innovative.

In a continually shifting cloud and machine learning landscape, how can you recognize the good from the bad, the ones hawking "end-to-end real-time e-services that incubate and disintermediate virtual channels" and true practicality? I generated that description at "Tech Bullshit Generator" (makebullshit.com), but I'm sure you will instantly recognize the type of sales gibberish that is found at just about any tech site.

Innovation has saturated every industry, including the ones that make productivity tools. Everywhere you turn, there is a new metaphor or a new analytics "dashboard" that measures all your KPIs, including the ones that rule the world of innovation. Real-world experience dictates that most tools are just that, tools. It's what you do with them.

So, what are the best solutions for business? There are more than 150 tools in the innovation space, with more coming every day. Here are a few, hopefully useful, suggestions.

Idea Management: Viima

There are at least 38 idea management applications, the largest innovation software category. Idea management tools accept input from either inside or outside an organization (crowdsourcing), or both. Captured ideas are typically ranked or filtered based on idea feedback or voting, sometimes using bubble chart analytics. Some offer idea implementation tracking, gamified challenges, incentives, mobile apps, and social media engagement. Prices range from free all the way to $65,000/mo. However, if one follows the dictum of a lean startup, how can you justify paying large sums of money for ideation? Finland-based Viima offers a visually appealing internal idea management tool you can try for free for up to 50 users. Other good options include Luxembourg-based Innovation Cloud and Denmark's Ideanote. Need open innovation? Try Oregon-based Collective Innovation's IdeaLab.

Innovation Management: Qmarkets Q-360

Organizations that require a complete set of solutions to manage their innovation efforts usually turn to innovation management applications. While many vendors claim to offer innovation software, that generally means idea management. Innovation management applications typically add advanced analytics and reporting tools to track continuous innovation, plus much more. Israel-based Qmarkets offers the Q-360 suite, which manages M&A scouting with optional Q-scout module, and multi-lingual gamification challenges with Q-open. It's also possible to combine an idea management tool with crowdsourcing platforms such as Betterific or Innocentive to arrive at a less costly solution. Two other offerings worth exploring, both based in Germany, are Berlin-based CrowdWorx Innovation Engine and Nuremberg-based ITONICS. Both feature consulting services, while ITONICS even offers hosting.

Mind Mapping: MindMeister

A popular general productivity application is mind mapping, which is often used to brainstorm ideas within organizations. It can also be used to generate innovative concepts. Mind mapping software lets users create visual diagrams that illustrate relationships between topics. Because mind maps are free-form, they're ideally suited to supporting idea generation and innovation, allowing you to arrive at cutting-edge, innovative ideas. MindMeister from Munich-based MeisterLabs and its sister application, MeisterTask (right), feature easy to use interfaces that are optimized for customer experience. You can invite team members to each map with either editing or viewing-only privileges. Built-in templates and the ability to import XMind, Freemind and text files complete its feature set. MindMeister is available to use free of charge for up to three maps, or $4.99/mo. for unlimited maps, PDF export and printing.

Project Management: MeisterTask

If you want to hack together your own innovation management suite, you also need MeisterTask, which helps you manage ideas to their completion. Like MindMeister, MeisterTask is optimized for usability, featuring a beautiful interface with such nice touches as customizable wallpapers and inspirational or funny quotes, like the one shown here "Everything popular is wrong" — Oscar Wilde. MeisterTask's features include due dates, task tagging, audit trails, activity comments, task assignment and notes. Notifications can be displayed in browser, or you can also choose to receive e-mail alerts. Combining Viima, Mind Meister and MeisterTask provides a solid alternative for those looking for best-of-breed standalone applications. Also recommended: Airtable to manage large datasets. The Basic plan is free. An $8.25 Pro tier adds app integrations, like Slack, while a $20.75 Business plan adds groups and permissions.

The End Game

TL;DR — The reason why innovation is on a tear is due to life changes taking place at warp speed. The converging forces of the eight Ubertrends described in this book will make society spin like a kinetic flywheel, rendering our future even more unrecognizable than it already is.

Service Marketing

With most ads falling on deaf ears by either being tuned out, skipped or blocked, marketers may want to rethink the $560 billion spent on global advertising in 2018. What if you could boost brand awareness but also provide a useful service to the community? Duracell Rapid Responder trucks let victims of Hurricane Sandy charge their phones and check e-mail. [1] As part of a road-repair grant program, KFC offered cities free repairs of the estimated 350 million U.S. potholes. [2] In exchange, KFC requested that repaired potholes be branded with temporary chalk declaring the pothole "refreshed by KFC," as shown in Louisville, Ky., above. That's a big-bucket idea.

1. Jack Neff, "Duracell Brings Charging Stations To Battery Park After Hurricane Sandy," *AdAge*, 31-Oct-12.
2. By Emily Bryson York, "Need A Pothole Filled In Your City? Call KFC," *AdAge*, 25-Mar-09.

To wade through the fast flowing eddy of the future will require vision. It's a telltale sign that next year is 2020, a number that symbolizes perfect vision. Every successful enterprise begins with a vision. I hope this book helped build your worldview. It recounts so many unusual phenomena that your brain is probably fizzing with ideas.

It starts with the Digital Lifestyle, which is weaving a technology thread through the very fabric of our existence. Who can forget that teen who jumped in front of a truck to save her iPod? That we're willing to risk life and limb to rescue what is essentially an inanimate object speaks volumes. That lifeless object springs to life when you press a button and music begins pulsing through your earphones, enveloping you in your own world. Those digital tunes are so valuable it's worth suing a friend over them.

That's the gist of both the Digital Lifestyle and Unwired Ubertrends, they have made our love for technology intractable. A loyalty so extreme, we're willing to murder to defend our favorite digital brand. Alternatively, troll others on social media who chose the wrong device.

Extreme is the watchword for Generation X-tasy. This Ubertrend is all about our constant urge to maximize our earthly experience. It will drive up the price of admission, from dining out to attending live performances, for our blasé masses. We're going to have to learn to live with these newly acquired

"Chuckle" T-shirt Creatively Encourages Innovation

The biggest innovation hurdle, most frequently mentioned by attendees at my speaking engagements, is management's lack of enthusiasm to actually implement initiatives. Here's a meme that uses an emoji and/or hashtag that can be shared on social media by those who are passionate about renewal and change. The "Chuckle" emoji, combined with the hashtag #youcallthatinnovation, can be used in social media posts to "out" innovation laggards. Alternatively, the Chuckle t-shirt can be worn by those frustrated with the status quo around people who need a swift kick in the pants. Visit ubercool.com for more details about the Ubertrends book tour and to find out how to receive a free t-shirt...as long as it's used productively. 😊

habits a long time because the Fountain of Youth entices us with so many new opportunities to enhance the quality of life. New facial rejuvenation discoveries will open up entirely new undiscovered worlds for us.

Time Compression is blurring life. As is technology. When that iPod morphed into the iPhone, magic exploded inside a high-resolution screen that sucked us deeper into a digital divide. Unwiring from life brought everyone freedom. However, that freedom is strengthening our resolve to seek more control. Being always connected has made it easy to express thoughts, without much thought. This casual attitude has brought us to the precipice of civil war, with civility a casualty of the Casual Living Ubertrend.

Thanks to Voyeurgasm, life is becoming radically transparent, a welcome sign for those who desire more visibility. The prospect of living in a world where women have more say should excite us. Some may not like it, but a change in management would be welcomed by many.

Now that you have 2020 vision, it's up to you to change the future. That means unleashing a tsunami of innovation. From removing microplastics in the ocean to solving social media's growing negative influence, the world needs our help. Taking care of an increasingly marginal middle class will require the combined acumen of a 1,000 points of startup lights.

I hope that this eye-opening roller coaster ride through the landscape of now has inspired you to begin changing the world before it changes you.

Index

A

A4M 76. *See also American Academy for Anti-Aging Medicine*
Aaviksoo, Jaak 52
AbbVie 77
abdominal plastic surgery 103
ablative 110, 111
Abu Dhabi 12, 125
A C. elegans 83, 88
acne scars 107, 110
activewear 227, 229
ADD 12, 173. *See also attention deficit disorder*
addiction 12
Administrative innovation 315
Adobe Systems 28
adult entertainment 142
adult roundworm 84
Advanced Research Projects Agency. *See DARPA*
Advanced Television Systems Committee 250
Aerion
   Aerion AS2 171
Aerion Supersonic 171
aesthetic medicine 98
Afinitor 87, 88
age discrimination 78
Age Management 74, 78
age spots 110
aggressive driving 232, 233
Agile 322
AI. *See [also]artificial intelligence ; See also artificial intelligence*
Aibo 41
Airbnb 71, 164, 296, 297, 305, 313
Airbus 171
Air Canada 219
Airdome 150
AirStrip. *See also Apple*
AIST 40
Alcoa 227
Alcor Life Extension 75
Aldebaran 38, 41
Alexa 212, 213, 305, 306. *See also Amazon.com*
Alexified. *See Alexa*
Alkazar 140, 141
Allergan 101, 102, 106, 108
Alliance Manufacturing Company 204
Ally & Gargano 153, 168
Alminana, Dan 85
Almost Famous 144
Aloha Friday 226
Alphabet 40, 77, 291, 306
AlphaGo 59
Alpha Mom 270, 271

Amana Refrigeration 149
Amazon.com 24, 40, 42, 60, 61, 70, 109, 164, 176, 178, 187, 212, 220, 221, 250, 291, 304, 305, 314, 315, 316, 319, 324
Amazon Factor 61, 62
Amazon Robotics 42. *See also Amazon.com*
Amazon Web Services 305
Amelio, Gil 292
American Academy for Anti-Aging Medicine 76
American Paper Bottle Company 296
American Society for Aesthetic Plastic Surgery 104, 106
American Society of Plastic Surgeons 99, 100, 101, 107, 108
Ameritech 163
amoeba 39
Ampex 246, 250
amphetamine(s) 155, 156, 177
anabolic steroid
   androgenic anabolic steroid 81
An American Family 254
Andraka, Jack 193
Android 22, 41, 51, 208
Angry Birds 48, 49
Anne Nelson 81
anonymity 126, 232, 236
Anonymous 56, 57
Anthony, Susan 265, 286
API. *See Application Programming Interface*
app 26, 28, 59, 65, 71
Apple 10, 11, 13, 22, 24, 25, 26, 63, 64, 70, 71, 96, 119, 149, 165, 201, 206, 207, 208, 209, 212, 213, 221, 227, 256, 257, 291, 292, 294, 295, 297, 302, 304, 306, 308, 314
   iPod 10–11
Apple iPhone 4 256
Apple Pay 209
Apple Watch 63, 64, 71, 292, 294, 306. *See also Apple*
Apple Watch Series 4 65
Application Programming Interface 18
approval creep 198
App Store 208. *See also Apple*
Aquino, Corazon 269
Arab Spring 71, 210, 211
Aragon 68, 69
AR.Drone. *See Parrot*
area associates 165
Argentina 120, 139, 269
ARKit 209. *See also Apple*
Armstrong, Kristin 81
Armstrong, Lance 199
ARPANET 164, 200
Arrison, Sonia 86
Artefill. *See Bellafill*
artificial intelligence 14, 32, 43, 58, 59, 70, 249
artificial stimulants 198
AR View 209. *See also Amazon.com*

ASIMO 36, 37, 71
ASPS. *See American Society of Plastic Surgeons*
astroturfing 29
ASUS 40
A syndrome produced by diverse nocuous agents. *See Selye, Hans*
Atari Pong 45
athleisure 95, 96, 228, 229, 307
Ativan. *See benzodiazepine*
Atkins, Juan 31
Atlantic City 120
atrophic acne 107
ATSC. *See Advanced Television Systems Committee*
attaché case 15
attention deficit disorder 173, 178
Audi 22
Audible 179
Audiobooks 179
Autobiography of a Yogi 94
Automatic Speed Ramping 179
automobile 22, 24, 34, 112, 161, 182, 296, 297
avatar 29
Avatar 29, 45
Avita. *See retinoid*
AWS. *See also Amazon Web Services*
Ayerst Laboratories 87

B

baby boomers 77
Bacchus-F 158
Bachelet, Michelle 269
bachelor's degree 276
Bain, Alexander 163
Baja Beach Club 14
Baker, Darren 86
Balsillie, Jim 206
Bancor 68, 69
bandwidth 28
Barletta, Martha 266
Barry Bonds 80
Barry, Megan 283
Bass, Robert 171
Baum, Andrea 223
BBN Technology 164
Bear Stearns 227
beats per minute 161
Bebe 61, 175
Belkin 213
Bellafill 107
Bellagio 119
Belmonte, Izpisua 77
Benanti, Laura 230
BenchMade Modern 219
Benzedrine 155
benzodiazepine 183
Bernardski, P.J. 187
Betamovie BMC-100P 246
Betterific 325
Beyoncé 28, 249, 259, 279

Bezos, Jeff 42, 88
BHRT 79, 80. *See also Bio-Identical Hormone Replacement Therapy*
Bhutto, Benazir 269
Big Brother 254
billionaires 132, 133
BioForm Medical 108
Bio-Identical Hormone Replacement Therapy 79
Bispebjerg University Hospital 92
Bitcoin 28, 66, 67, 68, 69, 164
BlackBerry 12
Blade Runner 145
Blair's 16 Million Reserve 136
Blakely, Sara 308
Blanton, Kimberly 266
bleisure 173
blepharospasm 106
Blizzard Entertainment 46, 71
blockchain 66, 67, 68, 69, 260, 314
blood-forming stem cells 90
Bloomberg terminals 169
blue jeans. *See denim*
Blu-ray
    H.264 167
BMI. *See body mass index*
BOAC. *See British Overseas Airways Corporation*
Bob Chinn's Crab House 116
body contouring 98, 104
Body Contouring 78, 98, 99, 100, 104
body mass index 194
body sculpting 103. *See also body contouring*
body shaping 98, 99, 100, 103, 104
Boeing 707 152
Bolt Beranek and Newman. *See BBN Technology*
Bonds, Barry 80, 81, 199
bone marrow cells 89
Book of Revelation 238
Borden Company 296
Borders 61, 111
Boston Consulting Group 34, 43
Boston Dynamics 40
botnet 52
Botox 97, 99, 105, 106, 107, 108
bottled water 113
botulins 106
botulinum toxin 99, 105, 106
Bouazizi, Mohammed 210
boutique hotels 122
Bouton Darty 220, 221
Bow, Clara 252
Boyd, Pattie 94
BP 18
BPM. *See beats per minute*
Brain Age 47
Brandenburg, Karlheinz 166
Brave 68
breakbeats 31
Breakthrough Innovation 297
breast augmentation 101, 102
breast implants 102

As this book vividly illustrates, Michael Tchong is on an indefatigable quest to decode the future. Being at the forefront of emerging trends is a perpetual passion that led Michael to establish his first media startup, *MacWEEK*, which helped mainstream desktop publishing.

Michael's next startups demonstrated a similar ability to ride waves early, including CRM, internet analytics and digital marketing. His ability to pioneer sweeping changes was validated by the acquisition of *MacWEEK* by Ziff-Davis; CyberAtlas by Mecklermedia; ICONOCAST by Imagine Media.

AUTHOR & SPEAKER
UBERCOOL INNOVATION

Hooked on entrepreneurship, Michael next founded Atelier Systems, which developed a personal communication manager, dubbed "Hello," featuring a novel idea — a modularly extensible architecture enhanced by an innovative GUI. This feature set has yet to be matched nearly 30 years later.

Always pushing the innovation envelope, Michael is a leading advocate of easy-to-use digital tools and superior customer experiences. The rapid growth of technology and innovation have made him a sought-after catalyst for the advancement of both ecosystems.

Michael's public speaking career was launched during the late 1990s dotcom boom with the founding of ICONOCAST, an award-winning digital marketing trendsetter.

He has entertained audiences globally, inspiring them with riveting insights into the world's most scintillating lifestyle, innovation and technology trends.

A cerebral catalyst, Michael motivates attendees by challenging their creativity and inventiveness. His informative yet entertaining style fuses the emotional and rational brain to help foster a new culture of innovation, an urgent need in this day and age of time-compressed change.

His unique people-watching and trend-forecasting perspectives have earned Michael recognition as one of the great forward thinkers of the information age. The ability to distill the future led the U.K.'s *Daily Telegraph* to label Michael "America's most influential trendspotter."

Michael studied economics at Fordham University in the Bronx and thoroughly enjoyed his high-school education at Colegio Arubano in Aruba where he graduated at the top of his class.

He began his career at some of Madison Avenue's most creative ad agencies, including DDB, Chiat/Day and Ally & Gargano.

Michael is the founder of Ubercool Innovation, a thought-leading incubator that helps companies shape-shift market sectors by leveraging next-generation technologies and user experiences. More details can be found at ubercool.com.